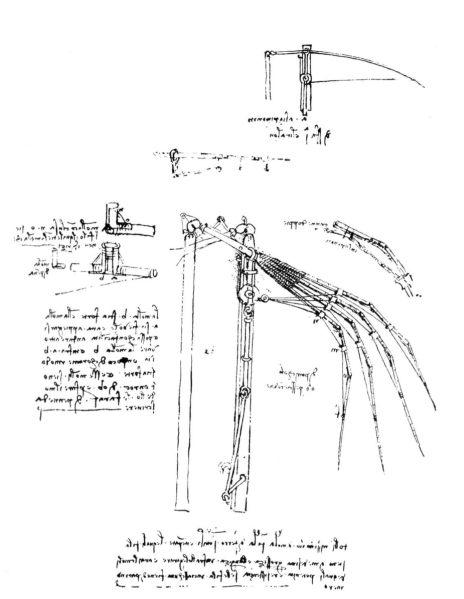

**Study of Mechanism of Wing of Flying Machine. Drawing by
Leonardo da Vinci. (Courtesy of Bettmann Archive.)**

Kinematics *of* Machines

Kinematics *of* Machines

by ROLLAND T. HINKLE

Professor of Mechanical Engineering
Michigan State University

SECOND EDITION

PRENTICE-HALL, INC.

Englewood Cliffs, N.J.

Library of Congress Catalog Card Number: 60-11501

First printing..........*April, 1960*
Second printing......*February, 1961*
Third printing.......*January, 1962*

PRINTED IN THE UNITED STATES OF AMERICA

51531—C

Preface to Second Edition

The material of the first edition has been retained in this edition. However, several of the topics have been rewritten and expanded. Coriolis' acceleration has been treated more extensively. The additions include: a discussion of the four-bar linkage in Chapter 2; the theory and application of independent-position equations, and finite difference equations for velocity and acceleration analyses in Chapter 6; the theory and application of complex variables for cam design in Chapter 7; and Bennett's linkage in Chapter 15. Chapters 12, 13, and 14 are entirely new.

The author is indebted to the many teachers who have commented on the first edition, made suggestions for the second edition, or read new portions of the manuscript. He is especially grateful to Professor Paul H. Black, Ohio University, Professor Francis H. Raven, Notre Dame University, and Dean M. Lawrence Price, Worcester Polytechnic Institute.

ROLLAND T. HINKLE

Preface to First Edition

Kinematics of machines is usually defined as the study of the relative motions of machine parts. The emphasis has been placed here rather than on the descriptions of mechanisms. However, a wide variety of mechanisms are used in the development of the theory and in the examples.

The basic concepts have been reduced to a minimum number. Their inclusion in the first two chapters makes it possible to omit sections in the remaining ten chapters without loss of continuity. Because of their basic importance, relative motion, inversion, and the angular velocity theorem are extensively treated. Some special constructions have been included in Chapter 6, not for their own sake, but to point out that basic theory can be used in many ways and that short cuts can often be developed.

The book presupposes a knowledge of engineering mechanics. However, calculus is sufficient if the reader spends additional time on the first two chapters.

The amount of material on cycloidal gears and flat belts has been reduced. New material has been included on velocity and acceleration polygons, equivalent linkages, special constructions, chains, rolling bodies, gears, and miscellaneous mechanisms. The derivation of Coriolis' acceleration is a special case, but it should make it possible for the reader to visualize the vector in magnitude and direction.

Problems of varying difficulty are included at the end of each chapter.

Material taken directly from other sources is acknowledged in the book. The author wishes to express appreciation to Professors L. C. Price and Ching-U Ip of Michigan State College for their help and encouragement during the writing of this volume.

ROLLAND T. HINKLE

Contents

CHAPTER 1

Terminology and Basic Concepts

1.1. Introductory. Certain phases of kinematics are as old as recorded history. One of the simplest devices, the wheel, has been used for five thousand years. The frontispiece in this book shows Leonardo da Vinci's (1452–1519) "Study of Mechanism of Wing of Flying Machine." A slider-crank mechanism is clearly shown. This slider crank is the basic mechanism of modern aircraft engines. Da Vinci would have been unable to calculate the acceleration of the slider. This is now considered a simple problem. In modern high-speed engines the inertia forces are often greater than the gas forces. An acceleration analysis is necessary for satisfactory design.

The Linotype shown in Fig. 1.1 is an example of a machine that contains many mechanisms. Its operation is almost as simple as that of the typewriter; an operator can write about 150 letters a minute. The rest is automatic. Cast slugs of the proper length, similar to that of Fig. 1.2, emerge from the machine. Most of the mechanisms are hidden from view. One series is shown in Fig. 1.3. When the key is pressed, a sequence of motions is started that in the end forms one letter in the slug. The cams in Fig. 7.1 actuate and control most of the mechanical actions of the Linotype.

A book filled with descriptions of mechanisms would be interesting and useful to the graduate engineer, but would be of little value to the person who is not well grounded in the theory of kinematics of machines. This book was written to present this groundwork. Terminology and the fundamentals of motion are presented first. This is followed with additional theory, and applications to specific mechanisms. The last chapter contains brief discussions of mechanisms not considered in earlier chapters.

1.2. Kinematics of machines treats of the relative motion of machine parts. The kinematic scheme of a machine can be investigated without regard to forces. This makes it possible to treat kinematics of machines as a separate subject.

1

Fig. 1.1.   Linotype machine.   (Courtesy of Mergenthaler Linotype Co.)

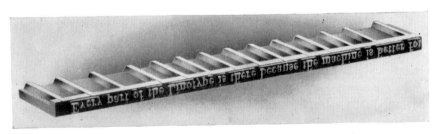

Fig. 1.2.   (Courtesy of Mergenthaler Linotype Co.)

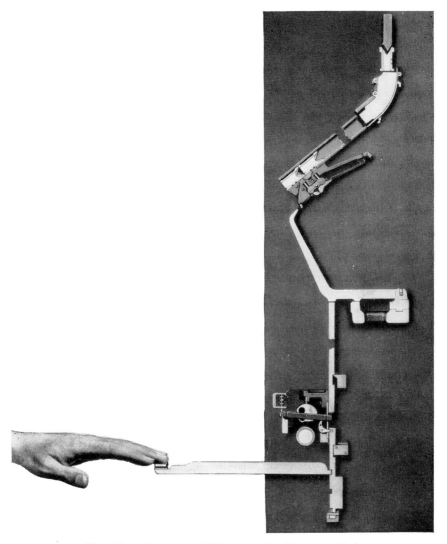

Fig. 1.3.   (Courtesy of Mergenthaler Linotype Co.)

The design of a machine may be divided into three steps:

1. Determination of the kinematic scheme
2. Determination of the forces
3. Proportioning of the parts

These three steps may not always be independent. When inertia forces are considered, the mass of the parts will contribute to the forces, and it might be necessary to alter the kinematic scheme to reduce accelerations. It is usually convenient, however, to consider the first two steps separately and then apply them in machine design, where the third step is considered. Forces will be considered briefly in several sections of this book.

1.3. Pairs. A pair is a joint that permits relative motion. As implied by the name, a pair has two elements. A slider-crank mechanism that is commonly used in gasoline engines is shown in Fig. 1.4, where A is a turning pair. The surface of the crankshaft that turns in the bearing is an element, and the surface of the bearing is the other element. Here B and C are similar turning pairs, and D is a pair. The surface of the piston and the surface of the cylinder form a sliding pair.

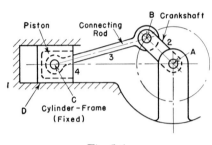

Fig. 1.4

In Fig. 1.5, the diameter of the journal with center at B has been increased in size so that it includes the shaft with center at A. This

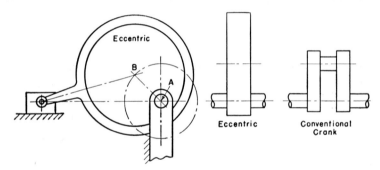

Fig. 1.5

type of crank is called an eccentric. An eccentric can be assembled with a one-piece connecting rod. Kinematically, the slider-crank mechanism in Fig. 1.5 is equivalent to Fig. 1.4.

A wheel and the surface on which it rolls form a rolling pair at the point of contact. A nut and screw form a helical pair (Fig. 1.7). A ball-and-socket joint forms a spherical pair (Fig. 1.8).

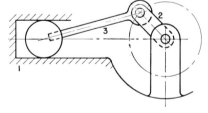

Fig. 1.6

1.4. Higher and lower pairs. If a pair has surface contact, it is a lower pair. If a pair has theoretical point or line contact, it is a higher pair. Thus A, B, C, and D in Fig. 1.4 are lower pairs. In Fig. 1.6, a mechanism is shown that is equivalent to Fig. 1.4.   The piston has been replaced by a sphere, rigidly fastened to the connecting rod.   The cylinder and sphere have line contact, and form a higher pair.   This would result in excessive wear, and is therefore not good design.   Kinematically, it makes no difference whether a pair is higher or lower.

1.5. Closed and unclosed pairs.   Elements of pairs that are held together mechanically are closed pairs.   The pairs of Figs. 1.4, 1.5, 1.6,

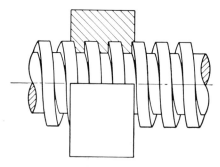

Fig. 1.7

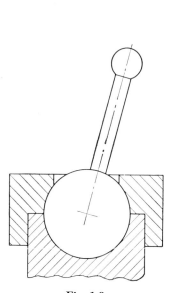

Fig. 1.8

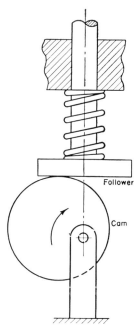

Fig. 1.9

1.7, and 1.8 are closed.   Pairs that are not held together mechanically are unclosed pairs.   The cam and follower shown in Fig. 1.9 form an unclosed pair.   The cam and follower are held in contact by the forces of gravity and the spring. At excessive speeds the cam and follower would not remain in contact at all times.

1.6. Kinematic link. A kinematic link is a rigid body with two or more elements of pairs. In Fig. 1.4, the crank and connecting rod have two elements of turning pairs each. The piston and frame have a turning element and a sliding element each. The master connecting rod of a nine-cylinder radial aircraft engine, shown in Fig. 1.10, has ten elements of turning pairs.

All materials have some elasticity, but in most cases the deformations are so small that they can be neglected in a kinematic analysis. Flexible connectors, such as belts and chains, act only in tension, and fluid in a tube acts in compression. While so acting, these can be treated as equivalent rigid links with elements of pairs.

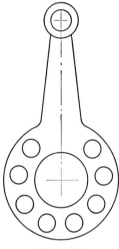

Fig. 1.10

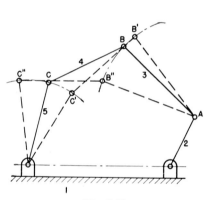

Fig. 1.11

1.7. Kinematic chain. When several links are joined in such a way that with one link fixed the others move according to a definite law, the chain of links is a kinematic chain. This type of motion is called con-

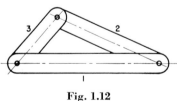

Fig. 1.12

strained motion. When the frame in Fig. 1.4 is fixed, the piston has a definite location for each position of the crank. This chain of links has constrained motion, and is a kinematic chain. The chain of links shown in Fig. 1.11 does not have constrained motion. For an assumed position of link 2, there is an infinite number of positions for links 3, 4, and 5. Two sets of positions are shown with broken lines. This chain of links is not a kinematic chain. The chain in Fig. 1.12 is a structure. When one link is fixed,

the others cannot be moved.   Only kinematic chains will be considered
in this book.

1.8. Mechanism.   When one link of a kinematic chain is fixed, the
chain becomes a mechanism.   This will be discussed further in Art. 2.8.

1.9. Machine.   A machine is a mechanism or a group of mechanisms
used to perform useful work.   Gasoline engines, lathes, and hoists are
examples of machines.   A watch is a mechanism.   The stored energy in
the spring is used to overcome friction and move the hands.   No external
work is done.

1.10. Plane motion.   If a body moves in such a way that all points
in it remain at constant distances from a reference plane, the body has
plane motion.   This reference plane is called the plane of motion.   The
three types of plane motion are described in the following three articles.

1.11. Plane rotation.   If a body has plane motion and moves in
such a way that each point in it remains a constant distance from a
fixed axis perpendicular to the plane of motion, the body has plane
rotation.   The crankshaft of the engine mechanism shown in Fig. 1.4
has plane rotation when the frame is fixed.

1.12. Plane translation.   If a body has plane motion and moves
in such a way that a line joining any two points in it (except lines normal
to the plane of motion) remains parallel to all previous positions, the
body has plane translation.   If, in addition to this, the body moves in a
straight line, it has rectilinear translation.   The piston in Fig. 1.4 has
rectilinear translation.   It is sometimes convenient to consider rectilinear translation as a special case of rotation, with an axis of rotation at
infinity.   The motion of a body moving with translation in a curved
path is called curvilinear translation.   The cars of a ferris wheel have
this type of motion.

1.13. Combined translation and rotation.   If a body has plane
motion that is neither pure rotation nor pure translation, it is a combina-

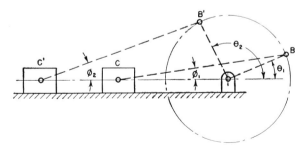

Fig. 1.13

tion of the two.   The motion of the connecting rod shown in Fig. 1.4 is
of this type.   This mechanism is shown again in Fig. 1.13.   Consider
the motion of the connecting rod as it moves from position CB to $C'B'$.

In Fig. 1.14, it is shown that this is equivalent to translation from CB to $C'B''$, and then rotation from $C'B''$ to $C'B'$. The same displacement could be accomplished as shown in Fig. 1.15. The connecting rod is

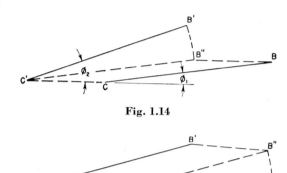

Fig. 1.14

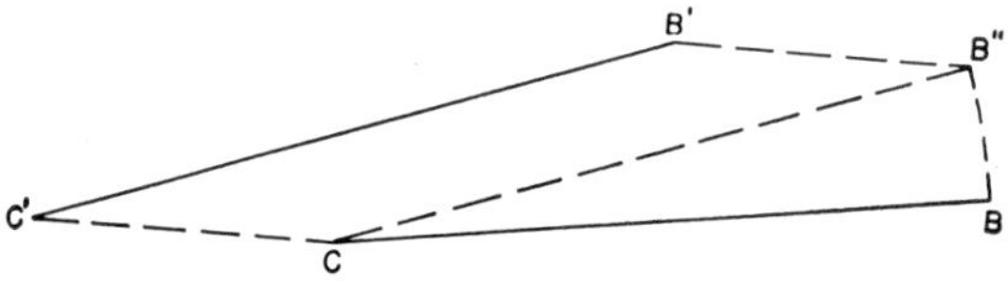

Fig. 1.15

rotated from CB to CB'' and then translated from CB'' to CB'. At any instant the motion of the connecting rod can be considered to be a combination of rotation about some point, and translation.

1.14. Helical motion. A body having rotation combined with translation along the axis of rotation has helical motion. A nut that is turned on a screw has helical motion (Fig. 1.7). This is three-dimensional motion.

1.15. Spherical motion. If each point in a body moving in space remains a constant distance from a fixed point, the body has spherical motion. The ball, and any part that is rigidly attached to the ball of the ball-and-socket joint shown in Fig. 1.8 have spherical motion. This is three-dimensional motion.

1.16. Phase, cycle, and period of motion. The simultaneous relative positions of the links of a mechanism or machine at any instant constitute a phase. The two phases of the mechanism shown in Fig. 1.13 can be indicated by specifying the position of the crank as θ_1 and θ_2. A machine completes a motion cycle when it starts from some phase, passes through all possible positions, and returns to the original phase. The slider-crank mechanism completes a motion cycle each time the crank turns one revolution. The valve mechanism of a 4-cycle gasoline engine requires two revolutions of the crank to complete one motion cycle. The period is the time required to complete one motion cycle.

1.17. Vectors. Quantities that have only magnitude, such as time, distance, and volume, are scalar quantities. Quantities that have both

magnitude and direction, such as displacement, velocity, and acceleration, are vector quantities. A vector quantity can be represented by a
straight line with an arrowhead. The length of the line represents the
magnitude; the angular orientation represents the line of action. The
arrowhead is called the *terminus*, and
the other end is called the *tail*, or *origin*
of the vector. If the origin of the vector is placed at the origin of the quantity that it represents, it is called a
localized vector. If the vector is drawn
anywhere else in the plane, it is called
a free vector. The localized vector and
a free vector representing the velocity
of crankpin A are shown in Fig. 1.16.

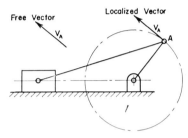

Fig. 1.16

1.18. Addition and subtraction of vectors. The symbols $\leftrightarrow$ and
$\rightarrow$ are commonly used to denote vector addition and subtraction. In
Fig. 1.17, let A and B represent successive displacements of a body.
These two displacements are equivalent to the single displacement
$A \leftrightarrow B$. All vector quantities can be added in this manner. The order
in which the vectors are added does not matter. Vector B can be
subtracted from A by changing the sign of B and adding, as shown in
Fig. 1.18. Vector A can be subtracted from B, as shown in Fig. 1.19.

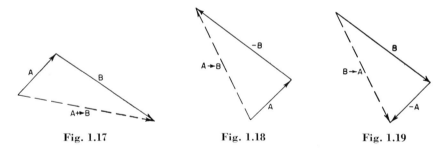

Fig. 1.17   Fig. 1.18   Fig. 1.19

An examination of Figs. 1.18 and 1.19 shows that $A \rightarrow B$ is equal and
opposite to $B \rightarrow A$, or $(A \leftrightarrow -B) = -(B \rightarrow A) = -(-A \leftrightarrow B)$.

1.19. Composition and resolution of vectors. The adding or
combining of vectors is called composition of vectors. The breaking up
or resolving of a vector into equivalent components is called resolution
of vectors. A vector can be resolved into an infinite number of combinations of components. It is often convenient to resolve a vector into two
components; for example, the components parallel to the x and y axes.

Two component vectors represent two magnitudes and two directions.
If any two of these four quantities are known, the other two can be deter-

mined. In Fig. 1.20, vector A is to be resolved into two components;
the magnitude and direction of one component, b, is known. This
known vector is laid off from the origin of vector A. The closing line
determines the other component, C. A second solution, B' and C', is
shown. This is equivalent to the solution B and C.

In Fig. 1.21, vector A is to be resolved into two components of magnitude b and c. Arcs of radii b and c are drawn from centers at the origin
and terminus of vector A. The intersections of the arcs determine two
distinct solutions, BC and $B'C'$. If the magnitudes b and c are equal,
there is one solution. If the sum of the magnitudes b and c is less than
the magnitude of A, there is no solution.

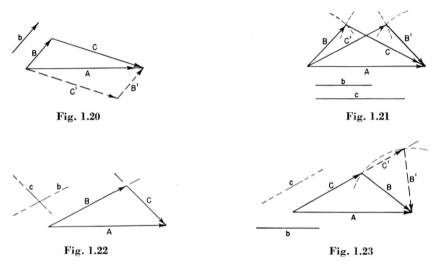

Fig. 1.20   Fig. 1.21

Fig. 1.22   Fig. 1.23

In Fig. 1.22, vector A is to be resolved into two components having
directions b and c. Lines parallel to b and c are drawn through the origin
and terminus of vector A. The intersection of these lines determines
the single solution, B and C.

In Fig. 1.23, vector A is to be resolved into two components; one is to
be of magnitude b and the other is to be in the direction c. A line parallel
to c is drawn through the origin of vector A. An arc of radius b is drawn
from a center at the terminus of vector A. The intersection of the arc
with the line of direction c determines two solutions, CB and $C'B'$. If
the arc is tangent to the line of direction c, there is one solution. If the
arc does not reach the line of direction c, there is no solution.

CHAPTER 2

Equations of Motion, Relative Motion, and Transmission of Motion

2.1. Displacement of a point. Displacement is the change of position of a moving point. In Fig. 2.1, point P moves from position D to E along the path C. The displacement of P is Δs. This displacement can be expressed by a single vector equation in terms of components parallel to the x and y axes.

$$\Delta s = \Delta x \nrightarrow \Delta y \quad \text{(graphically)} \tag{2.1}$$

Two algebraic equations are required to express this displacement. A vector symbol enclosed in bars represents the magnitude of the vector. The magnitude is

$$|\Delta s| = \sqrt{|\Delta x|^2 + |\Delta y|^2} \tag{2.2}$$

and the direction is

$$\beta = \tan^{-1} \left| \frac{\Delta y}{\Delta x} \right| \tag{2.3}$$

algebraically

In the limit, E approaches D and the chord Δs approaches the tangent at D. The direction of motion of a point as it moves along a path is therefore tangent to the path. *i.e. vel. is tangent to the path at the point.*

The angular displacement of point P can be expressed as the change in the angle made by its radius vector with respect to some reference point and line, in this case the origin and the x axis.

$$\Delta\theta = \theta_1 - \theta_2 \tag{2.4}$$

In order to obtain a relationship between linear and angular displacement, the displacement Δs (see Fig. 2.2) is written

$$\Delta s = R_1 \Delta\theta \nrightarrow \Delta R$$

In the limit,

$$ds = R_1\, d\theta \nrightarrow dR$$

For the important case of a circular path (see Fig. 2.3) dR is equal to zero, and

$$ds = R\, d\theta \quad \text{for circle} \tag{2.5}$$

11

rel. between angular displacement + linear displacement

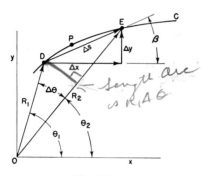

Fig. 2.1

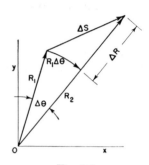

Fig. 2.2

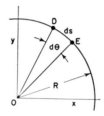

Fig. 2.3

2.2. Linear and angular velocity. Linear velocity is the time rate of change of linear displacement. In Fig. 2.1, point P moves from D to E in time Δt. The average velocity is

$$V = \frac{\Delta s}{\Delta t}$$

The instantaneous velocity of point P at position D is obtained by taking the limit

$$V = \underset{t=0}{\text{Limit}}\ \frac{\Delta s}{\Delta t} = \frac{ds}{dt} \tag{2.6}$$

The direction of the velocity is tangent to the path.

Angular velocity is the time rate of change of angular displacement. When the radius vector (Fig. 2.1) moves through an angle $\Delta\theta$ in time Δt, the average angular velocity is

$$\omega = \frac{\Delta\theta}{\Delta t}$$

where ω is radians per unit time. In the limit, the instantaneous angular velocity is

$$\omega = \frac{d\theta}{dt} \tag{2.7}$$

A relationship between linear and angular velocities for the case of circular motion can be obtained by substituting Eqs. (2.6) and (2.7) in Eq. (2.5), giving

$$V = R\omega \tag{2.8}$$

2.3. Linear and angular acceleration. The acceleration of a point having rectilinear motion will be considered first. Since the motion of the particle does not change in direction, the acceleration is due only to the change in magnitude of the velocity. Linear acceleration is the time rate of change of the magnitude of velocity. For a time interval Δt, the average acceleration is

$$A = \frac{V - V_0}{\Delta t} = \frac{\Delta V}{\Delta t} \tag{2.9}$$

where V_0 is the initial velocity and V is the final velocity for the time interval. In the limit, the instantaneous acceleration is

$$A = \frac{dV}{dt} = \frac{d^2s}{dt^2} \tag{2.10}$$

If the motion of the point is that of constant or uniform acceleration, the average acceleration for any time interval is equal to all the instantaneous values. For this special case the time interval can be of any value, and Eq. (2.9) can be written

$$A = \frac{V - V_0}{t} \qquad \text{or} \qquad V = V_0 + At \tag{2.11}$$

If a point has uniform velocity, the displacement s in time t is

$$s = Vt \tag{2.12}$$

If a point has variable velocity, the displacement is the product of the average velocity and the time. For uniform acceleration, the displacement is

$$s = \frac{1}{2}(V_0 + V)t \tag{2.13}$$

Substituting the value of V from Eq. (2.11) in Eq. (2.13) gives

$$s = V_0 t + \frac{1}{2}At^2 \tag{2.14}$$

Substituting the value of t from Eq. (2.11) in Eq. (2.13) gives

$$V^2 = V_0^2 + 2As \tag{2.15}$$

Angular acceleration α is the time rate of change of angular velocity. This is expressed as

$$\alpha = \frac{d\omega}{dt} = \frac{d^2\theta}{dt^2} \tag{2.16}$$

If a point moves in a circular path with uniform angular acceleration, and angular symbols θ, ω, and α are used in place of linear symbols s, V, and A, Eqs. (2.13), (2.14), and (2.15) will be derived in the form of (2.17), (2.18), and (2.19), respectively.

$$\theta = \frac{1}{2}(\omega_0 + \omega)t \tag{2.17}$$

$$\theta = \omega_0 t + \frac{1}{2}\alpha t^2 \tag{2.18}$$

$$\omega^2 = \omega_0^2 + 2\alpha\theta \tag{2.19}$$

$$V_f^2 = V_i^2 + 2a$$

2.4. Normal and tangential acceleration. When a point moves in a circular path, the velocity changes in direction, and may or may not change in magnitude. In Fig. 2.4, a point moves from position B to C in time dt. The initial velocity is V and the final velocity is $V + dV$. In Fig. 2.5, the change in velocity dV is resolved into two components dV^n and dV^t. Component dV^n is normal to the path; it results from the change in direction of the velocity. Component dV^t is tangent to the path; it results from the change in magnitude of the velocity.

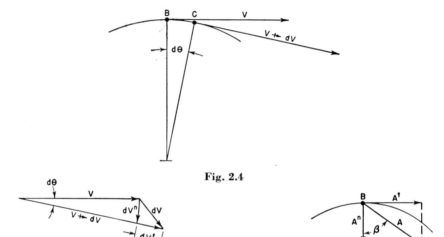

Fig. 2.4

Fig. 2.5   Fig. 2.6

The acceleration in the normal direction (A^n, normal acceleration) is the time rate of change of velocity in this direction.

$$A^n = \frac{dV^n}{dt} \tag{2.20}$$

From Fig. 2.5,

$$dV^n = V \, d\theta$$

Hence

$$A^n = V \frac{d\theta}{dt} \tag{2.21}$$

Substituting Eqs. (2.7) and (2.8) in (2.21) gives

$$A^n = V\omega = R\omega^2 = \frac{V^2}{R} \tag{2.22}$$

The acceleration in the tangential direction (A^t, tangential acceleration) is the time rate of change of the magnitude of the velocity. Equation (2.10) applies.

$$A^t = \frac{dV^t}{dt} \tag{2.23}$$

Substituting the derivative of Eq. (2.8) in (2.23) gives

$$A^t = R\frac{d\omega}{dt} = R\alpha \tag{2.24}$$

From Fig. 2.6, the magnitude of the total acceleration is

$$|A| = \sqrt{|A^n|^2 + |A^t|^2} \tag{2.25}$$

and the direction is

$$\beta = \tan^{-1}\left|\frac{A^t}{A^n}\right| \tag{2.26}$$

A point moving in a curved path always has normal acceleration. It has tangential acceleration if the magnitude of the velocity is changing. If a point has rectilinear motion, the normal acceleration is always

$$A^n = \frac{V^2}{R} = \frac{V^2}{\infty} = 0$$

Angular displacement, velocity, and acceleration are vector quantities. There are only two possible directions, clockwise (CW) and counterclockwise (CCW). The signs + and − will be used in place of +→ and →. In this book, the counterclockwise direction will be considered positive.

2.5. Simple harmonic motion. *When the acceleration of a particle having rectilinear motion is always proportional to the distance of the particle from a fixed point on the path and is directed toward the fixed point, the particle is said to have simple harmonic motion.* The relationship can be expressed by the equation

$$A = \frac{d^2x}{dt^2} = -Kx \tag{2.27}$$

in which A is the acceleration of the particle moving along the x axis, x is the position coordinate, and K is a constant. The negative sign indicates that the acceleration is to the left when the particle is to the right of the origin, and vice versa.

It is often convenient to consider simple harmonic motion as the motion of the projection, on a diameter, of a point moving in a circle with constant angular velocity. In Fig. 2.7, point Q moves in a circular path with constant angular velocity ω, and P is the projection of this point on a diameter. The displacement of P from the center O is

$$x = OP = r\cos\omega t \tag{2.28}$$

The velocity of point P is

$$V_P = \frac{dx}{dt} = -r\omega\sin\omega t \tag{2.29}$$

and the acceleration is

$$A_P = \frac{d^2x}{dt^2} = -r\omega^2\cos\omega t = -\omega^2 x \tag{2.30}$$

Here ω is a constant, and Eq. (2.30) is therefore the same as Eq. (2.27), which is the definition of simple harmonic motion.

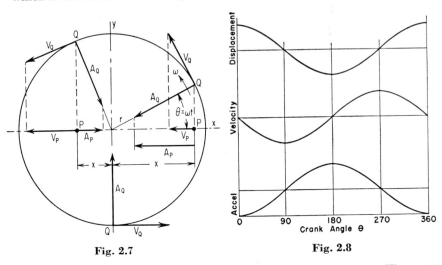

Fig. 2.7　　　　　　　　　　Fig. 2.8

2.6. Scotch yoke. A Scotch-yoke mechanism is shown in Fig. 2.9. A comparison of Figs. 2.9 and 2.7 shows that the horizontal slide performs simple harmonic motion when crank OQ rotates with constant angular

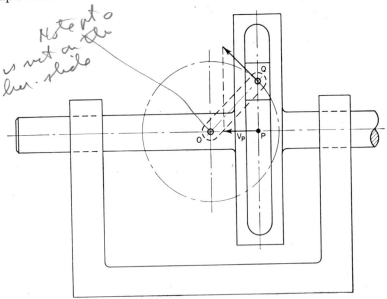

Fig. 2.9

velocity. Equations (2.28), (2.29), and (2.30) are plotted in Fig. 2.8. The nature of simple harmonic motion can be visualized by studying

Figs. 2.7 and 2.8.   When Q is at the extreme right, the velocity of P is zero and its acceleration is a maximum to the left.   As Q moves through the first quadrant, the velocity of P increases.   The acceleration continues to the left, but at a diminishing rate.   When Q has moved through 90°, the velocity of P is a maximum and the acceleration is zero.   As Q moves through the second quadrant, the velocity of P decreases and the acceleration is to the right.

2.7. Relative motion.   The motions previously considered were absolute motions.   The motions were defined with respect to axes or a body considered to be at absolute rest.   There is no point in the universe that is known to be at absolute rest.   For most purposes the earth can be considered to be at absolute rest, and in many cases the frame of a machine can be considered to be at absolute rest even though it is moving with respect to the earth.   An investigation of crankshaft failures in certain military trucks revealed that the gyroscopic effect of the flywheel resulting from the frame movement while operating over rough terrain was a contributing factor.   This theory is covered in dynamics, and not in kinematics.   In this book, unless otherwise stated, the frame will be at absolute rest.

The relative motion of a point or body is the motion with respect to some other point or body.   The two following examples will help to clarify the concept of relative motion.

Example 1.   Consider two automobiles, A and B, having respective velocities of 50 and 65 mph relative to the earth, as shown in Fig. 2.10.   The velocity of

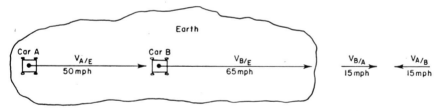

Fig. 2.10

car B relative to car A (written $V_{B/A}$) is the velocity of car B that would be apparent to an observer in car A if he thought of himself as being fixed; $V_{B/A}$ would be 15 mph to the right.   The velocity of A relative to B, $V_{A/B}$, would be the velocity of car A that would be apparent to an observer in car B if he considered himself fixed.   To such an observer, car A would appear to be backing at the rate of 15 mph.   Note that $V_{A/B} = -V_{B/A}$.

It can be seen that

$$V_{A/B} = V_{A/E} \rightarrow V_{B/E}$$

and

$$V_{B/A} = V_{B/E} \rightarrow V_{A/E}$$

In everyday life, most motions are observed as absolute motions. Train passengers are often confused by relative motion.   A passenger seated in a train that is in a station may observe that the train on the adjacent track is backing. A glance at the platform reveals that the adjacent train is stationary and that his train is moving forward.

Example 2. Consider two ships, A and B, that have absolute velocities represented by the vectors $V_{A/E}$ and $V_{B/E}$, shown in Fig. 2.11. An observer on ship B thinks of himself as being fixed. Like the train passenger, he can do this by considering that the sea is moving backwards with a velocity of $-V_{B/E}$ (see Fig. 2.12).

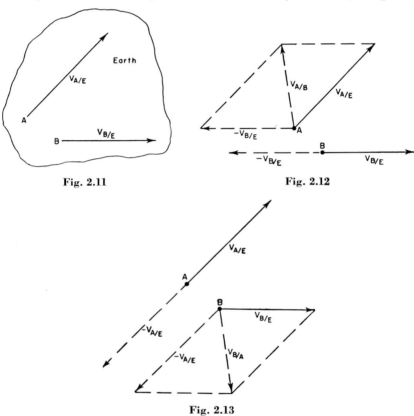

Fig. 2.11   Fig. 2.12

Fig. 2.13

From the observer's point of view, this assumed motion of the sea, $-V_{B/E}$, also carries ship A backwards, with the result that the observed velocity of A relative to B is $V_{A/B}$, as shown. In this example, as in the one above, use was made of the important principle, *the addition of equal velocities to two bodies does not change the relative velocities of the two bodies.*

In a similar manner, the velocity of B relative to A is determined in Fig. 2.13. Note again that

$$V_{A/B} = V_{A/E} \rightarrow V_{B/E}$$
$$V_{B/A} = V_{B/E} \rightarrow V_{A/E}$$

and
$$V_{A/B} = -V_{B/A}$$

$V_{A/B}$ means vel of A relative to B if B is considered as standing still & this can be done & readily F to be moving in a dee neg te vel of B & at same mag.

In vector equations, the terms can be transposed and the subscripts reversed if the signs are changed.   For example,

$$V_{A/B} = -V_{E/A} \rightarrow V_{B/E}$$
$$V_{A/E} = V_{A/B} \nrightarrow V_{B/E}$$
$$-V_{E/B} = V_{A/E} \nrightarrow V_{B/A}$$

etc.   These equations can be verified by drawing vector diagrams.

The motion of one body relative to a second body can be defined as the motion of the first body minus the motion of the second body, or, simply stated, *relative motion is the vector difference*.   If the motion of the second body is zero, the motion of the first body relative to the second body is the same as the absolute motion of the first body.   Absolute motion is a special case of relative motion.   When a vector symbol has only one subscript, for example V_A, it is under-stood that this represents the absolute velocity of A.

In Fig. 2.14, the rigid link AB is pinned to the frame at point A.   Point B cannot move towards or away from A, as this would cause failure of the link.   An observer attached to link 2 at A would not observe any motion of point B as link 2 rotates; i.e., the observer is attached to link 2 and rotates with it.   Point A is a double point; it is common to both 1 and 2.   If an observer is attached to link 1 at A, he would observe the

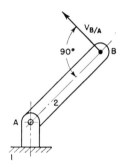

Fig. 2.14

motion of B as link 2 rotates.   This is understood when it is stated that *a point in a rigid body moves relative to another point in the same body, but in a direction at right angles to the line joining the two points.*

Leonardo da Vinci understood the concept of relative motion; he wrote, "But when the bird finds itself within the wind, it can sustain itself above it without beating its wings, because the function which the wing performs against the air when the air is motionless is the same as that of the air moved against the wings when they are without motion."[*] In wind tunnels, the airplane or model is stationary, and the air is caused to move.

In Art. 1.2, it was stated that kinematics of machines treats of the relative motion of machine parts.   It is essential that the concept of relative motion be understood.

2.8. Inversion is the making of different mechanisms by fixing different links in a kinematic chain.   As many mechanisms as there are links can be made from a given chain.   The slider-crank chain has four links, and the four mechanisms made from this chain are shown in Figs. 2.15 to 2.18.

[*] *The Notebooks of Leonardo da Vinci*, MacCurdy, ed., London: Jonathan Cape, Ltd.

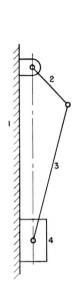

Fig. 2.15

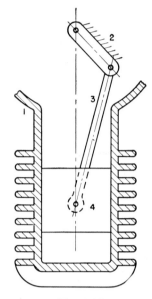

Fig. 2.16

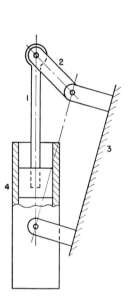

Fig. 2.17

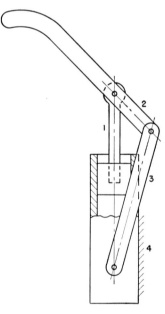

Fig. 2.18

The mechanism shown in Fig. 2.16 was used in the Gnome aircraft engine during World War I. The crankshaft was held stationary and the crankcase and cylinders rotated. The propeller was attached to the crankcase. This inversion is also used for a quick-return mechanism.

The mechanism shown in Fig. 2.17 is used in toy steam engines, and in the past has been used in marine engines. The piston of Fig. 2.15 has now become an oscillating cylinder. As crank 2 rotates, the piston slides in the cylinder and causes it to oscillate. This oscillatory motion of the cylinder is used to open and close steam ports, thus making a separate valve mechanism unnecessary.

The fourth inversion, shown in Fig. 2.18, is used for a pump.

2.9. Inversion and relative motion. A slider-crank chain is shown in Fig. 1.13. When the crank is moved from position θ_1 to θ_2, measured from the center line through the crank bearing and the wrist pin, the slider moves along this center line from position C to C'. This will always be true, regardless of which link is fixed. The motion of a point or link in a kinematic chain relative to some other point or link in the same chain is a property of the chain, and not of the mechanism. It does not matter which link is fixed. *Inversion has no effect upon relative motion.* This law will be used throughout the book.

2.10. Methods of transmitting motion. The four methods of transmitting motions are: (1) direct contact, Fig. 2.19; (2) intermediate rigid link, Fig. 2.20; (3) flexible connector, Fig. 2.21; (4) nonmaterial connectors, such as magnetic forces. The latter will not be considered in this book.

The driver is the link that receives motion from an external source. The driver imparts motion to the follower. In Fig. 2.19, the driver, link 2, rotates in a counterclockwise direction and imparts clockwise rotation to the follower, link 4. Link 4 could be the driver in a counterclockwise direction.

In Fig. 2.20, either link 2 or 4 can be the driver in either direction. The driver imparts motion to the follower through the intermediate rigid link 3. Link 3 can act in either tension or compression. The link connecting the driver and follower of a four-bar linkage is called the *coupler.*

Either pulley in Fig. 2.21 can be the driver in either direction. The driver imparts motion to the follower through the flexible belt 3. One side of the belt is always in tension.

2.11. Line of transmission. The driver imparts motion to the follower along the line of transmission. In Fig. 2.20, the line of transmission lies along link 3. Link 3 is pin-connected at P_2 and P_4. It can transmit motion and force only in tension and compression.

In Fig. 2.21, the line of transmission lies along the tension side of the belt. The belt is flexible, and can therefore transmit motion or force only along the centerline of the tension side.

In Fig. 2.19, the driver imparts motion to the follower along the common normal to the surfaces at the point of contact. The common normal and the line of transmission are the same line. The point of contact is a double point; it is designated P_2, a point in link 2, and P_4, a point in link 4. The center of rotation of 2 relative to 1 is designated O_{21}, a point common to 2 and 1. The center of rotation of 4 relative to 1 is designated O_{41}. Let the vector P_2R_2, perpendicular to $O_{21}P_2$, represent the velocity of point P_2. Then P_2R_2 is resolved into two components, P_2Q along the common normal, and P_2S_2 along the common tangent;

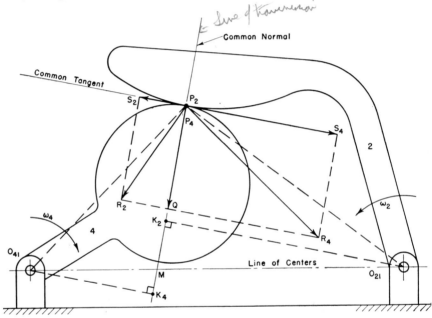

Fig. 2.19

P_2Q along the common normal is the driving component and P_2S_2 is the sliding component. The velocity of P_4 must be perpendicular to the line $O_{41}P_4$. It is represented by P_4R_4. The component of P_4R_4 along the common normal must equal P_2Q. If the component is greater, link 4 will leave contact with link 2. If the component is less, one of the links must bend or break. The driving component P_2Q then determines the length of vector P_4R_4. The sliding component P_4S_4 is then obtained. The vector difference of P_2S_2 and P_4S_4 represents the velocity of sliding of P_2 and P_4 due to the motion of both links.

 2.12. Angular velocity ratio theorem. *The angular velocities of driver and follower are inversely as the segments on the line of centers cut by the line of transmission or inversely as the perpendiculars from the centers to the line of transmission.*

Referring to Fig. 2.19, the theorem is expressed by the equation

$$\frac{\omega_2}{\omega_4} = \frac{O_{41}M}{O_{21}M} = \frac{O_{41}k_4}{O_{21}k_2} \tag{2.31}$$

The proof that follows is from Fig. 2.19.

have $V = kw$

$$\omega_2 = \frac{V}{R} = \frac{P_2R_2}{P_2O_{21}} \quad \text{and} \quad \omega_4 = \frac{P_4R_4}{P_4O_{41}}$$

$$\frac{\omega_2}{\omega_4} = \frac{P_2R_2}{P_2O_{21}} \times \frac{P_4O_{41}}{P_4R_4} \tag{2.32}$$

Triangles QR_2P_2 and $k_2P_2O_{21}$ are similar since their sides are mutually perpendicular. From these triangles

$$\frac{P_2R_2}{P_2O_{21}} = \frac{P_2Q}{O_{21}k_2} \tag{2.33}$$

From similar triangles QR_4P_4 and $k_4P_4O_{41}$

$$\frac{P_4R_4}{P_4O_{41}} = \frac{P_4Q}{O_{41}k_4} \tag{2.34}$$

Dividing Eq. (2.33) by (2.34) gives

$$\frac{R_2P_2}{P_2O_{21}} \times \frac{P_4O_{41}}{P_4R_4} = \frac{P_2Q}{O_{21}k_2} \times \frac{O_{41}k_4}{P_4Q} = \frac{O_{41}k_4}{O_{21}k_2} \tag{2.35}$$

Substituting Eq. (2.35) in (2.32) gives

$$\frac{\omega_2}{\omega_4} = \frac{O_{41}k_4}{O_{21}k_2}$$

From similar triangles $O_{41}k_4M$ and $O_{21}k_2M$,

$$\frac{O_{41}k_4}{O_{21}k_2} = \frac{O_{41}M}{O_{21}M}$$

Hence

$$\frac{\omega_2}{\omega_4} = \frac{O_{41}M}{O_{21}M}$$

It is convenient to determine the angular-velocity ratio by drawing the common normal. When the intersection of the common normal and the line of centers lies off the paper, the perpendiculars can be used.

The notation in Fig. 2.20 is similar to that in Fig. 2.19. The same proof applies in this case.

The proof of the angular-velocity ratio theorem for Fig. 2.21 is simpler than that for the two previous cases, but is not so general. Let pulley 2 be the driver and V be the velocity of the belt.

$$P_2Q'' = V = r\omega_2 \quad \text{and} \quad P_4Q' = V = R\omega_4$$

Eliminating V from these two equations gives

$$\frac{\omega_2}{\omega_4} = \frac{R}{r}$$

where R and r are perpendiculars from the centers of rotation to the line of transmission.   Triangles $MO_{41}P_4$ and $MO_{21}P_2$ are similar; hence

$$\frac{R}{r} = \frac{O_{41}M}{O_{21}M}$$

Therefore

$$\frac{\omega_2}{\omega_4} = \frac{O_{41}M}{O_{21}M}$$

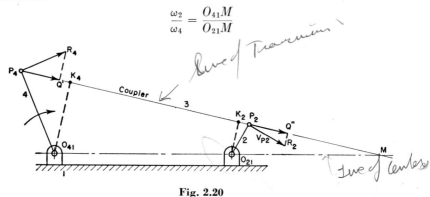

Fig. 2.20

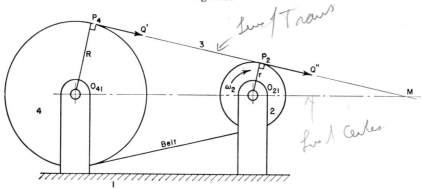

Fig. 2.21

2.13. Constant angular-velocity ratio. The   center   distance $O_{41}O_{21}$ is fixed.   It follows that, *for constant angular-velocity ratio of driver and follower, the line of transmission must cut the line of centers at a fixed point.*

2.14. Directional relationship of driver and follower. In Fig. 2.19, the line of transmission cuts the line of centers between the centers, and links 2 and 4 rotate in opposite directions.   In Fig. 2.20, the line of transmission cuts the line of centers outside of the centers, and links 2 and 4 rotate in the same direction.   This is always true.   It can be stated that *when the line of transmission cuts the line of centers between the centers the driver and follower rotate in opposite directions; when the line of transmission cuts the line of centers outside of the centers the driver and follower rotate in the same direction.*

2.15. Dead-center phase. In Fig. 2.22, link 2 is the driver. The line of transmission passes through the center of rotation of the follower. It can be seen that link 2 cannot drive 4. Link 2 merely subjects link 4 to compression. For dead-center phases, the angular-velocity ratio of follower to driver from Eq. (2.31) is infinity. In Fig. 2.23, a slider-crank mechanism is shown in top dead-center or head-end dead-center phase. A force applied to the piston will not cause rotation of the follower, link 2, because the line of transmission lies along link 3, which is collinear with the follower and passes through center O_{21}. A fly-wheel is necessary in engines to carry the links through the dead phases. The two slider-crank mechanisms of a steam locomotive are arranged with the cranks at 90° to each other so that both cannot be in dead phases at the same time. Sometimes failure occurs and the locomotive must operate with one cylinder. When this

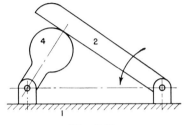

Fig. 2.22

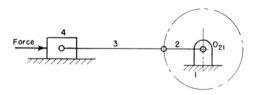

Fig. 2.23

happens the engineer must not stop the locomotive with the working cylinder on a dead phase, otherwise he would not be able to start again.

When the slider-crank mechanism is used for a compressor or pump, the crank is the driver, and there are no dead phases.

In Fig. 2.19, it can be seen that 2, when rotating clockwise, will not drive 4. For positive driving, the component of motion of the driver along the common normal must be directed toward the follower.

It can be stated that *for positive driving the line of transmission must not pass through the center of rotation of the follower, and the motion of the driver along the common normal must be directed toward the follower.*

2.16. Rolling contact. The direct-contact mechanism shown in Fig. 2.24 has contact on the line of centers for the phase shown. Let link 2 be the driver, and let the velocity of point P_2 be represented by the vector P_2R_2. The driving component along the common normal is P_2Q, and the sliding component is P_2S_2. The velocity of P_4 is P_4R_4. It will be equal to P_2R_2 since they coincide, and their components along the common normal must be equal. The sliding components P_2S_2 and P_4S_4

are equal. The velocity of sliding is the vector difference of P_2S_2 and P_4S_4. Since these vectors are equal, the sliding is zero.

When the point of contact is not on the line of centers, as shown in Fig. 2.19, vectors P_2R_2 and P_4R_4 do not coincide and the vector difference of P_2S_2 and P_4S_4 is not zero. Sliding exists. It can be stated that, in *direct-contact mechanisms, pure rolling exists when the point of contact lies on the line of centers.*

In Fig. 2.24, the line of transmission cuts the line of centers at the point of contact. The contact radii are equal to the segments into which

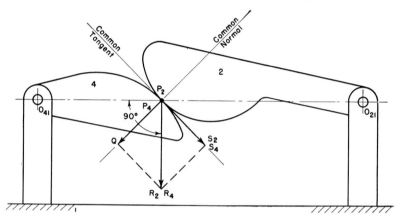

Fig. 2.24

the line of transmission cuts the line of centers. It can be stated that *the angular velocity ratio of driver and follower of mechanisms having rolling contact is inversely proportional to the contact radii.*

2.17. Huckert's theorem.* The nature of motion transfer can be summarized in a theorem: *The transfer of motion from one rigid body to another in a mechanism fulfills the necessary and sufficient conditions for turning when the relative displacement of the coincident particles is continuously zero; for rolling when the relative displacement is not zero and normal to the profiles at the point of contact; and for sliding when the relative displacement is not zero and along the tangent to the profiles at the point of contact.*

A motion transfer not defined by one of these conditions is a combination. A key pressing against a wheel hub exemplifies turning; a piston moving in a cylinder exemplifies sliding. The cycloid will illustrate rolling. In Fig. 2.25, cylinder 2 is placed between flat surfaces 1 and 3. When 3 is moved horizontally, 2 rolls between 1 and 3. A point P_2', on 2, will trace a cycloid on member 1, and P_2' will contact 1 at the coincident point P_1P_2. This is a cusp in the cycloid. The two branches have

---

* Jesse Huckert, *Analytical Kinematics of Plane Motion Mechanisms*, The Macmillan Co., New York, 1958. Huckert did not name this theorem but he was the first to bring together and state concisely the concepts.

a common vertical tangent.   The relative velocity of P_2 to P_1 is actually
zero at the point of contact; the relative displacement changes from
approach to recess.   Points P_2 and P_1
come together and then move apart with
relative motion along the common normal.   All points on the roller make contact in this manner.   In many cases all
three types of motion transfer are present.   At the point of contact in Fig. 2.19,
turning, sliding, and rolling are present.

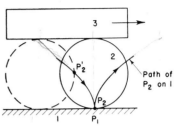

Fig. 2.25

2.18. Four-bar linkages.   A complex mechanism is sometimes defined as
a mechanism with one or more links with three or more elements of pairs.
In Chapter 14 it is shown that only four-bar linkages are composed entirely
of binary links.   The slider crank is a special case of the four-bar linkage,
and a direct contact mechanism, Fig. 2.19, is usually considered to be
an incomplete four-bar linkage.   The classification of four-bar linkages
given below follows that of Hrones and Nelson.*

Class A.   Crank and rocker mechanism.   One crank is capable of rotation through a complete revolution while the second crank can only oscillate, Figs. 2.26 and 2.27.

Requirements:

(1) Drive link must be the shortest link.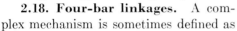

(2) $a < c + d - b$

(3) $a > c - d + b$

Class B.   Drag link mechanism.   Both cranks are capable of rotating
through 360°, Fig. 2.28.

Requirements:

(1) Line of centers must be shortest link.

(2) $a < c + d - b$

(3) $a > c - d + b$

Class C.   Double rocker mechanism.   Both cranks oscillate, but neither
can rotate through a complete revolution, Figs. 2.29 and 2.30.

Requirements:

(1) All cases where the connecting rod (coupler) is the shortest link.

(2) All linkages in which (2) and (3) for classes A and B are not
satisfied.

One extreme position for the rocker, link d, (Fig. 2.26) occurs when
b and c are coincident.   This is shown by the dotted links, where, for
clarity, the links have not quite reached the coincident position.   Now,
if c is shorter than b, say c', then link d must be greater than a, in Fig. 2.26

* J. A. Hrones and G. L. Nelson, *Analysis of the Four-Bar Linkage*, published
jointly by The Technology Press of the Massachusetts Institute of Technology and
John Wiley & Sons, Inc., New York, 1951.

it must be at least d' long.   It can be seen that b cannot have complete rotation because the distance between arc F' and the right portion of the circle traced by D is greater than link c'.   An inversion of the linkage with c as the fixed link is shown in Fig. 2.27.   Using the preceeding argument, it can be seen that link a must be greater than link b.

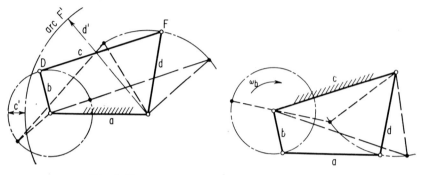

| Fig. 2.26 | Fig. 2.27 |

The links for the limiting position of the rocker for the condition of collinearity of links b and c are shown by broken lines in Fig. 2.26.   From this configuration we can write.

$$a + d > b + c \qquad (2.36)$$

For the other extreme position of the rocker which occurs when links b and c are coincident, we may use the fact that one side of a triangle is always greater than the difference of the other two sides and write

$$a - d < c - b \qquad (2.37)$$

In expressions of the type shown above, terms can be transposed if their signs are changed.   By adding the larger sides of Eqs. (2.36) and (2.37), and then adding the smaller sides, we can write

$$a + d + c - b > b + c + a - d \qquad \text{or} \qquad d > b$$

This completes the proof for the first requirement of class A linkages; i.e., the drive link must be the shortest link.   By transposing d in Eq. (2.37) to the other side we obtain the second requirement, and by transposing d in Eq. (2.36) we obtain the third requirement.

Inversion can be considered as the superimposing of a moving reference frame.   In Fig. 2.27, assume that link b rotates with constant angular velocity ω_b.   Link d oscillates while link a has combined oscillation and translation.   This latter motion can be considered as a type of oscillation. If a reference frame having rotation $-\omega_b$ is superimposed on the linkage, link b will be fixed, Fig. 2.28, and link c will have uniform rotation of $-\omega_b$. Link a will have the oscillation that it had in Fig. 2.27 with $-\omega_b$ superimposed on it.   This inversion then transforms a class A linkage into a

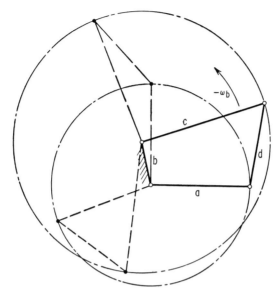

Fig. 2.28

class B linkage.   Drag link mechanisms are often used to convert uniform rotation (link c) to variable rotation (link a).   Since this linkage is an inversion of class A linkages, the requirements follow directly from those of class A.

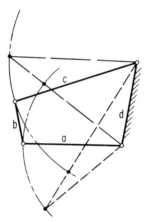

Fig. 2.29

Class C linkages can also be obtained from class A linkages by fixing link d, Fig. 2.29.   Links a and c now become rockers that cannot rotate through a complete revolution.   The two extreme positions, shown with dotted lines and with broken lines, have dead centers and should be avoided; i.e., the practical range of motion is less than the theoretical maximum. In Fig. 2.26, link b has complete rotation while link d has oscillation. Hence, if we fix d, link b should still be capable of continuous rotation. This is actually possible. In Fig. 2.29, move the linkage from the position shown with solid lines to the extreme position shown with broken lines. Now flex the joint between links a and b, and bring the linkage back in a crossed relationship. At the other extreme position which is shown with dotted lines, control the joint so that the linkage is brought back in the open arrangement shown. By continuing this process, link b can be made to rotate. This type of motion would be impractical; it is mentioned here to show that the theory of inversion holds without exception.

The linkage shown in Fig. 2.30 does not satisfy class A or class B requirements. Therefore it is a class C linkage regardless of which link is fixed. It should be noted that class A and B linkages can be used for class C linkages by limiting the motion.

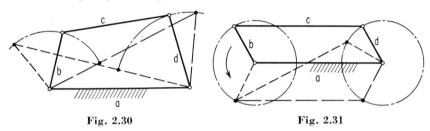

Fig. 2.30   Fig. 2.31

The parallel linkage, Fig. 2.31, is a special case where $a + d = b + c$ and $a - d = c - b$. When the driver (link b) and c are coincident, links a and d are collinear. Further turning of link b in a counter-clockwise direction will cause link d either to continue in a counter-clockwise direction as shown with broken lines, or to bend back and form a crossed linkage as shown with dotted lines. This crossed linkage is sometimes called the elliptical four-bar linkage because the displacement relationship of b and d is the same as for rolling ellipses. This is discussed in Chapter 8. The open and crossed linkages shown in Fig. 2.31 are not practical for continuous rotation unless means are taken to insure that the follower joint is carried through the dead centers.

PROBLEMS

2.1. For the crank and rocker mechanism shown in Fig. P 2.1, plot point D for each 30° displacement of crank 2. Draw a smooth curve through these points. (A tracing paper overlay containing link 3 with points B, C, and D can be helpful. Using the overlay, it is only necessary to locate B at each point, locate C on the circular arc traced by C, then prick through the overlay to obtain D on the drawing.)

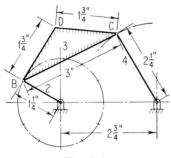

Fig. P 2.1

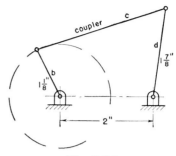

Fig. P 2.2

2.2. In Fig. P 2.2, link *b* is to rotate continuously, and *d* is to oscillate. Determine the theoretical maximum and minimum lengths for coupler *c*. Why, in practice, should the length be greater than the minimum and less than the maximum?

2.3. The Scott-Russell straight-line mechanism is shown in Fig. P 2.3. Here $OC = CB = DC$, and DCB is a rigid link. Show that D moves in a straight line that passes through O and is perpendicular to OB.

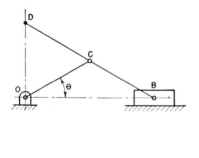

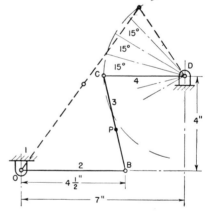

Fig. P 2.3 (above)
Fig. P 2.4 (right)

2.4. The Watt straight-line mechanism is shown in Fig. P 2.4. When the proportions are $CP/BP = OB/CD$ a portion of the path of P is very nearly straight. Plot the path of P using 15° intervals and the limiting positions for link CD. One limiting position is shown dotted.

2.5. A steel cylinder 10 in. in diameter is to be machined in a lathe. The cutting speed is to be 95 fpm. Determine the required speed of rotation in rpm.

2.6. An automobile wheel 28 in. in diameter is rotating at 550 rpm. Determine the speed of the automobile in (a) mph, (b) fps, and (c) the angular speed of the wheel in radians per sec.

2.7. The relative velocity of two points lying on a radial line of a revolving disk is 40 fps. The points are 4 in. apart. Determine the rpm of the disk.

2.8. An automobile starts from rest and accelerates at the rate of 5 fps² until a speed of 60 mph is attained. Determine the time in seconds and the distance traveled in feet.

2.9. A body starts from rest and accelerates uniformly for a distance of 4 ft and then decelerates uniformly for a distance of 2 ft and comes to rest. The total time is 4 sec. Determine the maximum (a) acceleration, (b) deceleration, (c) velocity.

2.10. Same as Prob. 2.9 except there is an additional travel of 2 ft at uniform velocity between the acceleration and deceleration periods.

2.11. A gasoline engine is started from rest and attains a speed of 3000 rpm in 5 sec. Assuming that the angular acceleration is constant determine (a) the angular acceleration of the crankshaft in radians per second squared (b) the number of revolutions made in coming up to speed.

2.12. A wheel 32 in. in diameter is turning with a speed of 420 rpm and is accelerating at the rate of 20 rps². Determine in feet and seconds: (a) the tangential acceleration of a point on the rim, (b) the normal acceleration, (c) the total acceleration.

2.13. A Scotch-yoke mechanism is shown in Fig. P 2.13. Let $\theta = 60°$, $R = 11$ in., and the speed of the crank be 175 rpm. Determine the velocity and acceleration of slider 3.

2.14. Referring to Fig. P 2.13, let the stroke of the slider 3 be 18 in. and the time for one stroke be 0.06 sec. Determine (a) the rpm of the crank, (b) the maximum velocity of the slider, (c) the maximum acceleration.

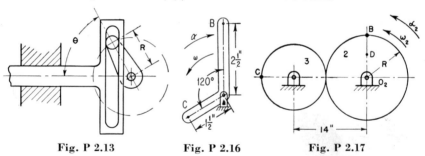

Fig. P 2.13   Fig. P 2.16   Fig. P 2.17

2.15. Measurements taken with a vibration meter show that a body is vibrating with harmonic motion at a frequency of 370 cycles per minute with a maximum acceleration of 260 in. per sec². Determine (a) amplitude of vibration, (b) maximum velocity.

2.16. In Fig. P 2.16, $\omega = 120$ rpm and $\alpha = 200$ radians per sec². Determine V_C, V_B, A_C^n, A_B^n, A_C^t, and A_B^t. Make a full size drawing of the figure and show the localized vectors to the following scales: velocity, 1 in. = 2 fps, acceleration, 1 in. = 20 fps². Determine graphically A_C, A_B, $A_{C/B}$ and $V_{C/B}$.

2.17. Two wheels that roll together are shown in Fig. P 2.17. Let $R = 9$ in., $\omega_2 = 250$ rpm, $\alpha_2 = 75$ radians per sec². Determine A_B^n, A_B^t, A_B, A_C^n, A_C^t, A_C, $A_{C/B}$.

EQUATIONS OF MOTION

2.18. Same as Prob. 2.17 except $\omega_2 = 340$ rpm, $\alpha_2 = 125$ radians per sec², $R = 10$ in., and D, located midway between B and O_2, is used instead of B.

2.19. In Fig. P 2.19, frame 2 moves to the left with a velocity of 40 mph. Wheels 4 and 3 are 72 in. and 42 in. in diameter, respectively. Determine the velocities V_{O_4}, V_{B/O_4}, V_B, $V_{B/C}$, ω_4, ω_3, $\omega_{4/3}$, $\omega_{3/4}$.

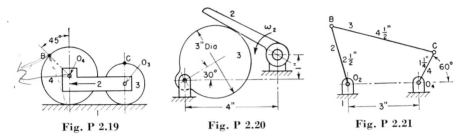

Fig. P 2.19   Fig. P 2.20   Fig. P 2.21

2.20. In Fig. P 2.20, $\omega_2 = 175$ rpm. Determine the angular velocity of member 3 in rpm and the velocity of sliding at the point of contact in fps.

2.21. In Fig. P 2.21, $\omega_2 = 150$ rpm CCW. Determine the angular velocity of member 4 in rpm.

2.22. Same as Prob. 2.21 except determine the angular velocity of link 3. (*Hint:* Use inversion, fix 2, and give proper ω to member 1; determine $\omega_{3/2}$, then absolute value of ω_3.)

CHAPTER 3

Velocities in Mechanisms

Instant Centers and Resolution

3.1. Introductory. There are two reasons why it is often necessary to make a velocity analysis: (1) The velocity analysis is used to determine cutting speeds in machine tools, to determine kinetic energy of parts that are designed to do work by virtue of their kinetic energy, to determine flow rates of fluids in machines such as engines and pumps, to determine load-carrying capacities of parts having film lubrication, etc. (2) The velocity analysis is a necessary step in making an acceleration analysis.

The illustrative examples that follow were chosen to represent the types of problems that are encountered in practice. The mechanisms are drawn in the simplest manner so that attention can be focused on the application of basic concepts to achieve the desired analysis.

3.2. Instant centers. An axis of rotation is an axis about which one body rotates relative to another body. In Fig. 3.1, member 2 rotates relative to member 1 about the axis O_{21}. This notation was first used in Art. 2.11. It can be written O_{21} or O_{12}. In plane motion, the motions of all points in a line perpendicular to the plane of motion are equal. It is not necessary to consider the thickness of the body; a study of the motion can be confined to one plane. The axis of rotation is often called the center of rotation.

An instant center of velocity is the point about which one body rotates relative to another for the particular phase being considered. It is a double point. The bodies have no linear velocity relative to each other at this point. At this point the two bodies have the same linear velocity relative to any other body.

Instant centers are of three types: fixed, permanent, and of a nature that is neither fixed nor permanent. These three types of centers occur in Fig. 3.5. Center O_{41} is a fixed instant center. It remains in the same place for all phases. Center O_{34} is the center about which link 3 rotates relative to 4 for the phase shown. This center moves when the mechanism moves, but the joint is of a permanent nature; O_{34} is a permanent instant center. It will be shown later that O_{31} is the point about which 3 rotates relative to 1 for the phase shown. Links 3 and 1 have no material connection at this point, and the location of the point varies for each phase. Center O_{31} is an instant center that is neither fixed nor permanent.

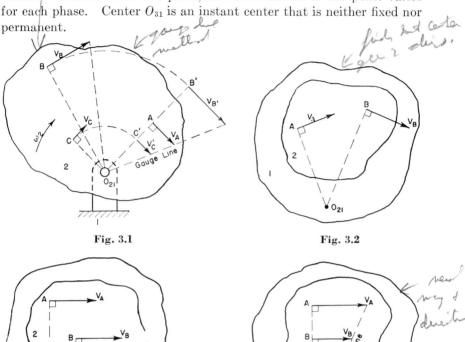

Fig. 3.1   Fig. 3.2

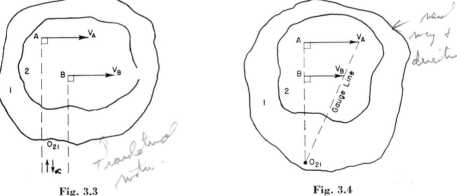

Fig. 3.3   Fig. 3.4

In Fig. 3.1, let V_A be the velocity of point A. From Art. 2.7 and Eq. (2.8) it is known that the direction of the velocity of any point in 2 relative to O_{21} is perpendicular to the line joining the point and O_{21}. The magnitude is $V = R\omega_2$. The value of ω_2 is the same for all points in the body; the velocity of any point in 2 is therefore proportional to R, the radius of the circular path described by the point. The velocity of point B can be determined graphically as follows. A gage line is drawn through the center of rotation O_{21} and the terminus of the known velocity vector V_A. An arc of radius $O_{21}B$ is drawn locating B'. The velocity of point B' is $V_{B'}$. When this vector is rotated back to B it becomes V_B; V_C is determined in the same manner.

If the directions of the velocities of two points in a body relative to a second body are known, the center of rotation can be determined. In Fig. 3.2, V_A and V_B are the known velocities of points A and B, respectively, relative to a fixed body 1. Perpendiculars erected to the vectors at A and B intersect at the instant center of rotation O_{21}.

In Fig. 3.3, perpendiculars erected to the known velocity directions at A and B are parallel. The center of rotation of 1 and 2 is at infinity. Member 2 must therefore have translation relative to member 1. If 2 is a rigid body, V_A and V_B must be equal.

In Fig. 3.4, perpendiculars erected to the known velocity directions at A and B are collinear. The location of the center cannot be determined unless the magnitudes of the velocities are known. If they are known, a gage line, as shown, can be drawn, locating center O_{21}.

3.3. Instant centers in mechanisms. A four-bar linkage is shown in Fig. 3.5. Points O_{41} and O_{21} are fixed centers, and points O_{34} and O_{23}

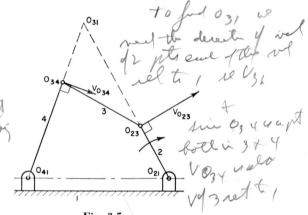

Fig. 3.5

are permanent centers. The direction of motion of O_{23} relative to 1, considered as a point in 2, is perpendicular to $O_{23}O_{21}$. Point O_{23} is also a point in 3; hence $V_{O_{23}}$ is also the velocity of point O_{23} relative to 1, considered as a point in 3. In a similar manner, $V_{O_{34}}$ is the velocity relative to 1 of point O_{34}, considered as a point in 3. The directions of motion of two points in 3 relative to 1 are known. The instant center O_{31} is located at the intersection of perpendiculars to these known velocities. Links 1 and 3 do not extend to include this point. If they did, it could be observed that links 1 and 3 have only relative rotation at this point.

Inversion does not affect relative motion (Art. 2.9). Only relative motions are being considered. Link 1 can be released and link 4 fixed, as shown in Fig. 3.6. The direction of $V_{O_{21}}$ is the direction of motion of point O_{21}, considered as a point in both 1 and 2, relative to 4. The direction of $V_{O_{23}}$ is the direction of motion of point O_{23}, considered as a point in both 2 and 3, relative to 4. The directions of motion of two points in 2 relative to 4 are known. The instant center of rotation O_{24} is located by drawing perpendiculars to these directions.

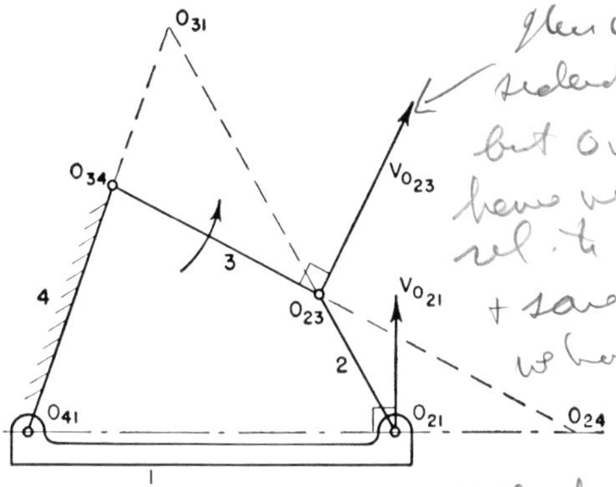

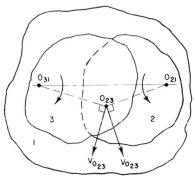

[margin note, handwritten:] rel. to 4 / there is need of pt O_{23}, con- / sidered as a pt on 3 / but O_{13} is also a but 2 / hence we have vel of pt O_{23} / rel. to 4 as a pt on 2 also. / + same with O_{21} the / we have vel of 2 pt as a / but 2 rel. to but / 4 + line is t / both direct intens at cent / 2 4

Fig. 3.6

The number of instant centers* in a mechanism is

$$\frac{n(n-1)}{2} \tag{3.1}$$

where n is the number of links. Locating the instant centers of a complex mechanism by the above method is tedious. A shorter method will be developed in the following articles.

3.4. Kennedy's theorem. *If three bodies have plane motion their instant centers lie on a straight line.* This theorem will be proved by showing that the third center cannot lie off the line passing through the other two, and then showing that it can lie on this line. In Fig. 3.7, center O_{21} is the instant center of 2 and 1, and O_{31} is the instant center of 3 and 1. Center O_{23} is assumed to lie off the line passing through O_{31} and O_{21}, as shown. The velocity of point O_{23} as a point in 3 is perpendicular to $O_{31}O_{23}$. The velocity of point O_{23} as a point in 2 is perpendicular to $O_{23}O_{21}$. These two velocities do not coincide. At this point, member 2 has linear velocity relative to member 3. This is contrary to

Fig. 3.7

* The number of pairs of links (or the number of instant centers) is the number of combinations of n links taken two at a time, which is

$$_nC_2 = \frac{n!}{2!(n-2)!} = \frac{n(n-1)}{2}$$

the definition of an instant center. In Fig. 3.8, center O_{23} is assumed to lie on the line $O_{31}O_{23}$. In this case the velocity of O_{23} as a point in 3 coincides with the velocity of O_{23} as a point in 2. There is no relative linear velocity between the parts of this double point. The exact location of O_{23} on the line depends on the directions and magnitudes of the angular velocities of 2 and 3 relative to 1.

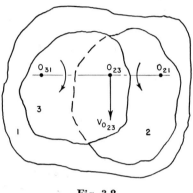

In Fig. 3.6, note that the instant centers of 1, 3, and 4 (O_{41}, O_{34}, O_{31}) lie on a line, the instant centers of 3, 2, and 4 (O_{34}, O_{23}, O_{24}) lie on a line, etc.

Fig. 3.8

3.5. Direct-contact mechanisms. In Fig. 3.9, the point of contact of 2 and 4 is the double point P_2P_4. The velocity of P_2 relative to the frame is the velocity vector P_2R_2, and the velocity of P_4 relative to the frame is P_4R_4 (see Fig. 2.19). The only velocity that P_4 can have relative to P_2 is sliding along the common tangent. The velocity of sliding of P_4 on P_2 is V_{P_4/P_2}. The center of rotation of 2 and 4 lies on the

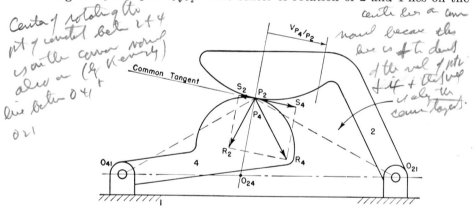

Fig. 3.9

perpendicular (the common normal) through the origin of this vector. The velocity of sliding V_{P_2/P_4} is equal and opposite to V_{P_4/P_2}. This is not an independent vector, but just another way of stating what is already known. Additional information can be obtained from Kennedy's theorem. It is known that center O_{24} lies on a line through O_{41} and O_{21}. The intersection of this line with the common normal locates center O_{24}.

3.6. Linear velocities. If the linear velocity of any point in a mechanism relative to the fixed member is known, the velocity of any other point in the mechanism relative to the fixed member can be determined by the use of instant centers. In Fig. 3.10, $V_{O_{23}}$ is the known velocity of O_{23} considered as a point in 2. The velocity of O_{34} as a point in 4 can be determined as follows. Using O_{21} as a center, rotate vector $V_{O_{23}}$ to the position B on the line of centers. This vector is indicated as $V'_{O_{23}}$. It should be remembered that if link 2 is extended to include B, then $V'_{O_{23}}$ would be the velocity of this point in link 2. A gage line through the center O_{21} and the terminus of vector $V'_{O_{23}}$ is used to determine the velocity of point O_{24} considered as a point in 2. Point O_{24} is also a point in 4. A gage line through center O_{41} and the terminus of $V_{O_{24}}$ can be used to determine the velocity of any other point in member 4. Using O_{41} as a center, an arc from O_{34} is drawn to C on the line of centers.

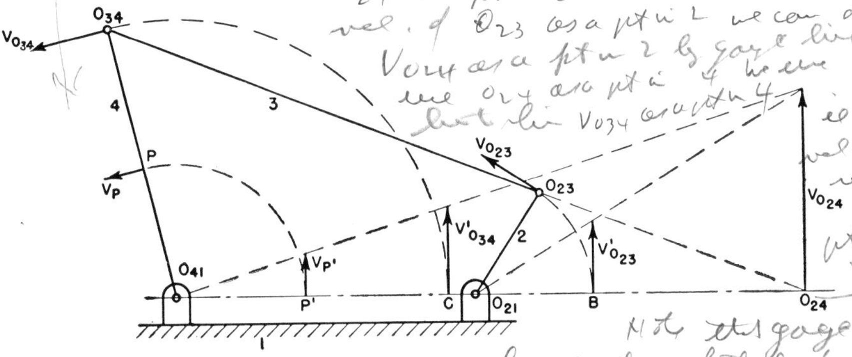

Fig. 3.10

Velocity $V'_{O_{34}}$ is the velocity of point C as a point in 4; $V'_{O_{34}}$ is rotated to position $V_{O_{34}}$, giving the desired vector.

In the above example, O_{24} was used as a transfer point. It was used to transfer from the known member 2 to the unknown, 4. This method is general. From Kennedy's theorem, the centers of rotation of known and unknown members and their common center or transfer point lie on a line.

The above example could have been solved in another manner, as shown in Fig. 3.11. Points O_{23} and O_{34} are both in member 3. The velocity of O_{23} as a point in 3 relative to 1 is known. A gage line through O_{31} and the terminus of $V_{O_{23}}$ can be used to determine the velocity of any other point in member 3. $V_{O_{34}}$ is determined as shown.

If $V_{O_{23}}$ is given, and it is desired to determine the velocity V_P, then $V_{O_{34}}$ must be determined first; then a gage line through O_{41} and the terminus of $V_{O_{34}}$ is used to determine V_P. By the method used in Fig. 3.10, V_P can be found without first determining $V_{O_{34}}$.

If the velocity of one point in a mechanism relative to some other point in the mechanism is desired, the absolute velocities are determined

first. These are used to determine the relative velocity, as explained
in Art. 2.7. *el welg relativ sol equat*

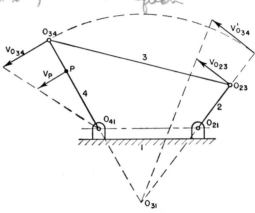

Fig. 3.11

3.7. Parallel line construction. A four-bar linkage is shown in
Fig. 3.12. The velocities of D and C are to be determined from the

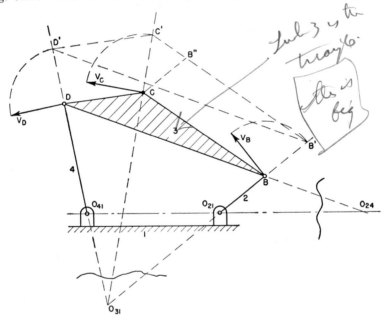

Fig. 3.12

known velocity of B. Assume that O_{24} and O_{31} lie off the paper and are
not available for making constructions. The desired velocities can be
determined as follows. Lay off BB' equal to V_B along the line $O_{21}B$
which passes through the center O_{31}. Construct $B'C'D'$ by drawing

lines parallel to the sides of link BCD. Then CC' is equal to $|V_C|$; the direction of V_C is perpendicular to CC'. This construction can be proved as follows. Draw CB'' parallel to BB'. Triangles $O_{31}BC$ and $CB''C'$ are similar. The velocities of points in a rotating body are proportional to their distances from the center of rotation; hence

$$\frac{V_B}{V_C} = \frac{O_{31}B}{O_{31}C} = \frac{CB''}{CC'} = \frac{BB'}{CC'}$$

Since BB' was made equal to $|V_B|$, CC' is equal to $|V_C|$; and V_D is determined in a similar way.

The parallel line construction is used for determining the velocities of points in a link from the known velocity of a point in the same link.

3.8. Angular velocities. Angular velocities can be determined from linear velocities, and vice versa. If, in Fig. 3.10, ω_2 is known, $V_{O_{23}}$ can be determined from the equation

$$V_{O_{23}} = R\omega = (O_{21}O_{23})\omega_2$$

and $V_{O_{34}}$ is determined by one of the methods of the previous articles. Then ω_4 is

$$\omega_4 = \frac{V}{R} = \frac{V_{O_{34}}}{O_{41}O_{34}}$$

A more direct method of obtaining ω_4 from ω_2 is to use O_{24} as a transfer point. The term $V_{O_{24}}$ is a velocity of points in 2 and 4.

$$\omega_2 = \frac{V}{R} = \frac{V_{O_{24}}}{O_{21}O_{24}}, \qquad \omega_4 = \frac{V_{O_{24}}}{O_{41}O_{24}}$$

Dividing the second equation by the first gives

$$\frac{\omega_4}{\omega_2} = \frac{V_{O_{24}}}{O_{41}O_{24}} \times \frac{O_{21}O_{24}}{V_{O_{24}}} = \frac{O_{21}O_{24}}{O_{41}O_{24}} \tag{3.2}$$

or

$$\omega_4 = \omega_2 \frac{O_{21}O_{24}}{O_{41}O_{24}}$$

In the same manner, ω_3 can be determined from ω_2 (see Fig. 3.11). Here $V_{O_{23}}$ is the velocity of points in 2 and 3; ω_2 and the centers of rotation O_{21} and O_{31} are known; hence

$$\omega_3 = \omega_2 \frac{O_{21}O_{23}}{O_{31}O_{23}}$$

Equation (3.2) can be stated as a theorem: *The angular velocities of two members are inversely proportional to the distances from the centers of rotation of the two members to their instant center (the third center located by Kennedy's theorem).*

Compare Fig. 3.9 with Fig. 2.19. Note that point M in Fig. 2.19 corresponds to O_{24} in Fig. 3.9. Make the same comparison with Fig. 3.10 and Fig. 2.20. It is always true that the intersection of the line of centers and the common normal of driver and follower is the instant center of driver and follower.   The above theorem is equivalent to the angular velocity theorem of Art. 2.12.

3.9. Obvious centers.   In order to locate instant centers, using Kennedy's theorem, it is first necessary to locate all the obvious centers. If these are not located, some of the others cannot be found.   In direct-contact mechanisms such as Fig. 3.9, the intersection of the common normal with the line of centers of driver and follower should be recognized as an instant center.   The mechanism shown in Fig. 3.13 is of no practical value, but is shown because it includes all other types of obvious centers.   Wheel 4 rolls on track 1; it pushes the slider 2 on the

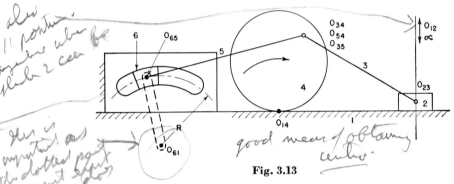

Fig. 3.13

horizontal surface of 1, and pulls slider 6 in the curved slot in 1.   All centers shown are obvious and must be indicated before Kennedy's theorem can be applied for locating the other centers.   The pin connections in the sliders are O_{23} and O_{65}.   Members 3, 4, and 5 are pinned at one point.   Centers O_{34}, O_{54}, and O_{35} are located here.   Wheel 4 rolls on the track without sliding.   At the point of contact the wheel and track have no relative linear motion.   This point is therefore the instant center O_{14}.   If block 6 is extended, as shown by broken lines, and pinned to 1 at the center of curvature of the slot, block 6 will have the same motion that it has when moving in the guide.   Point O_{61} is the instant center of 6 and 1.   Block 2 has rectilinear motion relative to 1.   The center of curvature of the path of 2 relative to 1 is at infinity.   Point O_{12} is therefore at infinity (see Fig. 3.3).

Example 1.   Locate all the instant centers for the mechanism shown in Fig. 3.14.   The number of instant centers is

$$\frac{n(n-1)}{2} = \frac{4(4-1)}{2} = 6$$

The obvious centers O_{34}, O_{23}, O_{21}, and O_{41} are located first.   From Kennedy's theorem it is known that O_{31} lies on a line through O_{21} and O_{32}.   It also lies on a line through O_{41} and O_{34}.   It therefore lies at the intersection of these two lines. Center O_{24} will be located at the intersection of lines $O_{34}O_{23}$ and $O_{41}O_{21}$.   Line $O_{41}O_{21}$ is at infinity.   Point O_{24} therefore lies on line $\overline{O_{34}O_{23}}$ at infinity.

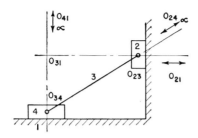

Fig. 3.14

Example 2. A steam-locomotive mechanism is shown in Fig. 3.15. The motion of the frame relative to the track will be considered. The number of instant centers is

$$\frac{6(6-1)}{2} = 15$$

When a mechanism has a large number of instant centers, some simple method of recording them is desirable. One method is shown in Fig. 3.16. Points with numbers corresponding to the links are located in a circular arrangement. When

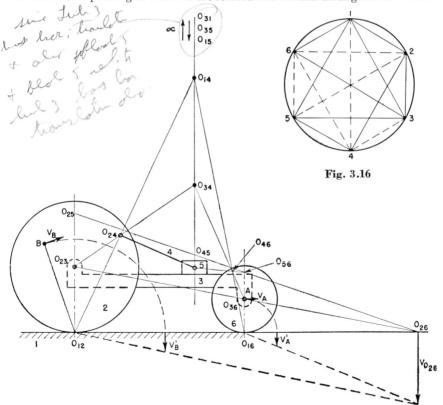

Fig. 3.16

Fig. 3.15

a center is located on the mechanism, a line is drawn joining the corresponding points in Fig. 3.16. Point O_{23} is an obvious center. It is indicated on the mechanism, and then a line is drawn from 2 to 3 in Fig. 3.16. The other obvious centers are located and recorded with solid lines.

The broken lines in Fig. 3.16 represent the centers that are located with the use of Kennedy's theorem. There is no definite order for locating these points. Point O_{34} can be located next. In Fig. 3.16, solid lines exist from 2 to 3 and 2 to 4. A line through these available centers O_{23} and O_{24} contains O_{34}. A solid line connects 1 and 3 but not 1 and 4. Center O_{41} is not yet known. This condition exists at point 6. From point 5, solid lines extend to 3 and 4. These centers are available, and a line through O_{35} and O_{45} can be drawn and O_{34} located. A solid line is now drawn from 3 to 4, indicating that O_{34} is available for use in determining other centers. The remaining centers are located in a similar manner.

Assume that the velocity of the locomotive is known. It is desired to determine the velocity of point B in wheel 2 relative to the track. The velocity of frame 3 is that of the locomotive. This known velocity is laid off as V_A at point A on the frame. This is also a point in 6. Point O_{26} is used as a transfer point to obtain the velocity of B in 2. The velocity V_A could have been laid off at O_{23}, thus obtaining the velocity of a point in 2 directly.

3.10. Linear velocities by resolution. In Art. 1.13, it was shown that the displacement of a body having plane motion can be considered separate rotational and translational displacements. It was stated that the motion at any instant can be considered a combination of rotation and translation relative to some point. This will now be shown. In Fig. 3.17, body 2 has rotation ω_2 about instant center O_{21}. This completely defines the motion of 2 relative to 1 for the instant shown. The velocity of B is V_B.

If a point in 1 other than O_{21} is chosen for the reference point, the motion must be specified as a rotation with angular velocity ω_2 about the new point, plus a translation. A translation component can be assumed and the new reference point determined, or a reference point can be chosen and the translation determined. The first case will be considered first.

If an arbitrary translational velocity is added to body 2, the linear velocity of every point in the body relative to 1 will be changed, but ω_2, the relative angular velocity of the bodies, will not be changed since no angular velocity is added. A translational velocity $V_B(t)$ is added to the body. The velocity of B relative to 1 is now $V_B(r)$, the vector sum of $V_B(t)$ and V_B. The new instant center will lie on a perpendicular at the origin of vector $V_B(r)$. Since ω_2 is unchanged, the location of this center can be calculated from the equation

$$BD = \frac{V_B(r)}{\omega_2}$$

or can be obtained graphically by making θ' equal to θ. The double point D_1D_2 is the instant center. If body 2 is now given translation V_{D_2/D_1}, equal but opposite to $V_B(t)$, the instantaneous motion will be restored to its original state. The original motion can therefore be specified as a rotation ω_2 about D_1 and a translation V_{D_2/D_1}. The second case will now be considered.

In Fig. 3.18, the motion of body 2 is ω_2 about O_{21} which produces the total velocity V_B. After arbitrarily choosing a reference point $D_1 D_2$, the velocity V_{D_2/D_1} is determined from the gauge line as shown. The rotational component $V_B(r)$ may be obtained by subtracting the translational component from the total velocity, or from equation $V_B(r) = BD\omega_2$. The original motion may then be specified as rotation ω_2 about D_1 and translation V_{D_2/D_1}.

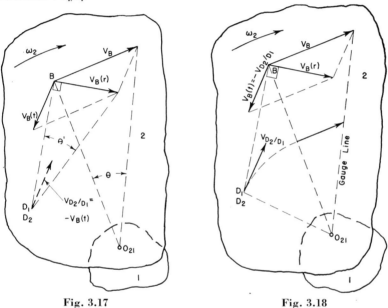

Fig. 3.17   Fig. 3.18

In the resolution method for determining linear velocities, it is convenient to use a particular reference point. Link BC is shown in Fig. 3.19. The velocity of B is known and the direction of V_C is known. The instant center of the link O_{21} can be located as shown. The reference point D_1 that is used in the resolution method can be determined by drawing a perpendicular from the center O_{21} to the line joining the points of known velocity and known velocity direction. The translation component V_{D_2/D_1} can be determined from gage line [1] as shown, and V_{D_2/D_1} lies along line BC. This is why D_1 was so chosen. All points in link 2 have this translation component. In the resolution method, all the instant centers are not available. The reference point is obtained in a different manner. The translation component $V_B(t)$ is obtained by drawing EF perpendicular to BC. Then $V_C(t)$, the translation component of V_C, is equal to $V_B(t)$. The perpendicular at the terminus of

$V_C(t)$ determines the magnitude of V_C. The rotational components $V_B(r)$ and $V_C(r)$ are determined by completing the rectangles as shown. Gage line [2] through the termini of $V_B(r)$ and $V_C(r)$ locates the reference point D_1D_2.

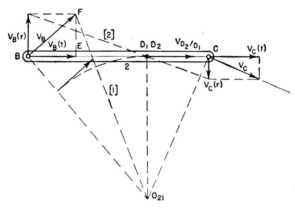

Fig. 3.19

Example 3. A four-bar linkage is shown in Fig. 3.20. The velocity of B is known, and it is desired to determine the velocities of C and E. The translational component $V_B(t)$ along line BC is determined by drawing a perpendicular from the terminus of V_B to line BC. Velocity $V_C(t)$ is equal to $V_B(t)$. The direction of V_C is perpendicular to CO_{21}. A perpendicular to BC at the terminus of $V_C(t)$

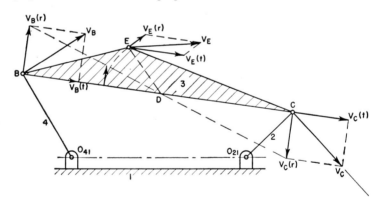

Fig. 3.20

determines the magnitude of V_C. The center of rotation D is determined from the gage line through the termini of $V_B(r)$ and $V_C(r)$. Then $V_E(r)$, the rotational component of E, is determined from this gage line. The translational component $V_E(t)$ is equal to $V_B(t)$, and V_E is the vector sum of $V_E(r)$ and $V_E(t)$.

Example 4. In Fig. 3.21, the velocity V_{B_2} is known, and the velocities of D and E are desired. The component of V_{B_2} that lies along the common normal of 2 and 4 (see Fig. 2.19) is V_{B_4}. The translational component along B_4C, obtained by drawing a perpendicular from the terminus of V_{B_4} to B_4C, is zero. This results from the fact that the instant center O_{41} and the reference point D_1 coincide (see Fig. 3.19). The value of V_C is determined from the gage line as shown. The translational component of V_C along link 5 is $V_C(t)5$. The translational com-

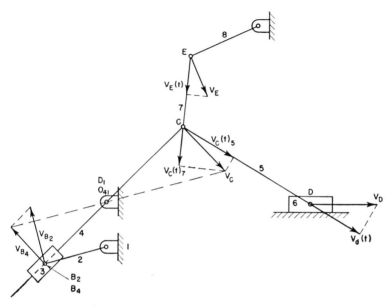

Fig. 3.21

ponent of D, velocity $V_D(t)$, is equal to $V_C(t)5$. The resultant velocity of D is horizontal. It is determined from the known component $Vd(t)$. Velocity $V_C(t)7$ is the translational component of V_C along link CE, and V_E is determined from the component $V_E(t)$.

PROBLEMS

3.1. Locate all the instant centers for the mechanism shown in Fig. P 3.1.

3.2. Locate all the instant centers for the mechanism shown in Fig. P 3.2.

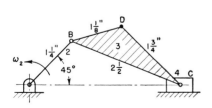

Fig. P 3.1

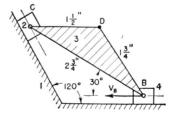

Fig. P 3.2

3.3. Locate all the instant centers for the mechanism shown in Fig. P 3.3.

3.4. Locate all the instant centers for the mechanism shown in Fig. P 3.4.

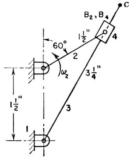

Fig. P 3.3

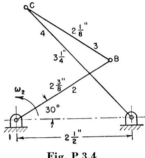

Fig. P 3.4

3.5. Locate all the instant centers for the mechanism shown in Fig. P 3.5.

3.6. Locate all the instant centers for the mechanism shown in Fig. P 3.6.

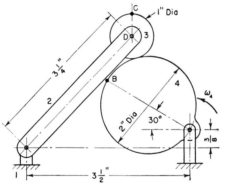

Fig. P 3.5

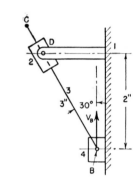

Fig. P 3.6

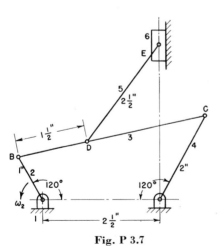

Fig. P 3.7

Fig. P 3.8

3.7. Locate all the instant centers for the mechanism shown in Fig. P 3.7.

3.8. Locate all the instant centers for the mechanism shown in Fig. P 3.8.

3.9. In Fig. P 3.1, let V_B be represented by a vector 1 in. long. Determine the vectors V_D and V_C.

3.10. In Fig. P 3.2, let V_B be represented by a vector 1 in. long. Determine the vectors V_D and V_C.

3.11. In Fig. P 3.3, let V_{B_2} be represented by a vector 1 in. long. Determine the vector V_C.

3.12. In Fig. P 3.4, let V_B be represented by a vector 1 in. long. Determine the vector V_C.

3.13. In Fig. P 3.5, let V_B be represented by a vector 1 in. long. Determine the vector V_C.

3.14. In Fig. P 3.6, let V_B be represented by a vector 1 in. long. Determine the vector V_C.

3.15. In Fig. P 3.7, let V_B be represented by a vector 1 in. long. Determine the vector V_E.

3.16. In Fig. P 3.8, let V_{B_2} be represented by a vector 1 in. long. Determine the vectors V_C, V_E, and V_D.

3.17. In Fig. P 3.1, let $\omega_2 = 150$ rpm. Determine ω_3.

3.18. In Fig. P 3.2, let $V_B = 20$ fps. Determine ω_3.

3.19. In Fig. P 3.3, let $\omega_2 = 250$ rpm. Determine ω_3.

3.20. In Fig. P 3.4, let $\omega_2 = 75$ rpm. Determine ω_3 and ω_4.

3.21. In Fig. P 3.5, let $\omega_4 = 100$ rpm. Determine ω_2 and ω_3.

3.22. In Fig. P 3.6, let $V_B = 30$ fps. Determine ω_3.

3.23. In Fig. P 3.7, let $\omega_2 = 80$ rpm. Determine ω_3, ω_4, ω_5, and ω_6.

3.24. In Fig. P 3.8, let $\omega_2 = 90$ rpm. Determine ω_3, ω_4, ω_5, and ω_6.

3.25. Using Fig. 2.19, show that the velocity of sliding at the point of contact is $(\omega_2 + \omega_4)PM$. When M lies outside the centers, show that the velocity of sliding is $(\omega_2 - \omega_4)PM$. (*Hint: M* is an instant center.)

3.26. In Fig. P 3.1, let V_B be represented by a vector 1 in. long. Determine V_C and V_D. Use the resolution method.

3.27. In Fig. P 3.6, let V_B be represented by a vector 1 in. long. Determine the vector V_C. Use the resolution method.

3.28. In Fig. P 3.7, let V_B be represented by a vector 1 in. long. Determine V_C, V_D, and V_E. Use the resolution method.

3.29. In Fig. P 3.8, let V_B be represented by a vector 1 in. long. Determine V_C, V_D, and V_E. Use the resolution method.

CHAPTER 4

Velocity Polygons

4.1. Velocity polygons. The velocity polygon or relative velocity method is a very useful and rapid way of determining linear and angular velocities in mechanisms. This method has the additional advantage over the instant center and resolution methods that it can be extended to make acceleration analyses. This will be considered in the next chapter. The key to the construction is, *the velocity of any point in a link relative to any other point in the same link is perpendicular to the line joining the two points.*

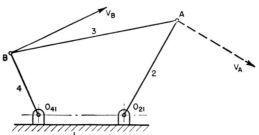

Fig. 4.1

Linear velocities are obtained by the use of the key and equations of relative velocity. In Fig. 4.1 the velocity of B is known, and the velocity of A is desired. A vector equation involving A and B is

$$V_{A/B} = V_A \rightarrow V_B$$

This equation can be written in the form

$$V_A = V_B \nleftrightarrow V_{A/B} \qquad (4.1)$$

The direction of V_A is known, V_B is known in magnitude and direction, and the direction of $V_{A/B}$ is known. This information is sufficient for solving the equation. In Fig. 4.2, V_B is laid off and a line in the direction of $V_{A/B}$ (perpendicular to BA) is drawn through the terminus of V_B. The origin of V_A will lie at the origin of V_B and the terminus of V_A will lie on the line containing $V_{A/B}$. A line is drawn through the origin of V_B in the direction of V_A. The intersection determines the magnitudes of V_A and

50

$V_{A/B}$.   The notation that will be used in this book is shown in Fig. 4.3, where ob represents V_B, oa represents V_A, ba represents $V_{A/B}$, and ab represents $V_{B/A}$.   The pole o is the point of zero velocity.

The mechanism in Fig. 4.4 is similar to that of Fig. 4.1.   It is desired to determine the velocities of all lettered points.   The velocity of B is known and V_A is determined as in the example above.   The velocity of C

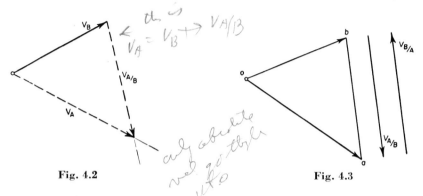

Fig. 4.2   Fig. 4.3

can now be determined from the known velocities of B and A.   An equation involving C and B is

$$V_C = V_B \nleftrightarrow V_{C/B} \tag{4.2}$$

The magnitude and direction of V_B and the direction of $V_{C/B}$ are known. This information is not sufficient to solve the equation.   An equation involving C and A is

$$V_C = V_A \nleftrightarrow V_{C/A} \tag{4.3}$$

There is not sufficient information to solve this equation.   Equations (4.2) and (4.3) can be solved simultaneously as shown in Fig. 4.5.   From Eq. (4.2), V_B is laid off as ob.   A line through b in the direction $V_{C/B}$ (perpendicular to BC) will contain the terminus of V_C.   From Eq. (4.3), V_A is laid off as oa.   A line through a in the direction $V_{C/A}$ (perpendicular to CA) will contain the terminus of V_C.   Then oc is the vector V_C.   In working problems separate diagrams are not drawn for determination of the velocity of each point.   All work is done on one diagram or velocity polygon.   Figures 4.3 and 4.5 are combined in Fig. 4.6.   Point a on the diagram was determined by drawing lines of known direction through known points o and b, and c was determined by drawing lines of known direction through known points a and b.   The directions of the velocities of $V_{D/B}$, $V_{D/C}$, and $V_{D/A}$ are known.   Point d can be located by drawing lines of known direction containing the terminus of V_D through b and c or through c and a.

Point d can also be located by proportion.   Each link in Fig. 4.4 has an image in Fig. 4.6 that is similar.   Line ob is perpendicular to

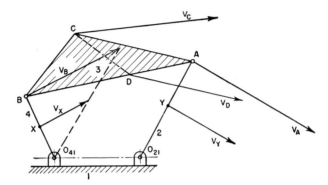

Fig. 4.4

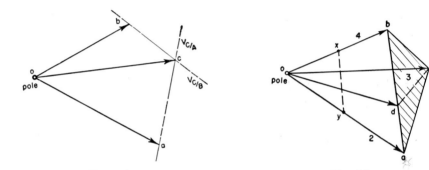

Fig. 4.5   Fig. 4.6

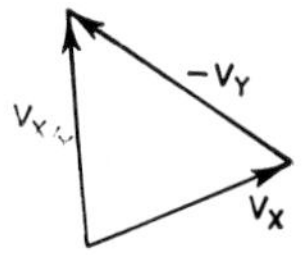

Fig. 4.7

$O_{41}B$, ba is perpendicular to BA, cd is perpendicular to CD, etc. These velocity images are rotated 90° relative to the links in the original mechanism. The frame has zero velocity. Its image is a point at the pole o. Then d can be located from the ratio

$$\frac{bd}{ba} = \frac{BD}{BA}$$

Now V_X can be determined from a gage line as shown in Fig. 4.4. It can also be obtained by properly locating x on ob, the velocity image of link 4. From similar triangles

$$\frac{V_X}{V_B} = \frac{O_{41}X}{O_{41}B}$$

Then ob represents V_B, ox will represent V_X if it is obtained from the ratio

$$\frac{ox}{ob} = \frac{O_{41}X}{O_{41}B}$$

and oy representing V_Y can be obtained in a similar manner.

The velocity of X relative to Y is

$$V_{X/Y} = V_X \rightarrow V_Y$$

This construction is shown in Fig. 4.7. The vector $V_{X/Y}$ is equal to the line from y to x in Fig. 4.6, and $V_{Y/X}$ is the line from x to y. Lines from the pole to points on the velocity polygon represent absolute velocities of the corresponding points on the mechanism. A line joining any two points on the velocity polygon represents the vector difference of the absolute velocities. From this it can be stated that *the velocity of any point on a mechanism relative to any other point on the mechanism is represented by the line joining the corresponding points on the velocity polygon.*

4.2. Angular velocities. The angular velocity of a link can be determined by dividing the velocity of a point in the link relative to any other point in the link by the distance between them. The angular velocity of link 3 in Fig. 4.4 is

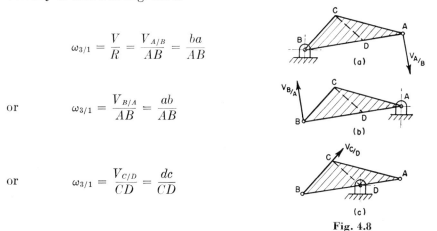

$$\omega_{3/1} = \frac{V}{R} = \frac{V_{A/B}}{AB} = \frac{ba}{AB}$$

or

$$\omega_{3/1} = \frac{V_{B/A}}{AB} = \frac{ab}{AB}$$

or

$$\omega_{3/1} = \frac{V_{C/D}}{CD} = \frac{dc}{CD}$$

Fig. 4.8

etc. In the first case the velocity of A relative to B is taken. This means that B is thought of as being fixed. It is shown fixed in Fig. 4.8(a), and the vector $V_{A/B}$ is placed at A. It can be seen that link 3 has clockwise rotation. When considering a point fixed as is done above, the translation component that is associated with this reference point is eliminated. This does not affect the angular velocity.

Example 1. In Fig. 4.9 the angular velocity of link 2 is 443 rpm CCW. The velocity of C and the angular velocity of link 5 are desired. The velocity polygon is shown in Fig. 4.10. All data apply to the original drawing. The velocity of A is

$$V_A = AO_{21}\omega_2 = \frac{1.125}{12} \times \frac{2\pi 443}{60} = 4.36 \quad \text{fps}$$

This is laid off as oa to an assumed velocity scale of 1 in. $= k_v = 2$ fps. The velocity of B relative to A is perpendicular to BA. A line through a in this direction contains b. The velocity of B relative to O_{41} is perpendicular to BO_{41}. A line through pole o in this direction contains b. Thus b is located at the intersection of these two lines. The motion of C relative to the frame is horizontal. A horizontal line through o contains c. The velocity of C relative to B is perpendicular to CB. A line through b in this direction contains c. Thus c is

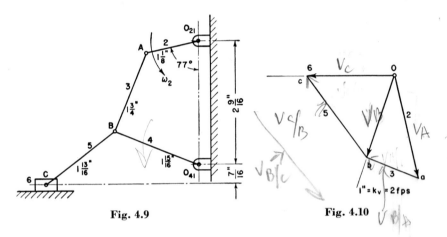

Fig. 4.9   **Fig. 4.10**

located at the intersection of these two lines. On the drawing oc scales 1.9 in. The velocity of C is

$$V_C = ock_v = 1.9 \times 2 = 3.8 \quad \text{fps}$$

Block 6 has rectilinear translation relative to the frame. All points in it have the same velocity. The velocity image of 6 is a point at c. The value of $V_{B/C}$ is obtained from the velocity polygon and is used to determine the angular velocity of link 5.

$$\omega_5 = \frac{V_{B/C}}{BC} = \frac{4.26}{1.8125/12} = 28.2 \quad \text{radians per sec CW}$$

Example 2. A direct-contact mechanism is shown in Fig. 4.11. Here ω_2 is known and the velocity of B is desired. Velocity V_{D_2} is the product of the radius D_2O_{21} and ω_2. This vector is laid off as od_2 in Fig. 4.12. The only motion that D_4 can have relative to D_2 is sliding along the common tangent at the point of contact. A line through d_2 in this direction contains d_4. The motion of D_4 relative to the frame is perpendicular to D_4O_{41}. A line through o in this direction contains d_4, and d_4 is located at the intersection of these two lines. To aid in visualizing the problem, BD_4O_{41} is indicated as a triangular member. For the phase shown this triangular link has the same angular velocity as the circular link. Point b is determined from the known points o and d_4.

Example 3. A quick-return mechanism is shown in Fig. 4.13. Velocity V_{B_2} is known and the velocity of D is desired. Velocity V_{B_2} is laid off as ob_2 in Fig. 4.14. The direction of motion of B_4 is perpendicular to link CO_{41}. A line through o in this direction contains b_4. The motion of B_4 relative to B_2 is sliding along the link CO_{41}. A line through b_2 in this direction contains b_4, and b_4 is located at the intersection of these two lines. Then c is located by proportion. It is

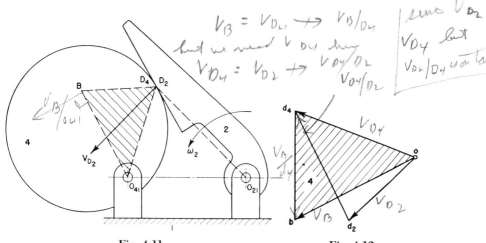

Fig. 4.11   Fig. 4.12

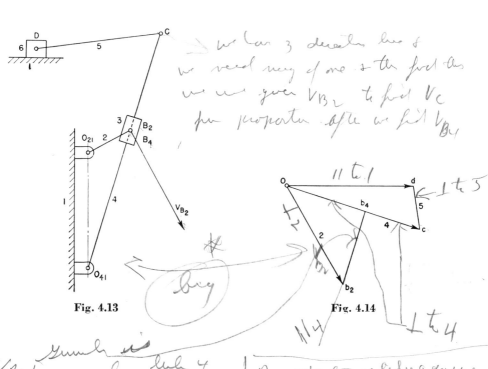

Fig. 4.13   Fig. 4.14

known that link $O_{41}B_4C$ has a velocity image similar to it. Then b_4c is determined from the proportion

$$\frac{b_4c}{ob_4} = \frac{B_4C}{O_{41}B_4}$$

Point d is determined from the known points c and o.

Example 4. An oscillating cylinder mechanism is shown in Fig. 4.15. Here V_A is known and the velocity of point B is desired. Velocity V_A is laid off as oa in Fig. 4.16. The direction of motion of B is not known. It is necessary to select some point in 3 of known velocity direction. Member 3 is extended to include

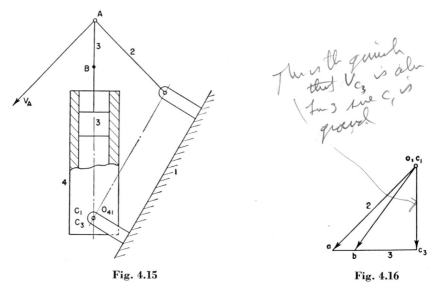

Fig. 4.15   Fig. 4.16

point O_{41}. This does not alter the motions of the links. Point O_{41} is also indicated at C_1C_3, a double point in 1 and 3. The direction of motion of C_3 relative to C_1 is along the line AC_1. A line through o in this direction contains C_3. The direction of motion of C_3 relative to A is perpendicular to C_3A. A line through a in this direction contains c_3, and c_3 is located at the intersection of these lines. Then ac_3 is the velocity image of AC_3, and b is located by proportion.

Example 5. Trial solution. A quick return mechanism is shown in Fig. 4.17. Here V_{B_2} is known and the velocity of point D is desired. Velocity V_{B_2} is laid off as ob_2 in Fig. 4.18. A horizontal line through o contains d, a vertical line through o contains c, and a line through b_2 parallel to link 4 contains b_4. This information is not sufficient to locate a point in link 4. It is necessary to use a trial solution. It is known that link 4 will have a velocity image that is similar and perpendicular to DC. It is also known that one end of the image will lie on the line containing d, and the other end on the line containing c. A trial solution $(c)(d)$ is drawn and (b_4) is located by proportion. All conditions are satisfied except one: (b_4) does not lie on the line containing b_4. This solution is not correct. A second trial solution $((c)) ((d))$ is made and $((b_4))$ is located by proportion. This solution is not correct. A line through (b_4) and $((b_4))$ will be the locus of b_4 for all trial solutions

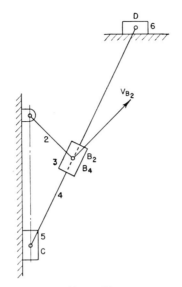

Fig. 4.17

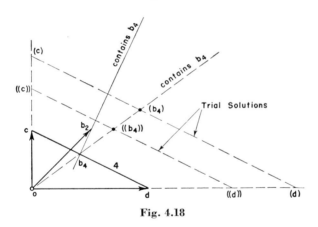

Fig. 4.18

and will therefore contain the correct b_4. The intersection of this line with the line through b_2 parallel to DC is the correct b_4. The correct image cb_4d is drawn. It can be seen that the line through (b_4) and $((b_4))$ passes through the intersection of the lines containing c and d. If this intersection is used only one trial solution is necessary.

Example 6. In Fig. 4.19 the velocity of B is known and the velocity of D is desired. Velocity V_{A_2} is determined from V_B as shown in Fig. 4.19. Wheels 2 and 3 have rolling contact; therefore $V_{A_2} = V_{A_3}$. Velocity V_F is determined from V_{A_3} as shown. Now V_B and V_F are laid off as ob and of, respectively, in Fig. 4.20. A line through f perpendicular to EF contains e, a line through b perpendicular to CB contains c, a vertical line through o contains d. A trial solution is necessary. Line $(e)(c)$ is drawn perpendicular to EC with one end on the line

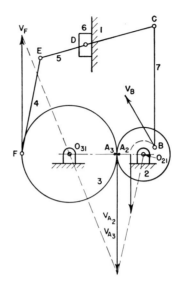

Fig. 4.19

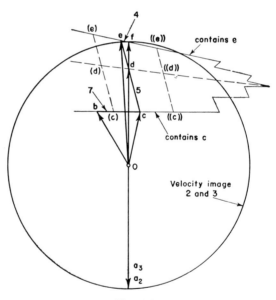

Fig. 4.20

containing e and the other end on the line containing c; (d) is located by proportion. The intersection of the lines containing e and c lies off the paper and is not available for use. A second trial solution $((e))((d))((c))$ is necessary. The intersection of the line through $(d)((d))$ and the vertical line containing d locates d.

The velocity images of 2 and 3 are shown. Both wheels have zero velocity at their centers and the same peripheral speed. One circle with its center at o

represents both wheels. The position of oa_2 relative to $O_{21}A_2$ shows that the
image of 2 is rotated 90° CCW relative to member 2 in Fig. 4.19. The relative
positions of oa_3 and $O_{31}A_3$ show that image 3 is rotated 90° CW relative to member 3.

Example 7. In Fig. 4.21 the velocity of A is known and the velocity of D is
desired. An attempt to solve this problem will lead to trial solutions for links

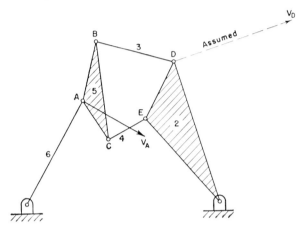

Fig. 4.21

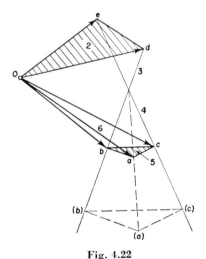

Fig. 4.22

3, 4, and 5. Information is not available to make this solution. A solution can
be obtained as shown in Fig. 4.22 by neglecting V_A and assuming a velocity vector
V_D. When this is done a trial solution is necessary only for link 5. The length
of oa is measured on the drawing, and the velocity scale is calculated, using this
length and the known value of V_A. All other velocities can be determined from
Fig. 4.22 and this scale.

4.3. Simultaneous trial solutions for two links. A Walschaert valve gear that is used on steam locomotives is shown in Fig. 4.23. The construction of the velocity polygon for this mechanism requires trial solutions for links 6 and 8. The reversing lever is stationary most of the time, and H will be assumed fixed. The piston and crosshead 4,

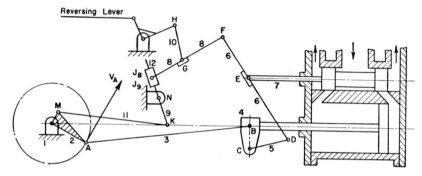

Fig. 4.23

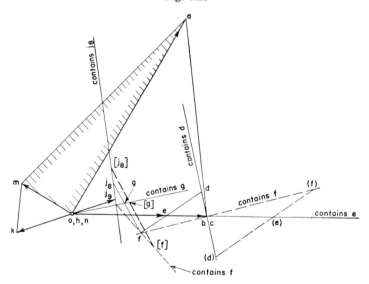

Fig. 4.24

connecting rod 3, crank 2, and frame 1 form a simple slider crank mechanism. The valve 7 receives motion from the crosshead at C and the crank at M. The velocity of crank pin A is known. The velocity polygon for the entire mechanism is shown in Fig. 4.24. Points a, m, b, k, and j_9 are determined in the usual manner. The velocity of C is equal to that of B; therefore c coincides with b in Fig. 4.24. A trial solution for link 6 will be made first. A line through c perpendicular to CD contains d. A line through o in the direction of sliding of valve 7 will contain e.

Line $(d)(e)$ is laid off perpendicular to DE; (f) is located by proportion. A line through (f) and the intersection of lines containing e and d will contain the correct location for point f. No more can be done here. A trial solution for link 8 is required next. A line through j_9 parallel to the direction of sliding of block 12 on 9 contains j_8. A line through h perpendicular to GH contains g. Line $[j_8][g]$ is drawn perpendicular to J_8G, and $[f]$ is located by proportion. A line through $[f]$ and the intersection of lines containing j_8 and g contains f. The intersection of this line with the previously determined line containing f locates f. The correct images fed and fgj_8 are drawn.

4.4. Determination of mechanical advantage from the velocity polygon. In Art. 1.1 it was stated that kinematic schemes can be investigated without regard to forces. This is usually true except in cases where a mechanical advantage is specified. The linkage must be proportioned to give this mechanical advantage. The theory and one example will be given to show that the velocity polygon can be used to determine the mechanical advantage of a mechanism.

A simple lever supported at O is shown in Fig. 4.25. The mechanical advantage is CO/BO. If a force P is applied at C a balancing force Q is required at B. The ratio of the forces is

$$\frac{CO}{BO} = \frac{\text{force } Q}{\text{force } P}$$

The mechanical advantage can also be determined using the principle of virtual (infinitesimal) displacements, virtual velocities, or virtual work.

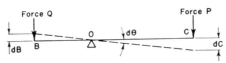

Fig. 4.25

Let the bar rotate through an angle $d\theta$. The displacement of C is $dC = OC\,d\theta$, and the displacement of B is $dB = OB\,d\theta$; then

$$\frac{dC}{dB} = \frac{OC\,d\theta}{OB\,d\theta} = \frac{OC}{OB} = \frac{\text{force } Q}{\text{force } P}$$

When the bar rotates through the angle $d\theta$ it has an angular velocity. The magnitude of this angular velocity does not matter. The linear velocity of point C is $V_C = OC\omega$ and the linear velocity of B is $V_B = OB\omega$; then

$$\frac{V_C}{V_B} = \frac{OC\omega}{OB\omega} = \frac{OC}{OB} = \frac{\text{force } Q}{\text{force } P}$$

This shows that instantaneous velocities can be considered to represent virtual displacements drawn to a large scale. Since a ratio is to be taken, the scale does not enter into the calculations and need not be considered.

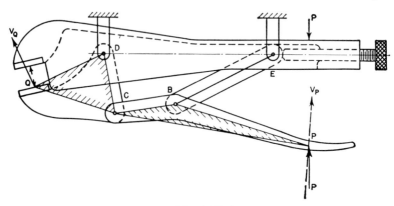

Fig. 4.26

Toggle pliers and the equivalent linkage are shown in Fig. 4.26. A force P is applied as shown. A velocity polygon can be drawn by assuming a velocity for some point in the linkage. The direction of the velocity of P is shown. This cannot be used as a starting point, since the direction is determined from the polygon. One of the points Q, C, or B can be chosen, since the links containing these points are pinned to the fixed member and the directions of motions are known. In this example V_Q is assumed and is laid off as oq in Fig. 4.27. The velocity polygon is completed in the usual manner. These velocities can be considered to represent virtual displacements on a large scale.

Work is the product of force and displacement. It is only the component of force that acts in the direction of the displacement that does work, or work is the product of the force and the component of displacement that is in the direction of the force. Force P is applied in a vertical direction; hence it does work along oP', the vertical component of the virtual displacement op. The component of displacement $P'p$ is perpendicular to the force. No work is done along this displacement. At Q work is done along the component oQ' that is perpendicular to the jaw. The work at P must equal that at Q.

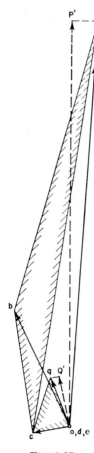

Fig. 4.27

$$\text{force } P \times oP' = \text{force } Q \times oQ'$$

$$\frac{oP'}{oQ'} = \frac{\text{force } Q}{\text{force } P} = \text{mechanical advantage}$$

If the mechanical advantage is not the desired value a study of Figs. 4.26 and 4.27 will indicate what links to alter to obtain this mechanical advantage. If the shape of the handle is altered so that force P is applied in the direction of the displacement op, the mechanical advantage will be greater. In this case op and oP' are nearly equal and there is little to be gained. The theory of virtual displacements is based on infinitesimal displacements. In practice the forces are large, and because of the elasticity of the materials, the displacements are small but measurable. If the piece being clamped in the jaws is round, the displacement component qQ' will cause a slight rolling of the piece. If the piece is flat the displacement component qQ' represents sliding or shear distortion of the piece. In this case work is done along the component qQ' and the mechanical advantage is not so great as that indicated above. In some types of clamping devices this action might be undesirable.

It is often necessary to determine the mechanical advantage of mechanisms in motion. This method can of course be used in these cases. The pliers were chosen to show that a problem in statics can be solved using a velocity polygon. The method is not only rapid but it reveals conditions that are not usually apparent from the conventional force analysis.

PROBLEMS

The following problems are to be solved by the velocity polygon method. Label the velocity images. The directions as well as magnitudes of angular velocities should be determined. Let the scale of the velocity polygons be 1 in. $= k_v = 10$ fps except where otherwise stated.

4.1. (a) Construct the velocity polygon for Fig. P 4.1. Let the length of $V_B = 2$ in. Place vectors V_E, V_C, and V_F on the configuration (space) diagram.
    (b) Determine ω_2, ω_3, and ω_4.

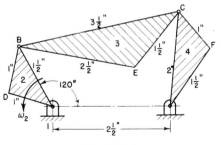

Fig. P 4.1

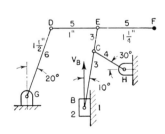

Fig. P 4.2

4.2. (a) Construct the velocity polygon for Fig. P 4.2. Let the length of $V_B = 1\frac{1}{4}$ in., $BC = 1\frac{1}{4}$ in., $CE = \frac{1}{2}$ in., $CH = \frac{3}{4}$ in.
    (b) Determine ω_3, ω_4, and ω_5.

4.3. (a) Construct the velocity polygon for Fig. P 4.3. Let the length of $V_B = 2$ in. Wheels 2 and 4 roll on 1.

(b) Determine ω_2, ω_4, and ω_3.

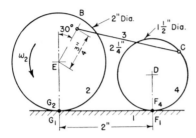
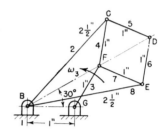

Fig. P 4.3   Fig. P 4.4

4.4. (a) Construct the velocity polygon for Peaucellier's straight-line mechanism shown in Fig. P 4.4. Let the length of $V_F = 1\frac{1}{2}$ in.

(b) Determine ω_2, ω_3, and ω_5.

4.5. (a) Construct the velocity polygon for Fig. P 3.1. Let the length of $V_B = 2$ in.

(b) Determine ω_2, ω_3, and ω_4.

4.6. (a) Construct the velocity polygon for Fig. P 3.2. Let the length of $V_B = 2$ in.

(b) Determine ω_3.

4.7. (a) Construct the velocity polygon for Fig. P 3.3. Let the length of $V_{B_2} = 2$ in.

(b) Determine ω_3.

4.8. (a) Construct the velocity polygon for Fig. P 3.4. Let the length of $V_B = \frac{1}{2}$ in.

(b) Determine ω_3 and ω_4.

4.9. (a) Construct the velocity polygon for Fig. P 3.5. Let the length of $V_B = 2$ in.

(b) Determine ω_2 and ω_3.

4.10. (a) Construct the velocity polygon for Fig. P 3.6. Let the length of $V_B = 2$ in.

(b) Determine ω_3.

4.11. (a) Construct the velocity polygon for Fig. P 3.7. Let the length of $V_B = 2$ in.

(b) Determine ω_3, ω_4, and ω_5.

4.12. (a) Construct the velocity polygon for Fig. P 3.8. Let the length of $V_{B_2} = 2$ in.

(b) Determine ω_3, ω_4, and ω_5.

4.13. (a) Construct the velocity polygon for Fig. P 4.13. Let the length of $V_{B_2} = 2$ in.

(b) Determine ω_3 and ω_4.

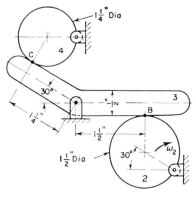

Fig. P 4.13

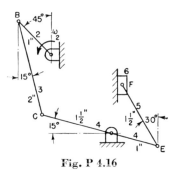

Fig. P 4.14

4.14. (a) Construct the velocity polygon for Fig. P 4.14. Let the length of $V_F = 2$ in.

(b) Determine ω_3, ω_4, ω_5, and ω_6.

4.15. (a) Construct the velocity polygon for Fig. P 4.15. Let the length of $V_{B_2} = 2$ in. $GC = 2$ in., $FD = 6$ in., $ED = 2$ in.

(b) Determine ω_4 and ω_7.

4.16. (a) Construct the velocity polygon for Fig. P 4.16. Let the length of $V_B = 1\frac{1}{2}$ in.

(b) Determine ω_3, ω_4, and ω_5.

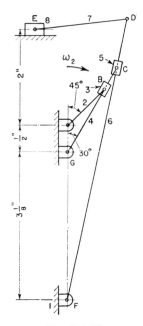

Fig. P 4.16

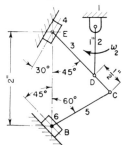

Fig. P 4.15

Fig. P 4.17

4.17. (a) Construct the velocity polygon for Fig. P 4.17. Let the length of $V_D = \frac{1}{2}$ in.

(b) Determine ω_3 and ω_5.

4.18. (a) Construct the velocity polygon for Fig. P 4.18. Let the length of $V_B = 1$ in. Wheels 2 and 7 have rolling contact.

(b) Determine ω_3, ω_4, and ω_6.

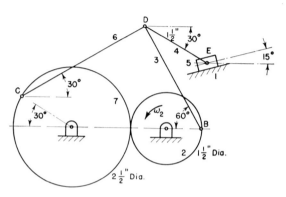

Fig. P 4.18

4.19. Construct a velocity polygon for Fig. P 4.19. Assume a vector 2 in. long to represent the velocity of a point that leads to a simple solution.

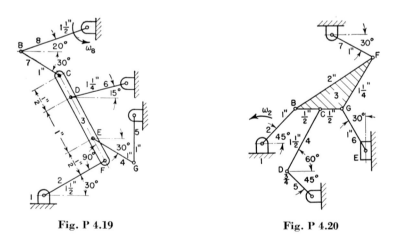

Fig. P 4.19   **Fig. P 4.20**

4.20. Construct a velocity polygon for Fig. P 4.20. Assume a vector to represent the velocity of a point that leads to a simple solution.

4.21. (a) Construct the velocity polygon for Fig. P 4.21. Let the length of $V_B = \frac{1}{2}$ in.

(b) Explain how this problem could be solved without using a trial solution.

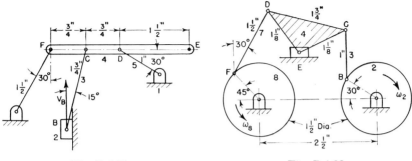

Fig. P 4.21   Fig. P 4.22

4.22. Construct the velocity polygon for Fig. P 4.22. Let $\omega_2 = 400$ rpm and $\omega_8 = 800$ rpm. Let the velocity scale be 1 in. $= K_v = 2.5$ fps.

4.23. Construct the velocity polygon for Fig. P 4.23. Let the length of the $V_G = 1\frac{1}{2}$ in.

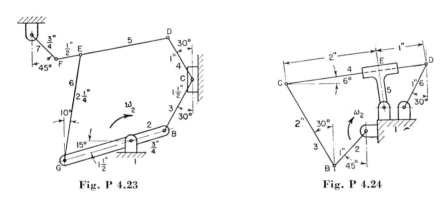

Fig. P 4.23   Fig. P 4.24

4.24. Construct the velocity polygon for Fig. P 4.24. Let the length of $V_B = 1\frac{1}{2}$ in.

4.25. A modified computor linkage is shown in Fig. P 4.25. Let the input velocities be represented by vectors $V_G = 1\frac{1}{2}$ in. and $V_F = 3$ in. Construct the velocity polygon.

4.26. A toggle mechanism is shown in Fig. P 4.26. Here 2 is the input member and 6 the output member. Assume a force at B and determine the mechanical advantage.

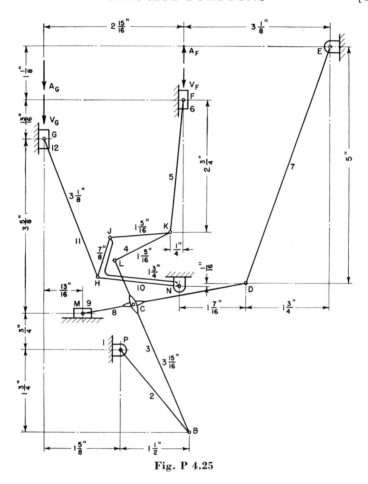

Fig. P 4.25

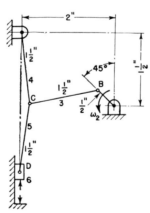

Fig. P 4.26

CHAPTER 5

Acceleration

5.1. Introductory. The development of engineering materials, manufacturing processes, and other phases of engineering makes it possible to build machines that operate at higher speeds than were considered possible a few years ago. Since the normal acceleration is proportional to the square of the speed, the doubling of a machine speed will increase four times the stresses due to centrifugal forces. When a high-speed machine is designed, the acceleration analysis is one of the most important steps. The development of machinery is continually increasing the complexity of mechanisms. Some of these present a challenge to the engineer when an acceleration analysis is required. Methods of dealing with these mechanisms are treated in this chapter. As in the chapters on velocity, the mechanisms are drawn in the simplest manner so that attention can be focused on the application of basic concepts.

5.2. Acceleration polygons. One advantage of the use of velocity polygons is that the method can be extended to make acceleration analyses. The notation used in the acceleration polygon is similar to that used in the velocity polygon except the letters are primed. The pole o' of the acceleration polygon represents the point of zero acceleration. Lines from the pole to points in the acceleration polygon represent absolute accelerations. A line joining two points in the acceleration polygon represents the relative acceleration of the corresponding points on the mechanism. It will be shown later that acceleration images are similar to the corresponding links in the mechanism. The key to the construction of acceleration polygons is, *the normal and tangential accelerations of a point are perpendicular to each other*. In addition to the concepts used for velocity polygons and the key above, the following equations will be used.

$$A^n = \frac{V^2}{R} = R\omega^2 = V\omega \tag{5.1}$$

$$A^t = R\alpha \tag{5.2}$$

$$A = A^n + A^t \tag{5.3}$$

$$\text{Coriolis' acceleration} = 2V\omega \tag{5.4}$$

Coriolis' acceleration will be considered in a later article

5.3. Linear acceleration.   An example will be used to illustrate the method for determining linear accelerations.   In Fig. 5.1 the crank rotates with uniform angular velocity as shown.   The acceleration of C is desired.   The velocity polygon is shown in Fig. 5.2 and the acceleration polygon in Fig. 5.3.   The acceleration of C can be determined from the equation

$$A_C = A_B +\!\!\!\!+ A_{C/B} = A_B^n +\!\!\!\!+ A_B^t +\!\!\!\!+ A_{C/B}^n +\!\!\!\!+ A_{C/B}^t$$

The acceleration polygon is the graphical solution of this equation. Point C moves in a horizontal path.   A horizontal line through pole o'

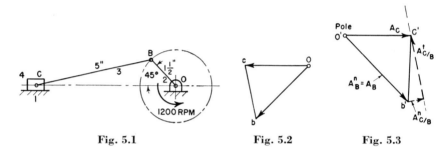

Fig. 5.1   Fig. 5.2   Fig. 5.3

contains c', the terminus of A_C.   The normal acceleration* of B is

$$A_B^n = BO\omega_2^2 = \frac{1.5}{12}\left(\frac{1200 \times 2\pi}{60}\right)^2 = 1975 \quad \text{fps}^2$$

Since A_B^t is zero, $A_B^n = A_B$.   This is laid off as $o'b'$ in the direction of B to O.   Then $A_{C/B}^n$ is calculated by using the value of $V_{C/B}$ from the velocity polygon.

$$A_{C/B}^n = \frac{V_{C/B}^2}{CB} = \frac{(11.5)^2}{\frac{5}{12}} = 318 \quad \text{fps}^2$$

This is laid off from b' in the direction C to B.   The direction of $A_{C/B}^t$ is perpendicular to $A_{C/B}^n$.   A line through the terminus of $A_{C/B}^n$ in this direction contains c', the terminus of $A_{C/B}^t$.   The intersection of this line with the horizontal line through o' containing c' locates c', and $o'c'$ represents A_C.   It scales 1410 fps².

5.4. Acceleration images.   In Fig. 5.4 the angular velocity and acceleration of link 2 are given.   The velocity and acceleration polygons are shown in Figs. 5.5 and 5.6.   Here A_D can be determined from the equation

$$A_D = A_C +\!\!\!\!+ A_{D/C}$$

This can be written

$$A_D^n +\!\!\!\!+ A_D^t = A_C^n +\!\!\!\!+ A_C^t +\!\!\!\!+ A_{D/C}^n +\!\!\!\!+ A_{D/C}^t$$

* The unit of acceleration, feet per second per second, is abbreviated as fps² throughout this text.

The value of A_D^n is obtained from Eq. (5.1), using the value of V_D from the velocity polygon. This vector is laid off from o'. A perpendicular at the terminus of A_D^n contains d', the terminus of A_D^t. The vectors on the right side of the equation are laid off starting from o'. The values

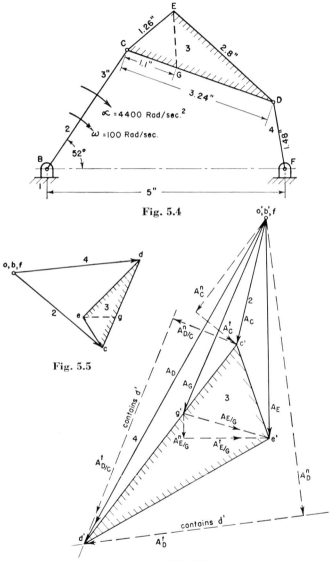

Fig. 5.4

Fig. 5.5

Fig. 5.6

of A_C^n and A_C^t are calculated from the known motion of link 2 and laid off as shown. The vector sum of A_C^n and A_C^t is A_C. This is represented by $o'c'$, and $A_{D/C}^n$ is calculated using the value of $V_{D/C}$ from the velocity polygon and is laid off from c'. A perpendicular at the terminus of $A_{D/C}^n$ contains d', the terminus of $A_{D/C}^t$. The intersection of this line with the previously determined line containing d' locates d'. Then $o'd'$ represents the vector A_D.

The point e' can be located in a similar manner by laying off $A_{E/C}^n$ from c' and $A_{E/D}^n$ from d' and obtaining the intersection of the perpendiculars to these vectors. A more rapid way is to construct the acceleration image $c'd'e'$ similar to CDE. The similarity of the link and image can be proved as follows.

$$A_{C/D} = A_{C/D}^n \leftrightarrow A_{C/D}^t = \omega_3^2 CD \leftrightarrow \alpha_3 CD$$

Since $A_{C/D}^n$ and $A_{C/D}^t$ are perpendicular to each other,

$$|A_{C/D}| = \sqrt{\omega_3^4 (CD)^2 + \alpha_3^2 (CD)^2} = CD \sqrt{\omega_3^4 + \alpha_3^2}$$

In like manner

$$|A_{E/C}| = EC \sqrt{\omega_3^4 + \alpha_3^2}$$
$$|A_{D/E}| = DE \sqrt{\omega_3^4 + \alpha_3^2}$$

etc. The magnitudes of relative accelerations of points on a link are equal to the distances between the points on the original link times a constant. Since distances between points on the acceleration image represent relative accelerations, these distances must be proportional to the corresponding distances on the link. Points d' and c' are located on the acceleration image. The acceleration image of link 3 can be completed from the proportions

$$\frac{c'd'}{CD} = \frac{c'e'}{CE} = \frac{e'd'}{ED} = \frac{c'g'}{CG}$$

The cyclic order must be maintained. If $CEDG$ is clockwise, $c'e'd'g'$ must be clockwise.

5.5. Angular acceleration. The angular acceleration of a link can be obtained from Eq. (5.2). The angular acceleration of a link is equal to the tangential acceleration of any point in the link relative to any other point in the link divided by the distance between the points. The value of $A_{D/C}^t$ can be taken from Fig. 5.6, and $A_{E/G}^t$ is obtained by resolving $A_{E/G}$ (Fig. 5.6) into its normal component parallel to EG, and tangential component perpendicular to EG. The angular acceleration of link 3 is

$$\alpha_3 = \frac{A_{D/C}^t}{DC} \text{ clockwise} \tag{a}$$

$$\alpha_3 = \frac{A_{C/D}^t}{CD} \text{ clockwise} \tag{b}$$

$$\alpha_3 = \frac{A_{E/G}^t}{EG} \text{ clockwise} \tag{c}$$

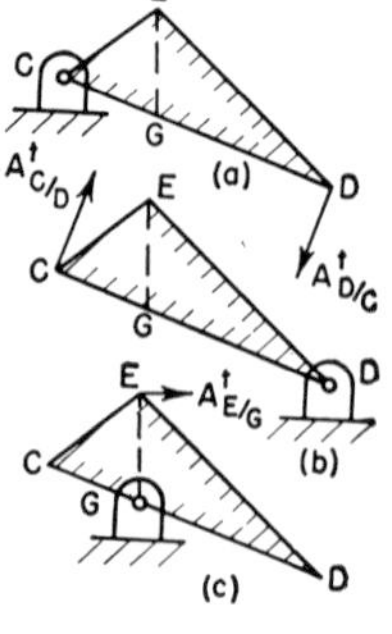

Fig. 5.7

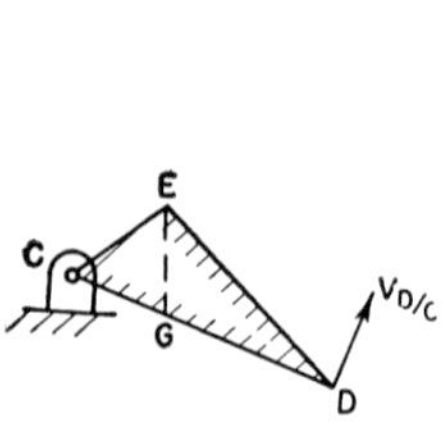

Fig. 5.8

The angular velocity of link 3 from Fig. 5.8 is counterclockwise. The angular velocity of link 3 is therefore decreasing.

5.6. Graphical determination of normal accelerations. The units used in making calculations and drawing polygons can be any of the standard units; however, it is customary to use feet and seconds. On the drawings of the mechanism, let the scale be 1 in. $= k_s$ ft. In drawing velocities, let the scale be 1 in. $= k_v$ fps. In drawing accelerations, let the scale be 1 in. $= k_a$ fps^2.

A rotating link BC is shown in Fig. 5.9. The velocity V_C is indicated as CV. These two values, the lengths BC and V_C, are drawn to the scales indicated above. A right triangle BVN is constructed as shown. Triangles BCV and CVN have perpendicular sides and are therefore similar. Then

$$\frac{CN}{CV} = \frac{CV}{BC} \quad \text{or} \quad CN = \frac{(CV)^2}{BC} \tag{5.5}$$

Let

$$\frac{CNk_a}{CVk_v} = \frac{CVk_v}{BCk_s} \quad \text{or} \quad CNk_a = \frac{(CVk_v)^2}{BCk_s} \tag{5.6}$$

Equation (5.6) holds if the scales have a certain relationship. This relationship can be obtained by dividing Eq. (5.6) by (5.5), giving

$$\frac{k_a}{k_v} = \frac{k_v}{k_s} \quad \text{or} \quad k_a = \frac{k_v^2}{k_s} \tag{5.7}$$

A dimensional check shows that the units chosen are correct.

$$\text{fps}^2 = \frac{(\text{fps})(\text{fps})}{\text{ft}} = \text{fps}^2 \tag{5.8}$$

By construction CVk_v is equal to V_C on the mechanism, and BCk_s is equal to the actual length of BC on the mechanism. Therefore CNk_a

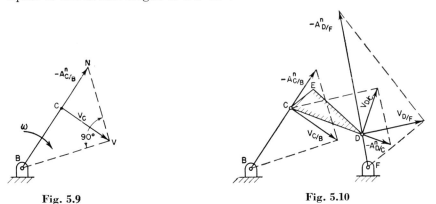

Fig. 5.9   **Fig. 5.10**

from Eq. (5.7) must represent the normal acceleration of C relative to B on the mechanism on the scale indicated above. In Fig. 5.9 it can be seen that the sense of this vector is reversed. When it is used in the acceleration polygon it must be drawn in the correct direction.

The mechanism of Fig. 5.4 is shown in Fig. 5.10, and the constructions for the determination of the normal accelerations are shown. This graphical construction reduces the time required to make an acceleration analysis. The velocities can be transferred from the polygon to the drawing of the mechanism with dividers. The normal accelerations can then be transferred to the acceleration polygon. None of the vectors need be scaled until the acceleration polygon is completed, and then only those desired need be scaled. Any two scales can be assumed and the third calculated using Eq. (5.7). Usually k_s and k_v are assumed.

5.7. Equivalent linkages. The acceleration analysis of a direct contact mechanism is often more difficult than for a four-bar linkage or a slider crank. In Fig. 5.11, let 2 and 4 be direct contact members of

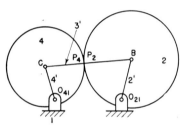

Fig. 5.11

circular form. Since the distances $O_{21}B$, BC, and $O_{41}C$ are constant for all phases, it can be seen that the linkage 1, 2', 3', 4' can replace the original linkage for the purpose of making an acceleration analysis; i.e., if link 2' is assigned the same angular velocity and acceleration as member 2, then link 4' will have the same angular velocity and acceleration as member 4.

Often the contours of the contacting members are not circular arcs, as shown in Fig. 5.12. Let R_2 be the radius of curvature of the contour of member 2 at P_2 with center at B, and let R_4 be the radius of curvature of the contour of member 4 at P_4 with center at C. Then, as in Fig. 5.11, the linkage 2', 3', 4' can replace the original direct contact mechanism. The circles shown in Fig. 5.12 are called osculating circles.* The osculating circle of a curve at a point has second order contact with the curve; i.e., the first and second derivatives of the circle are the same as for the curve, and can therefore replace the curve for the purpose of making a velocity and acceleration analysis.

In many contours, especially in cams, a point B, Fig. 5.13, will have two radii of curvature. R_2 is the radius of curvature of the curve at B as it is approached from C, and R_1 is the radius of curvature of the curve at B as it is approached from A. When point B is in contact with the mating member, there will be two equivalent linkages. The difference in the

---

* "The osculating circle of a curve at a given point is the circle which in the limiting position, if there is such, of the circle through the given point and two other points of the curve, as the latter two approach the fixed point along the curve; the circle which has contact of at least the second order with the curve." James, G. and R. C. James, *Mathematics Dictionary*, D. Van Nostrand Co. Inc., 1949.

accelerations of these two linkages represents the finite change in acceleration due to this discontinuity. Except for circular arcs, it must be remembered that the radii of curvatures at the point of contact differ for each phase.

Six additional equivalent linkages are shown in Figs. 5.14 through 5.19. In Fig. 5.17, the equivalent links $2'$ and $3'$ meet at infinity which leads to an indeterminant solution. In Fig. 5.18, the osculating circle of member 2 at point P_2 is made into a roller which is attached to link $2'$. This equivalent linkage is not simple to analyze but it leads to another equivalent linkage. Note that the center of the roller C traces the path BCD relative to member 4. While this is not the same path that C as a

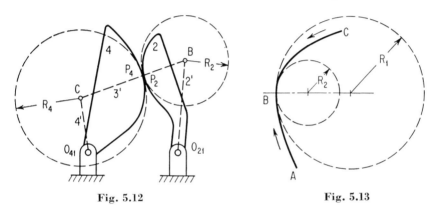

Fig. 5.12   **Fig. 5.13**

point in the original member 2 traces on 4, the two paths have second order contact at C, hence the path at C can be used for an acceleration analysis for this phase. The equivalent linkage* is shown in Fig. 5.19 where the flat face has been moved to BCD, and member 2 comes to a point at C so that C will trace a straight path. This linkage is an inverted slider crank which will be treated in the next Article.

5.8. Coriolis' acceleration. *If a point moves along a path that has rotation, the absolute acceleration of the point is the vector sum of the acceleration of the point relative to the coincident point in the path (i.e., relative to the path that is fixed to the rotating member), the absolute acceleration of the coincident point in the path, and a third component. The third component is called Coriolis' acceleration.*

In Fig. 5.20, rod 2 moves with constant angular velocity from position DE to DE' in time dt. During this time a slider moves outward along the rod with constant velocity V from position K_3 to K_3'. Consider the displacement of the slider from K_3 to K_3' in the following stages: K_3 to K_2' due to rotation of the rod, K_2' to P due to outward velocity V, and P to K_3' due to an acceleration perpendicular to the rod. This is Coriolis' accelera-

---

* D. K. Wright, Jr., "Discussion," *Trans.*, ASME, vol. 78, p. 142.

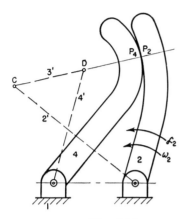

Fig. 5.14

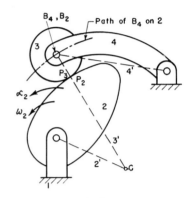

Fig. 5.15

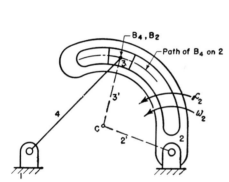

Fig. 5.16

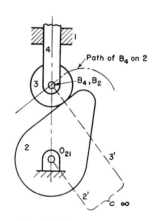

Fig. 5.17

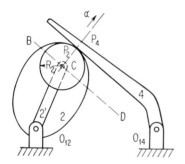

Fig. 5.18

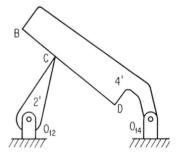

Fig. 5.19

tion.   An expression for it can be obtained as follows:

$$\text{arc } PK'_3 = \text{arc } LK'_3 - \text{arc } K_2 K'_2$$
$$PK'_3 = LD\,d\theta - K_2 D\,d\theta = K'_2 P\,d\theta = V\,dt\,\omega\,dt = V\omega\,dt^2 \quad (5.9)$$

The tangential velocity (perpendicular to the rod) of the block is $V^t = r\omega$.   Since ω is constant and r increases uniformly as a result of the constant velocity of the slider along the rod, V^t will increase uniformly.

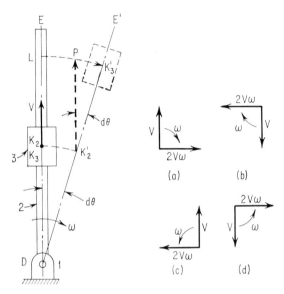

Fig. 5.20

This means that the acceleration perpendicular to the rod is constant. We can therefore write

$$PK'_3 = \frac{1}{2} A\,dt^2 \qquad\qquad (5.10)$$

Then, from Eqs. (5.9) and (5.10)

$$\frac{1}{2} A\,dt^2 = V\omega\,dt^2 \quad\text{or}\quad A = 2V\omega \quad \text{Coriolis' acceleration} \quad (5.11)$$

The directional relationship of V, ω, and $2V\omega$ for the case of Fig. 5.20 is shown at (a).   If the velocity of the slider is toward the center D the relationship will be that of (b).   If ω is reversed, the relationships for the two velocity directions will be according to (c) and (d).   Figure 5.20(a), (b), (c), and (d) can be used as a key for determining the direction of Coriolis' acceleration.   The key can be stated as follows: *the direction of Coriolis' acceleration is the direction of the relative velocity vector after it has been rotated 90° in the direction of the angular velocity of the path.*

The following is a derivation for another special case. The disk, (Fig. 5.21) which has a circular groove in it, rotates with a constant angular velocity ω_2. The sliding block, member 3, moves in the groove with a constant angular velocity ω_3. The velocities of the coincident points are: V_2, the absolute velocity of point P_2, and $V_{3/2}$, the velocity of P_3 relative to P_2. Then

$$A_3 = \frac{V_3^2}{r} = \frac{(V_2 + V_{3/2})^2}{r} = \frac{V_2^2 + V_{3/2}^2 + 2V_2V_{3/2}}{r}$$

$$= A_2^n + A_{3/2}^n + 2V_{3/2}\omega_2 \qquad (5.12)$$

In this expression, vector addition is not indicated because the vectors are parallel.

If, in Fig. 5.21, $\omega_2 = \omega_{3/2} = 1$ radian per sec, and $r = 1$ in., the velocities will be $V_2 = V_{3/2} = 1$ ips. The three components of acceleration, Fig. 5.21(a), will combine to give the absolute acceleration, $A_{P_3} = 4$ ips². In this example, it should be clear that accelerations determined

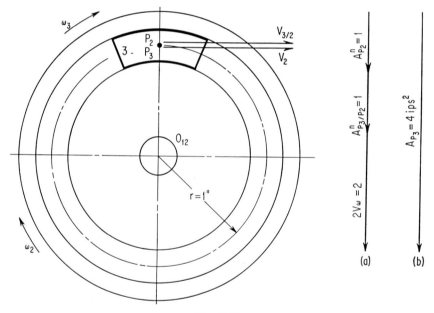

Fig. 5.21

by squaring individual relative velocities do not contain the cross product of the velocities. This cross product is added in the form of the Coriolis acceleration. When the path is not a part of a rotating member but is in a fixed plane, $\omega = 0$ and therefore the Coriolis component is zero. In this example the path on the rotating member traced by P_3 is coincident with the path traced on the fixed plane by P_3. However, when the fixed path is considered and the absolute velocity, $V_{P_3} = 2$ ips is used, the acceleration of P_3 is

$$A_{P_3} = \frac{(V_{P_3})^2}{r} = \frac{(2)^2}{1} = \quad 4 \text{ ips}^2$$

This is shown at (b) in Fig. 5.21.

Another example will be worked out to show that the Coriolis acceleration does not appear when the absolute path is used instead of a path on a rotating member. In Fig. 5.20, assume $\omega = 1$ radian per sec, and slider velocity $V_{K_3} = 1$ ips. The center of the slider, K_3, which traces a straight line path on the rotating rod, will trace an Archimedean spiral, DK_3S, in the fixed plane, Fig. 5.22. The equation of an Archimedean spiral is

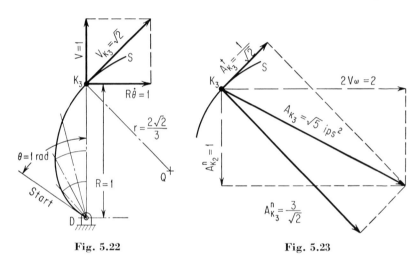

Fig. 5.22   Fig. 5.23

$R = C\theta$. After one second, $R = 1$ and $\theta = 1$, then $C = 1$. The equation of the fixed path DK_3S in Fig. 5.22 is $R = \theta$ which has derivatives $dR/d\theta = 1$ and $d^2R/d\theta^2 = 0$. The vertical and horizontal components of velocity of the slider for the position shown are 1 ips. The tangential velocity, $V_{K_3} = \sqrt{2}$, is obtained from these components. The radius of curvature of the spiral at K_3 can be determined as

$$r = \frac{\left[R^2 + \left(\dfrac{dR}{d\theta} \right)^2 \right]^{3/2}}{R^2 + 2\left(\dfrac{dR}{d\theta} \right)^2 - R\dfrac{d^2R}{d\theta^2}} = \frac{(1+1)^{3/2}}{1+2-0} = \frac{2\sqrt{2}}{3} \quad \text{in.} \quad (5.13)$$

The normal acceleration is

$$A^n_{K_3} = \frac{V^2_{K_3}}{r} = \frac{2}{2\sqrt{2/3}} = \frac{3}{\sqrt{2}} \quad \text{ips}^2$$

The tangential acceleration can be determined by differentiating the equation for the tangential velocity

$$V_{K_3} = [V^2 + (R\dot\theta)^2]^{1/2} \qquad (5.14)$$

$$A^t_{K_3} = \frac{dV_{K_3}}{dt} = \frac{1}{2}\frac{2(R\dot\theta)(R\ddot\theta + \dot\theta\dot R)}{[V^2 + (R\dot\theta)^2]^{1/2}} = \frac{1}{2}\frac{2(1)(0+1)}{(1+1)^{1/2}} = \frac{1}{\sqrt{2}} \qquad \text{ips}^2 \quad (5.15)$$

A_{K_3}, the total acceleration of the slider, is the vector sum of the normal and tangential accelerations to the path K_3S, Fig. 5.23. The same result can be obtained by considering the slider as it traces a straight line path along the rotating rod.

$$A_{K_3} = A^n_{K_2} \nrightarrow A^t_{K_2} \nrightarrow A^n_{K_3/K_2} \nrightarrow A^t_{K_3/K_2} \nrightarrow 2V_{K_3/K_2}\omega_{2/1} \qquad (5.16)$$
$$= 1 \nrightarrow 0 \nrightarrow 0 \nrightarrow 0 \nrightarrow 2$$

This solution is shown with broken lines in Fig. 5.23. From this example it should be clear that it is usually easier to work with the rotating path rather than with the absolute path. In the general case the path is curved and has angular acceleration, and the moving point has acceleration along the path. The proof for the general case is included in most engineering mechanics books.* Examples will be worked to illustrate the theory when applied to mechanisms.

Example 1. A governor mechanism is shown in Fig. 5.24(a). The links and their angular motions are shown in (b). The acceleration of P_3 is wanted. This problem will be worked without Coriolis' acceleration and then with the acceleration. The velocity polygon is shown in Fig. 5.25. The value of $V_{P_3/C}$ cannot be determined graphically. It is

$$V_{P_3/C} = R\omega_{3/1} = (1.56)(10) = 15.6 \quad \text{fps}$$

It should be remembered that the velocity of any point in a link relative to some other point in the link is the product of the distance between them and the absolute angular velocity of the link.

The accelerations are

$$A^n_c = CO\alpha^2_{2/1} = (1.4)(12)^2 = 202 \quad \text{fps}^2$$
$$A^t_c = CO\alpha_{2/1} = (1.4)(75) = 105 \quad \text{fps}^2$$
$$A^n_{P_3/C} = PC\omega^2_{3/1} = (1.56)(10)^2 = 156 \quad \text{fps}^2$$
$$A^t_{P_3/C} = PC\alpha_{3/1} = (1.56)(60) = 93.5 \quad \text{fps}^2$$

These vectors are laid off as solid lines in Fig. 5.26. Then $o'p'_3$ is the desired vector A_{P_3}.

The mechanism shown in Fig. 5.27 is equivalent to that of Fig. 5.24. The acceleration of P_3 is the vector sum of the accelerations of P_2 relative to the frame, the acceleration of P_3 relative to P_2, and Coriolis' acceleration.

$$A_{P_3} = A^n_{P_2} \nrightarrow A^t_{P_2} \nrightarrow A^n_{P_3/P_2} \nrightarrow A^t_{P_3/P_2} \nrightarrow 2V_{P_3/P_2}\omega_{2/1}$$

---

* Higdon and Stiles, *Engineering Mechanics*, 2nd Ed., New York: Prentice-Hall, Inc., 1955. Hall, A. S., "Teaching Coriolis' Law," *ASEE Journal*, June, 1948.

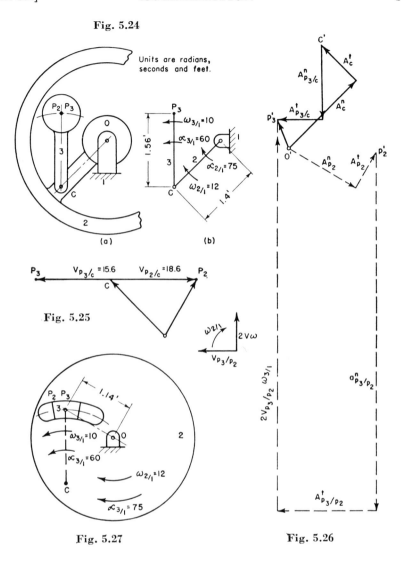

Fig. 5.24

Units are radians,
seconds and feet.

(a)

(b)

Fig. 5.25

Fig. 5.27   Fig. 5.26

The values are

$$A_{P_2}^n = PO\omega_{2/1}^2 = (1.14)(12)^2 = 163.5 \quad \text{fps}^2$$

$$A_{P_2}^t = PO\alpha_{2/1} = (1.14)(75) = 85.5 \quad \text{fps}^2$$

$$A_{P_3/P_2}^n = \frac{(V_{P_3/P_2})^2}{PC} = \frac{(V_{P_3/C} \rightarrow V_{P_2/C})^2}{PC} = \frac{[15.6 - (-18.6)]^2}{1.56} = 750 \quad \text{fps}^2$$

$$A_{P_3/P_2}^t = PC\alpha_{3/2} = PC(\alpha_{3/1} - \alpha_{2/1}) = (1.56)[60 - (-75)] = 210 \quad \text{fps}^2$$

$$2V_{P_3/P_2}\omega_{2/1} = (2)(34.2)(12) = 820 \quad \text{fps}^2$$

These vectors are laid off with broken lines in Fig. 5.26.   From the drawing, A_{P_3} scales 65 fps².

Example 2. A cam mechanism is shown in Fig. 5.28.   It is desired to determine the acceleration of the reciprocating follower 4.   The path that P_4 traces on 2 is shown.   The velocity polygon is shown in Fig. 5.29 and the acceleration polygon in Fig. 5.30.   The acceleration of P_4 is

$$A_{P_4} = A_{P_2}^n \nrightarrow A_{P_2}^t \nrightarrow A_{P_4/P_2}^t \nrightarrow A_{P_4/P_2}^n \nrightarrow 2V_{P_4/P_2}\omega_{2/1}$$

The components are

$$A_{P_2}^n = OP\omega_{2/1}^2 = \frac{1.72}{12}(15)^2 = 32.2 \quad \text{fps}^2$$

The cam has no angular acceleration; therefore

$$A_{P_2}^t = 0$$

$$A_{P_4/P_2}^n = \frac{V_{P_4/P_2}^2}{R} = \frac{V_{P_4/P_2}^2}{\infty} = 0$$

where R is the radius of curvature of the path of P_4 on 2 at the point of contact.

$$2V_{P_4/P_2}\omega_{2/1} = (2)(2.5)(15) = 75 \quad \text{fps}^2$$

These two vectors are laid off starting from o'.   The direction of A_{P_4/P_2}^t is tangent to the path that P_4 traces on 2.   A line in this direction through the terminus of

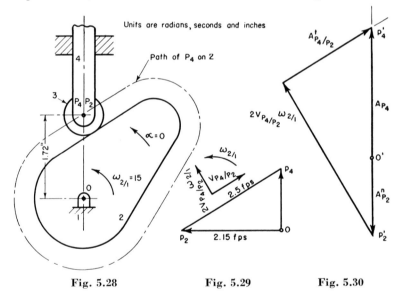

Fig. 5.28   Fig. 5.29   Fig. 5.30

$2V_{P_4P_2}\omega_{2/1}$ contains p_4'.   The acceleration of P_4 relative to the frame is along the centerline of the follower.   A line in this direction through o' contains p_4', and p_4' is located at the intersection of these two lines.   On the drawing A_{p_4} scales 54.8 fps².

Example 3. A quick-return mechanism is shown in Fig. 5.31.   Member 2 has constant angular velocity as shown.   The angular acceleration of link 3 is desired. The acceleration of P_3 must be determined first.   The equation is

$$A_{P_3} = A_{P_2}^n \nrightarrow A_{P_2}^t \nrightarrow A_{P_3/P_2}^t \nrightarrow A_{P_3/P_2}^n \nrightarrow 2V_{P_3/P_2}\omega_{2/1}$$

In order to solve this equation it is necessary to know the radius of curvature of the path that P_3 traces on 2. This is not known. The path that P_2 traces on 3 is a straight line along the link. This path can be used if the equation is written as though solving for the acceleration of P_2.

$$A_{P_2} = A_{P_3/C}^n \,\leftrightarrow\!\!\!+ A_{P_3/C}^t \,\leftrightarrow\!\!\!+ A_{P_2/P_3}^t \,\leftrightarrow\!\!\!+ A_{P_2/P_3}^n \,\leftrightarrow\!\!\!+ 2V_{P_2/P_3}\omega_{3/1}$$

The vectors that can be calculated are

$$A_{P_2} = P_2 O \omega_{2/1}^2 = \frac{6}{12}(20)^2 = 200 \quad \text{fps}^2$$

$$A_{P_3/C}^n = \frac{V_{P_3/C}^2}{P_3 C} = \frac{(5)^2}{\frac{10}{12}} = 30 \quad \text{fps}^2$$

$$A_{P_2/P_3}^n = 0$$

$$\omega_{3/1} = \frac{V_{P_3/C}}{P_3 C} = \frac{5}{\frac{10}{12}} = 6 \quad \text{radians per sec}$$

$$2V_{P_2/P_3}\omega_{3/1} = (2)(8.75)(6) = 105 \quad \text{fps}^2$$

The directions of A_{P_3/P_2}^t and $A_{P_3/C}^t$ are known. This information is sufficient for completing the polygon. One arrangement is shown in Fig. 5.33. The known

Units are radians, seconds and inches

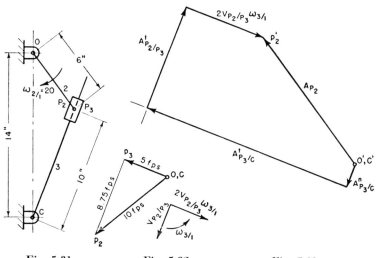

Fig. 5.31   **Fig. 5.32**   **Fig. 5.33**

vectors A_{P_2}, $A_{P_3/C}^n$, and $2V_{P_2/P_3}\omega_{3/1}$ are laid off as shown. Lines in the known directions of the other two vectors complete the polygon. Then $A_{P_3/C}^t$ scales 275 fps^2.

$$\alpha_{3/1} = \frac{A_{P_3/C}^t}{P_3 C} = \frac{275}{\frac{10}{12}} = 330 \quad \text{radians/sec}^2$$

5.9. Complex mechanisms.

In Chapter 4 it was found that some mechanisms require trial solutions in the construction of velocity polygons. If a trial solution is required for a link in a velocity polygon, a trial solution for the same link is required in the acceleration polygon. If simultaneous trial solutions are required for two links in a velocity polygon, simultaneous trial solutions are required for the same links in the acceleration polygon. The trial solution method for velocity polygons was made possible by the fact that the velocity image of a link is perpendicular to the link. The angular orientation of an acceleration image relative to the link is determined by the relationship between the normal and tangential accelerations. This relationship is not known until the polygon is completed. The normal accelerations can be calculated using velocities from the velocity polygon. When these are laid off on the acceleration polygon, only the tangential components are left. These are perpendicular to the link, and a trial solution for the tangential components can be made in the same manner as in a velocity polygon. No new basic concepts are required; those that have been used in the earlier part of this chapter are sufficient.

Example 4. In Fig. 5.34 the angular velocity and acceleration of link 2 are known. The velocity polygon is shown in Fig. 5.35. A trial solution was required for link 4. The acceleration polygon is shown in Fig. 5.36. The order in which the lines were drawn is indicated by numbers in brackets. Accelerations $A_{B/F}^n$ [1] and $A_{B/F}^t$ [2] are calculated and laid off, locating b'. Then $A_{D/B}^n$ [3] is calculated and laid off from b'. A line [4] perpendicular to $A_{D/B}^n$ will contain d', the terminus of $A_{D/B}^t$. Acceleration $A_{C/H}^n$ [5] is calculated and laid off from o'. A line [6] perpendicular to $A_{C/H}^n$ contains c', the terminus of $A_{C/H}^t$. Then $A_{E/G}^n$ [7] is calculated and laid off from o'. A line [8] perpendicular to $A_{E/G}^n$ contains e', the terminus of $A_{E/G}^t$. A trial solution is now necessary. A portion of Fig. 5.36 is shown in Fig. 5.37. For purposes of explanation it is assumed that the location of d' is known; $A_{E/D}^n$ is calculated and laid off from d' (this vector is shown with a broken line). A perpendicular to $A_{E/D}^n$ (shown broken) contains e', the terminus of $A_{E/D}^t$. The intersection of this line with line [8] containing e' locates e', and c' is located in a similar manner. This is the usual arrangement for laying off normal and tangential components. The acceleration image $c'd'e'$ of link 4 is shown. Accelerations $A_{E/D}^n$, $A_{E/D}^t$, $A_{C/D}^n$, and $A_{C/D}^t$ can be arranged differently, as shown by the solid line vectors. This latter arrangement is necessary in making trial solutions. In Fig. 5.36 $A_{E/D}^n$ [9] is laid off in an arbitrary position such that its terminus touches line [8] containing e'. A line [10] through the origin of $A_{E/D}^n$ and parallel to line [8] will contain the terminus of $A_{E/D}^t$, and $A_{C/D}^n$ [11] is laid off in an arbitrary position such that its terminus touches line [6] containing c'. A line [12] through the origin of $A_{C/D}^n$ and parallel to line [6] contains the terminus of $A_{C/D}^t$. A trial solution [13] for the tangential components $A_{E/D}^t$ and $A_{C/D}^t$ is made by drawing a line between [10] and [12] perpendicular to link EDC (Fig. 5.34). Point (d') is located by proportion from link EDC. A line [14] through (d') and the intersection of lines [10] and [12] contains (d') for all trial solutions. The intersections of lines [4] and [14] locates d'. Vectors [15], [16], [17], and [18] determine the acceleration image of link 4.

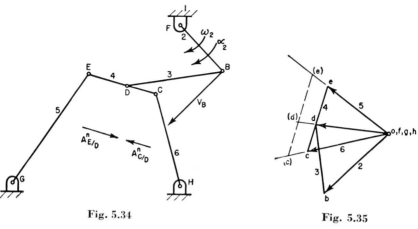

Fig. 5.34

Fig. 5.35

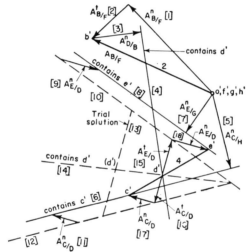

Fig. 5.36

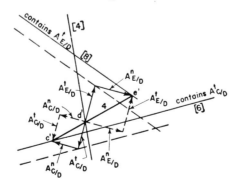

Fig. 5.37

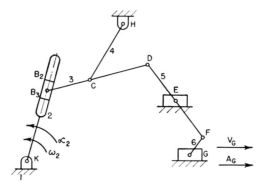

Fig. 5.38

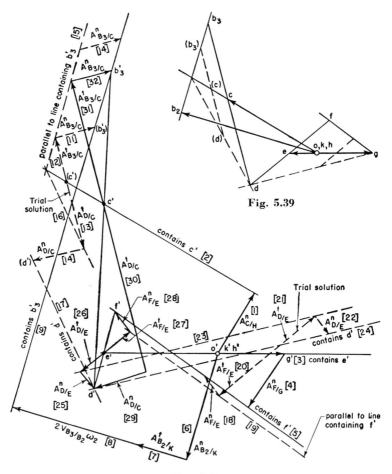

Fig. 5.39

Fig. 5.40

Example 5. A portion of a Walschaert valve gear is shown in Fig. 5.38. In order to reduce the number of lines in the acceleration polygon some of the links that require only elementary technique have been omitted. Member 2 has been given arbitrary angular velocity and acceleration, and point G has been given arbitrary linear velocity and acceleration. The velocity polygon, Fig. 5.39, is similar to a portion of Fig. 4.24. Links 3 and 5 require trial solutions. The acceleration polygon is shown in Fig. 5.40. The order in which the lines are drawn is indicated by numbers in brackets. First $A_{C/H}^n$ [1] is calculated and laid off. A perpendicular line [2] through the terminus of $A_{C/H}^n$ contains c', the terminus of $A_{C/H}^t$. The known value of A_G is laid off as $o'g'$[3]. The slider E has horizontal motion. Line [3] will also contain e'. Acceleration $A_{F/G}^n$ [4] is calculated and laid off from g'. A perpendicular line [5] through the terminus of $A_{F/G}^n$ contains f', the terminus of $A_{F/G}^t$. Acceleration $A_{B2/K}^n$ [6] is calculated and laid off. Then $A_{B_2/K}^t$ [7] and $2V_{B_3/B_2}\omega_2$ [8] are calculated and laid off as shown. A perpendicular line [9] through the terminus of $2V_{B_3/B_2}\omega_2$ contains b_3', the terminus of A_{B_3/B_2}^t. It is now necessary to make trial solutions. Link 3 will be considered first. Acceleration $A_{B_3/C}^n$ [11] is calculated and laid off in an arbitrary position such that its terminus touches line [9] containing b_3'. The perpendicular line [12] between the origin of $A_{B_3/C}^n$ [11] and line [2] is a trial solution for $A_{B_3/C}^t$. Acceleration $A_{D/C}^t$ [13] is laid off using the proportions of link 3, and $A_{D/C}^n$ [14] is calculated and laid off from the terminus at $A_{D/C}^t$. Lines [11], [12], [13], and [14] form a trial solution for link 3. If $A_{B_3/C}^n$ [14] is laid off again in some position other than [11] it can be seen that a line [15] through the origins of these two vectors is parallel to line [9]. Line [15] contains the termini of $A_{B_3/C}^t$ for all trial solutions. Line [16] through the terminus of $A_{D/C}^t$ [13] and the intersection of lines [2] and [15] contains the termini of $A_{D/C}^t$ for all trial solutions. Line [17] through the terminus of $A_{D/C}^n$ [14] and parallel to line [16] contains the termini of $A_{D/C}^n$ for all trial solutions. Line [17] therefore contains d'. A trial solution for link 5 is now necessary. It is made in a manner similar to that for link 3. Acceleration $A_{F/E}^n$ [18] is calculated and laid off with its terminus touching line [5] containing f'. Line [19] is drawn parallel to line [5]. The trial value of $A_{F/E}^t$ [20] is laid off as shown. Acceleration $A_{D/E}^t$ [21] is determined by proportions, and $A_{D/E}^n$ [22] is calculated and laid off from the terminus of $A_{D/E}^t$ [21]. Line [23] is drawn through the terminus of $A_{D/E}^t$ [21] and the intersection of lines [3] and [19]. Line [24] is drawn through the terminus of $A_{D/E}^n$ [22] parallel to line [23]. Line [24] contains d', so that d' is located at the intersection of lines [24] and [17]. Starting from d', the correct normal and tangential accelerations for links 3 and 5 can now be drawn.

5.10. Rolling contact.* The equations derived below are for rolling circles, however, they can be used for all rolling curves since the actual curves can be replaced by osculating circles. When a circle, member 4, Fig. 5.41, is rolled on a straight line, a point P_4 on the circumference of the circle will trace a cycloid relative to the straight line. When the circle is rolled on the inside of a larger circle, P_4 traces a hypocycloid,

---

* Ip, Ching U., I. E. Morse, Jr. and R. T. Hinkle, "How to Analyze Rolling-Contact Mechanisms for Acceleration Characteristics," *Machine Design*, July 26, 1956.

Fig. 5.42.   When a circle is rolled on the outside of another circle, P_4 traces an epicycloid, Fig. 5.43.   The following derivation for an equation to determine the acceleration of point P_4 relative to point P_2 when the two are in contact will be based on Fig. 5.43.

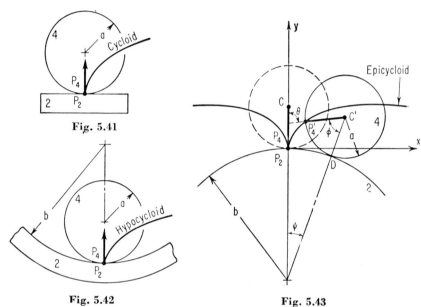

Fig. 5.41

Fig. 5.42   Fig. 5.43

The parametic equations for an epicycloid are

$$x = (a + b) \sin \psi - a \sin \left[\frac{(a + b)\psi}{a} \right] \qquad (5.17)$$

$$y = (a + b) \cos \psi - a \cos \left[\frac{(a + b)\psi}{a} \right] \qquad (5.18)$$

For pure rolling the arcs of contact are equal, i.e., $DP_2 = DP_4'$.   We can therefore write

$$a\phi = b\psi \qquad \text{or} \qquad \phi = \frac{b\psi}{a} \qquad (5.19)$$

From Fig. 5.43 we see that

$$\theta = \phi + \psi \qquad (5.20)$$

where θ is the angle rotated through by the radius a from position CP_4 to $C'P_4'$.   The angular velocity of body 4 relative to 2 is

$$\omega_{42} = \frac{d\theta}{dt} \qquad (5.21)$$

Substitution of the Eq. (5.19) value of ϕ into Eq. (5.20) gives

$$\psi = \frac{a\theta}{a + b} \qquad (5.22)$$

With this value of ψ, Eqs. (5.17) and (5.18) become

$$x = (a + b) \sin\left(\frac{a\theta}{a + b}\right) - a \sin\theta \qquad (5.23)$$

$$y = (a + b) \cos\left(\frac{a\theta}{a + b}\right) - a \cos\theta \qquad (5.24)$$

The x and y components of the relative velocity V_{P_4/P_2} are given by the expressions

$$\frac{dx}{dt} = \frac{dx}{d\theta}\frac{d\theta}{dt} = \frac{d\theta}{dt}\left[a\cos\left(\frac{a\theta}{a + b}\right) - a\cos\theta\right] \qquad (5.25)$$

$$\frac{dy}{dt} = \frac{dy}{d\theta}\frac{d\theta}{dt} = \frac{d\theta}{dt}\left[-a\sin\left(\frac{a\theta}{a + b}\right) + a\sin\theta\right] \qquad (5.26)$$

When P_2 and P_4 are in contact, $\psi = \theta = 0$ which gives $dx/dt = dy/dt = 0$. This is correct because P is the instant center of velocity.

The second derivatives of Eqs. (5.23) and (5.24) give the x and y components of the relative acceleration A_{P_4/P_2}. They are

$$\frac{d^2x}{dt^2} = \frac{d}{d\theta}\frac{dx}{dt}\frac{d\theta}{dt} = \left(\frac{d\theta}{dt}\right)^2\left[-\frac{a^2}{a + b}\sin\left(\frac{a\theta}{a + b}\right) + a\sin\theta\right] \qquad (5.27)$$

$$\frac{d^2y}{dt^2} = \frac{d}{d\theta}\frac{dy}{dt}\frac{d\theta}{dt} = \left(\frac{d\theta}{dt}\right)^2\left[-\frac{a^2}{a + b}\cos\left(\frac{a\theta}{a + b}\right) + a\cos\theta\right] \qquad (5.28)$$

When P_2 and P_4 are in contact, the acceleration along the x axis, or common tangent is

$$A^t_{P_4/2} = \frac{d^2x}{dt^2} = 0$$

The acceleration along the common normal (y axis) is then the total acceleration. It is

$$A_{P_4/P_2} = A^n_{P_4/P_2} = \frac{d^2y}{dt^2} = \frac{ab\omega_{42}^2}{a + b} \qquad (5.29)$$

By a similar development, the total acceleration for the hypocycloid case is

$$A_{P_4/P_2} = \frac{ab\omega_{42}^2}{a - b} \qquad (5.30)$$

For the cycloid, the acceleration is

$$A_{P_4/P_2} = a\omega_{42}^2 \qquad (5.31)$$

The cycloid formula can be found in the manner described above, or from either of the other two formulas as a special case for b of infinite magnitude. In all cases the acceleration vector is directed toward the center of the rolling circle.

5.11. Inversion. It was shown earlier how an acceleration analysis can be made for cam mechanisms of the type shown in Fig. 5.44 by using a special equivalent linkage. With the aid of inversion an analysis using the conventional linkage, shown with solid lines, will be made. In the original cam mechanism shown with dotted lines, A is the fixed center of rotation of cam 2, and C is the center of curvature of the cam contour at the point of contact P_2P_4. An attempt to solve this problem directly using the equivalent linkage shown will lead to indeterminate relationships because of the infinite links. The analysis can be made using inversion: link 4 is fixed. This is accomplished by superimposing a reference frame that has angular velocity and acceleration equal and opposite to the unknown quantities ω_4 and α_4 that exist when 1 is fixed. This will be illustrated numerically. (All data apply to the original drawing.)

With link 1 fixed, ω_4 is determined using the angular velocity ratio theorem.

$$\omega_4 = \omega_2 \frac{AH}{BH} = 1.00 \frac{0.86}{3.62} = 0.237 \qquad \text{radians per sec CW}$$

When link 4 is fixed, 0.237 radians per sec CCW (i.e., $-\omega_4$) must be added to the other links. The velocity polygon for this condition with link 4 fixed is shown at (b).

$$V_A = \omega_4(AB) = 0.237 \times 4.48 = 1.065 \qquad \text{ips}$$
$$V_{C/A} = (\omega_2 + \omega_4)CA = 1.237 \times 1.56 = 1.93 \qquad \text{ips}$$

By measurement

$$V_C = 2.06 \qquad \text{ips}$$

The acceleration polygon for the inversion with link 4 fixed is shown at (c). The order in which the lines were drawn is shown by numbers in brackets. The symbol $\{\alpha_4\}$ will be used to denote the acceleration that must be added to all links to bring about the inversion; i.e. $\alpha_4 = -\{\alpha_4\}$

$$A_A^n = \omega_4 V_A = 0.237 \times 1.065 = 2.035 \qquad \text{ips}^2$$
$$A_A^t \text{ is known in direction only}$$

$$A_{C/D} = A_{C/D}^t \qquad \text{since} \qquad A_{C/D}^n = 0 \qquad \text{because} \qquad CD = \infty$$
$$\text{(known in direction only)}$$

$$A_{C/A}^n = (\omega_2 + \omega_4)^2 CA = (1.237)^2 \times 1.56 = 2.38 \qquad \text{ips}^2$$

The terminus of this vector is c' and lies on line [3]. Line [4] representing, a possible solution for $A_{C/A}^n$ is drawn parallel to AC, and line [5] which contains the origin of this vector is drawn parallel to line [3].

$$A_{C/A}^t = (\alpha_2 + \{\alpha_4\})CA = \alpha_2 CA + \{\alpha_4\}CA$$

Only a part of this vector can be determined at this stage.

$$\alpha_2(CA) = 1.5 \times 1.56 = 2.34 \qquad \text{ips}^2$$

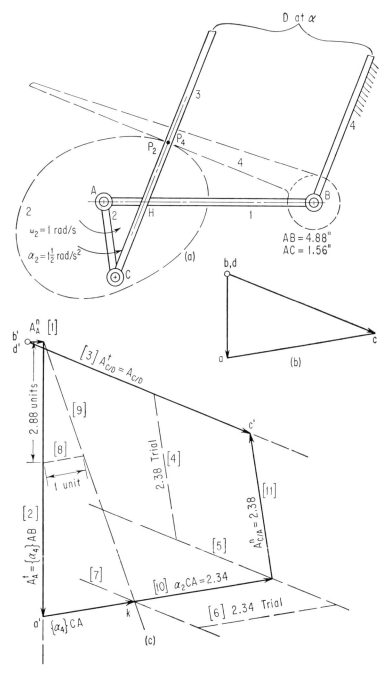

Fig. 5.44

This is laid off at any convenient place [6], and line [7] which contains the origin of this vector is drawn parallel to line [5].

It is obvious that the vectors $\{\alpha_4\}AB$ and $\{\alpha_4\}CA$ have the ratio

$$\frac{AB}{CA} = \frac{4.48}{1.56} = 2.88$$

2.88 units are laid off along line [2] as shown and line [8] one unit long is laid off perpendicular to CA as shown. Line [9] intersects [7] at k. Line [10] through k parallel to [8] satisfies the conditions,

$$\frac{\{\alpha_4\}AB}{\{\alpha_4\}CA} = 2.88, \quad \text{and} \quad \alpha_2(CA) = 2.34$$

Line [10] therefore gives the correct solution. By measurement

$$A_A^t = 4.40 \quad \text{ips}^2$$

then

$$\{\alpha_4\} = \frac{A_A^t}{AB} = 0.98 \quad \text{radians per second}^2 \text{ CCW}$$

and

$$\alpha_4 = -\{\alpha_4\} = 0.98 \text{ radians per second}^2 \text{ CW}$$

The above solution is more complex than the solution for the equivalent linkage shown in Fig. 5.19. It was included here to further explain the concept of inversion; i.e., inversion can be considered as the superposition of a rotating reference frame on a mechanism, the motion of the reference frame being equal but opposite to that of an arbitrarily chosen link in the mechanism.

5.12. Closure. In all probability, new methods for acceleration analysis will be developed; however, at the present time, a number of methods for analyzing complex mechanisms are available. They include the auxiliary point,[1] the three line construction,[2,3,4] the four line construction,[4] an indirect method,[5] and the method of influence coefficients.[6] Wolford and Hall[7] have made a thorough analysis of the second acceleration, (third derivative).

[1] A. S. Hall and E. S. Ault, "Auxiliary Points Aid Acceleration Analysis," *Machine Design*, November, 1943.

[2] H. H. Mabie and F. W. Ocvirk, *Mechanisms and Dynamics of Machinery*, John Wiley & Sons, Inc., New York, 1957.

[3] C. D. Albert and F. S. Rogers, *Kinematics of Machinery*, John Wiley & Sons, Inc., New York, 1938.

[4] J. A. Dent and A. C. Harper, *Kinematics and Kinetics of Machinery*, John Wiley & Sons, Inc., New York, 1921.

[5] T. P. Goodman, "An Indirect Method for Determining Accelerations in Complex Mechanisms," ASME Paper No. 57-A-108.

[6] J. Modrey, "Analysis of Complex Chains With Influence Coefficients," ASME Paper No. 58-A-74.

[7] J. C. Wolford and A. S. Hall, "Second-Acceleration Analysis of Plane Mechanisms," ASME Paper No. 57-A-52.

PROBLEMS

5.1. (a) Construct the acceleration polygon for Fig. P 4.1. Here ω_2 is constant. Use data of Prob. 4.1 and assume a suitable acceleration scale or use the graphical construction of Art. 5.6. Draw vectors A_E, A_C, and A_F on the configuration diagram. Indicate their numerical values in fps².

(b) Determine α_3 and α_4. Indicate whether the links are increasing or decreasing in angular speed.

5.2. (a) Construct the acceleration polygon for Fig. P 3.1. Here ω_2 is constant. Use data of Prob. 4.5.

(b) Determine α_3 and α_4. Indicate whether the links are increasing or decreasing in angular speed.

5.3. (a) Construct the acceleration polygon for Fig. P 3.2. Velocity V_B is constant. Use data of Prob. 4.6.

(b) Determine α_3. Indicate whether the link is increasing or decreasing in angular speed.

5.4. (a) Construct the acceleration polygon for Fig. P 3.4. Here ω_2 is constant. Use data of Prob. 4.8.

(b) Determine α_3 and α_4. Indicate whether the links are increasing or decreasing in angular speed.

5.5. (a) Construct the acceleration polygon for Fig. P 4.2. Velocity V_B is constant. Use data of Prob. 4.2.

(b) Determine α_5.

5.6. (a) Construct the acceleration polygon for Fig. P 4.16. Here ω_2 is constant. Use data of Prob. 4.16.

(b) Determine α_3 and α_4.

5.7. Determine the vectors A_C and A_E for Fig. P 4.17. Here ω_2 is constant. Use data of Prob. 4.17.

5.8. Construct the acceleration polygon for Fig. P 4.18. Here ω_2 is constant. Use data of Prob. 4.18.

5.9. Construct the acceleration polygon for Fig. P 4.19. Here ω_6 is constant in a CCW direction. Let the length of V_D be represented by a vector $1\frac{1}{4}$ in. long. Use the graphical construction of Art. 5.6.

5.10. Construct the acceleration polygon for Fig. P 4.14. Here $\omega_2 = 60$ rpm, $\alpha_2 = 0$.

5.11. Determine α_2 for Fig. P 3.5. Here $\omega_4 = 80$ rpm, $\alpha_4 = 0$.

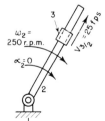

Fig. P 5.12

5.12. Determine the acceleration of slider 3 in Fig. P 5.12. The speed of 3 along link 2 is constant. The slider is 14 in. from the center of rotation of member 2.

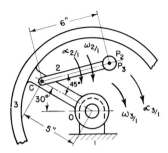

Fig. P 5.13

5.13. In Fig. P 5.13, $\omega_{3/1} = 60$ radians per sec, $\omega_{2/1} = 25$ radians per sec, $\alpha_{3/1} = \alpha_{2/1} = 0$.

(a) Determine A_{P_2} without using Coriolis' law.

(b) Determine A_{P_2} using Coriolis' law.

5.14. Determine A_C for Fig. P 3.3. Here $\omega_2 = 120$ rpm, $\alpha_2 = 0$.

5.15. Construct the acceleration polygon for Fig. P 4.21. Let the magnitude of the velocity $V_B = \frac{1}{2}$ in. and the acceleration $A_B = 1$ in. The velocity and acceleration are both in the direction of V_B in Fig. P 4.21. Use the graphical construction of Art. 5.6.

5.16. Construct the acceleration polygon for Fig. P 4.25. Velocity $V_G = 1\frac{1}{2}$ in., $V_F = 3$ in., $A_G = 2\frac{1}{2}$ in., $A_F = 2\frac{3}{4}$ in. Use the graphical construction of Art. 5.6.

5.17. Construct the acceleration polygon for Fig. P 5.17. Use scales 1 in. = $k_v = 5$ fps and 1 in. = $k_a = 100$ fps².

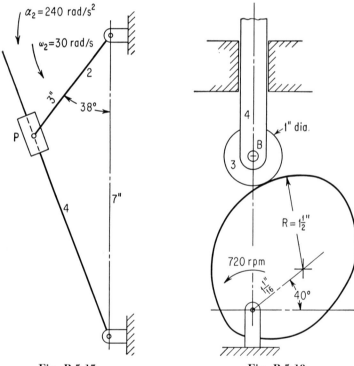

Fig. P 5.17   **Fig. P 5.18**

5.18. Construct acceleration polygons for Fig. P 5.18 using two methods. Use scales 1 in. = $k_v = 4$ fps and 1 in. = $k_a = 300$ fps².

CHAPTER 6

Velocity and Acceleration Graphs, Special Constructions, Analytical Methods

In the preceding chapters, methods were developed for determining velocities and accelerations in mechanisms for a chosen phase. Usually it is necessary to determine the velocities and accelerations of the links for a complete cycle. This can be done by determining the values for a series of phases through the cycle, plotting these values, and drawing curves through the points. In this chapter, graphs and special constructions will be considered.

6.1. Graphical differentiation. A velocity-time graph can be obtained from a displacement-time graph, and an acceleration-time graph can be obtained from a velocity-time graph using graphical differentiation.

A displacement-time graph is shown in Fig. 6.1. The velocity of point P is $V = ds/dt$. A line BD is drawn tangent to the curve at P. A line parallel to the time axis is drawn through B, and a line parallel to the displacement axis is drawn through D forming a right triangle BCD. The velocity is then

$$V = \frac{DCk_s}{BCk_t}$$

The fact that DCk_s and BCk_t are not infinitesimal does not matter since they were constructed in such a manner that their ratio is equal to the ratio of the corresponding infinitesimal quantities. Their ratio gives the correct slope at point P. The velocity can be plotted to any scale desired. However, it is convenient to use a particular scale. The velocity graph derived from the displacement graph is shown below it. The velocity of P is plotted as DC. This can be done with dividers. The velocity scale corresponding to this is

$$1 \text{ in.} = k_v = \frac{\text{velocity of point on machine}}{\text{length of line on drawing that represents velocity}}$$

$$= \frac{DCk_s/BCk_t}{DC} = \frac{k_s}{BCk_t} \tag{6.1}$$

95

The velocity graph was obtained by constructing tangent triangles, using a constant value for BC, at a series of points along the displacement graph. A constant BC produces a constant k_v scale.

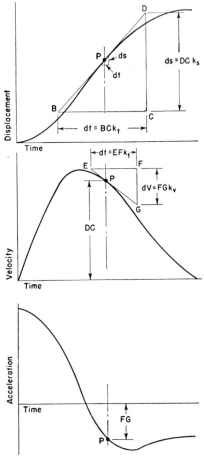

Fig. 6.1

The acceleration graph shown below the velocity graph was obtained in the same manner.

$$A^t = \frac{dV}{dt} = \frac{FGk_v}{EFk_t}$$

When the vertical leg of the triangle is used to represent the acceleration, the scale is

$$1 \text{ in.} = k_a = \frac{FGk_v/EFk_t}{FG} = \frac{k_v}{EFk_t} \tag{6.2}$$

The horizontal leg EF is again an assumed constant. The acceleration is indicated above as the tangential component since it is determined from the change in magnitude of velocity. If the point moves in a curved path the normal acceleration must be determined in some other manner.

The hypodermic gun shown in Fig. 6.2 is an example where graphical differentiation can be useful. In operation the nozzle is held against the flesh. When the springs are released they drive the piston forward at a high velocity causing the jet from the nozzle to enter the flesh. If certain assumptions are made the velocity of the jet can be calculated. The validity of the assumptions can be determined only by experiment. If a scale is attached to the frame and a pointer to the piston rod, a high-speed motion picture can be taken to obtain data for plotting a displacement-time graph. The velocity graph for the piston can be obtained by

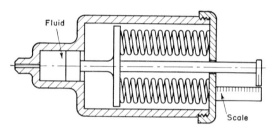

Fig. 6.2

using graphical differentiation. The velocity of the jet at any instant will be

$$\text{vel. of jet} = \text{vel. of piston} \times \frac{\text{area of piston}}{\text{area of nozzle}}$$

The constructions in the previous chapters can be made quite accurately since points are determined from intersecting lines. In graphical differentiation judgment must be used in drawing tangents. Sufficient points must be plotted and a smooth curve carefully drawn. The use of a reflecting bar will increase the accuracy. The cross section of the reflecting bar is rectangular. The bar is laid across the curve and rotated to a position such that the visible curve and the reflection form a smooth curve. The edge of the bar is then normal to the curve.

If the slope of the tangent to a curve is 74° (Fig. 6.3) and an error of 1° is made in drawing the tangent, the resulting relative error is

$$\text{relative error} = \left(\frac{\tan 74° - \tan 75°}{\tan 74°}\right) 100 = 7\%$$

At P_2 the relative error is approximately the same. The relative error curve for 1° error in the tangent is shown in Fig. 6.4. When the slope is small or large the relative error is large. For small slopes the absolute error is small. When the tangent is horizontal any error in drawing the tangent will produce an infinite relative error even though the absolute error is negligible. Steep slopes should be avoided. This can usually be accomplished by choosing a suitable time scale. Errors made in deriving a velocity graph from a displacement graph are not cumulative. If an acceleration curve is derived from this curve and errors are

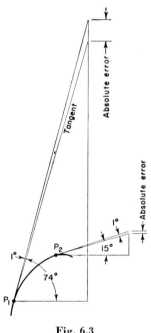

Fig. 6.3

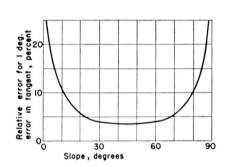

Fig. 6.4

made, the errors in the corresponding points for the two curves may be cumulative.

6.2. Revolved polygon. When it is necessary to determine velocities in a mechanism for many phases, or if in the early stages of design it is necessary to investigate similar mechanisms of different proportions, time can often be saved by using revolved polygons. In the revolved polygon the images are parallel to the links. The use of the revolved polygon will be illustrated with two examples.

Example 1. A slider crank is shown in Fig. 6.5(a). All data apply to the original drawing. The crank has uniform rotation of 200 rpm clockwise. The velocity of the piston C will be determined for 12 equally spaced positions of the crank. The velocity polygon for the number one phase is shown at (b). In (c) the polygon is revolved 90°. The velocity images are parallel to the links. The velocity scale is calculated so that vector ob is equal to O_2B on the drawing.

$$V_B = \frac{2.875}{12} \times \frac{200 \times 2\pi}{60} = 5 \quad \text{fps}$$

Since O_2B on the drawing is 1.4375 in., the velocity scale is

$$1 \text{ in.} = k_v = \frac{5}{1.4375} = 3.48 \quad \text{fps}$$

The revolved polygon is shown superimposed upon the original mechanism so that ob coincides with the crank. Line O_2c represents the magnitude of the velocity of

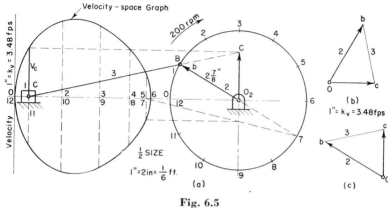

Fig. 6.5

C. For any position of the piston, point c is located on the vertical line through O_2 at the intersection with the connecting rod or the rod extended. The construction is also shown for position 7.

The velocities for the 12 positions are plotted against time in Fig. 6.6. Since the crank rotates uniformly and the positions are equally spaced on the crank

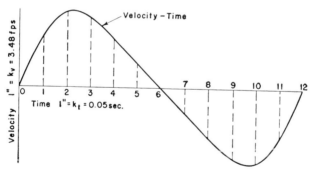

Fig. 6.6

circle, the time intervals are equal. The time for one revolution is $\frac{60}{200} = 0.3$ sec. The time axis is 6 in. long. The time scale is 1 in. $= k_t = 0.3/6 = 0.05$ sec.

Example 2. A quick-return mechanism is shown in Fig. 6.7(a). Crank 2 rotates with constant velocity. The velocity polygon is shown at (b) and the revolved polygon at (c). The velocity scale is chosen so that ob_2 is equal to O_2B_2 on the drawing (d). The revolved polygon is shown superimposed upon the mechanism. The line through O_2 that is parallel to link 4 contains b_4 and c_4. Point b_4 is located by drawing a perpendicular to link 4 through b_2. The intersection D is obtained by extending this line. A line through D and C locates c_4. From similar triangles it can be shown that $c_4b_4/b_4O_2 = C_4B_4/B_4O_4$. Point c_5 is located on the perpendicular to link 4 passing through c_4. This construction can be used for all phases except for vertical positions of the crank. For these two

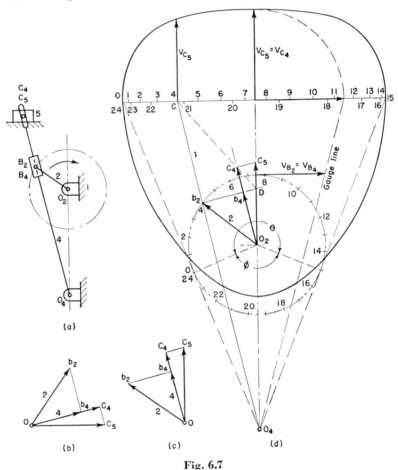

Fig. 6.7

position V_{B_2} can be laid off as shown, and V_{C_5} can be determined from a gage line. For these phases $V_{C_4} = V_{C_5}$.

The time required for the stroke from left to right is the time required for the crank to turn through the angle θ. The time for the return stroke is the time required for the crank to turn through angle ϕ. The ratio of these angles can be altered by altering the proportions of the mechanisms.

There are no general rules for constructing a revolved polygon. A method must be developed for each mechanism.

6.3. Polar velocity graphs. A slider crank is shown in Fig. 6.8. In the previous article it was shown that O_2c represents the velocity of the piston if the crank is turning uniformly and the velocity scale is chosen so that the velocity of B is represented by the length O_2B on the drawing. These values can be plotted by rotating c about O_2 to the crank. The resulting curves are shown. The velocity of the piston for

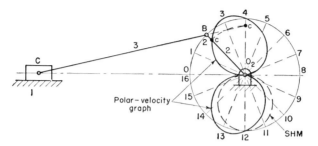

Fig. 6.8

any phase can be determined by drawing the crank in the phase and measuring the distance along the crank from O_2 to the curve.

As the ratio of the length of the connecting rod and crank is increased the motion of the piston approaches simple harmonic motion. The polar velocity graph approaches the circle shown.

A four-bar linkage is shown in Fig. 6.9. The velocity of B is laid off radially outward along crank 2. When 2 rotates uniformly Bb is con-

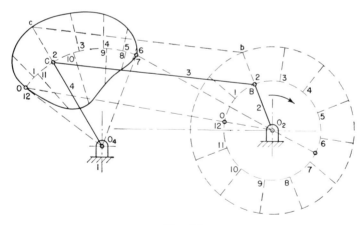

Fig. 6.9

stant and the polar velocity graph for B is a circle with center at O_2. The velocity of C is Cc. Here c is the intersection of a line through b parallel to link 3, and link 4 extended. This is the parallel line construction that was proved in Art. 3.7. Any velocity scale can be assumed.

6.4. Angular velocity graphs. It is sometimes necessary to plot angular velocity graphs. A rapid method that can be used with many

mechanisms will be described.   A Geneva stop is shown in Fig. 6.10(a).
The driver, member 2, rotates with uniform motion.   While 2 is rotating
uniformly through one-fourth revolution, 4 is rotating with a variable
angular velocity through one-fourth revolution; and 4 is stationary while

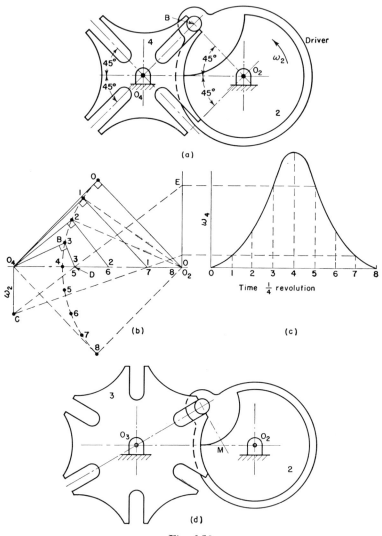

Fig. 6.10

2 is rotating through the remaining three-fourths revolution.   The
angular velocity time curve will be plotted for member 4.   In Art. 2.12
it was shown that the angular velocities of driver and follower are
inversely proportional to the segments into which the common normal
(line of transmission) cuts the line of centers.   The constructions for

determining the intersections of the common normal and the line of centers are shown in (b) for positions 0 to 4. For position 3 the angular velocity ratio is

$$\frac{\omega_4}{\omega_2} = \frac{O_2D}{O_4D}$$

Here ω_2 is laid off vertically from O_4 to a chosen scale. A line through C and D will intersect a vertical line through O_2 at E, forming similar triangles O_4CD and DEO_2. Then

$$\frac{\omega_4}{\omega_2} = \frac{O_2D}{O_4D} = \frac{O_2E}{O_4C}$$

and O_2E will represent ω_4 on the same scale that O_4C represents ω_2. The angular velocity time graph is shown at (c).

The Geneva stop shown at (d) has 6 slots; 3 will make $\frac{1}{6}$ turn for each turn of 2. The line of transmission intersects the line of centers at M for the phase where motion begins. This will cause impact loading. Except for low speeds, member 2 should be designed with center O_2 at M.

6.5. Ritterhaus construction. The slider crank mechanism is of such importance that special constructions have been developed for rapid

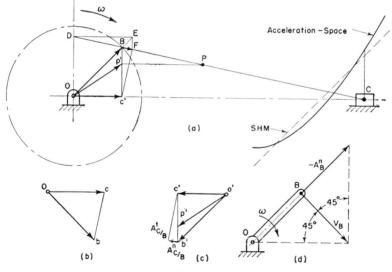

Fig. 6.11

determination of accelerations. One of these, the Ritterhaus construction, is shown in Fig. 6.11(a). The crank rotates with uniform angular velocity. The velocity polygon is shown at (b). The velocity scale was chosen in accordance with Art. 6.2; that is, the vector ob is equal to the length of the crank OB on the drawing. The acceleration polygon is shown at (c). Since there is no tangential acceleration of B, the image $o'b'$ is parallel to OB. If the acceleration scale is chosen so that the length of the vector $o'b'$ is equal to the length of the crank on the drawing, the polygon, when rotated 180°, will fit on the mechanism as shown in (a). The directions of all accelerations are reversed. The graphical construction for determining normal accelerations (Art. 5.6) is shown at (d). The length of V_B was made equal to the crank OB. It can be seen that the normal acceleration vector is also equal to the length of the crank. The scale relationship of Eq. (5.7) therefore holds for the Ritterhaus construction.

The construction is made as follows: extend the connecting rod to the vertical center line through O, obtaining intersection D; through D draw a horizontal line; extend the crank to obtain E; a vertical line through E intersects the connecting rod at F; a perpendicular to the connecting rod at F intersects the horizontal centerline at c'. This construction can be proved as follows. Triangles OCB and DBE are similar. Triangles DOB and BEF are similar. Then

$$\frac{DB}{BC} = \frac{BE}{BO} \quad \text{and} \quad \frac{BF}{BD} = \frac{BE}{BO}$$

Eliminating BE/BO from these equations gives

$$\frac{BD}{BC} = \frac{BF}{BD} \quad \text{or} \quad BF = \frac{(BD)^2}{BC}$$

where BD represents $V_{C/B}$ and BC is the corresponding radius. Hence $BF = A_{C/B}^n$.

This construction is indeterminate for the head-end and crank-end dead-center phases. The construction shown in Fig. 6.12 can be used

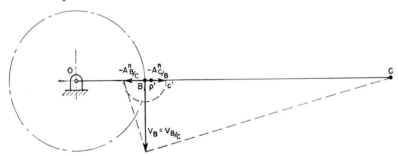

Fig. 6.12

to determine the piston acceleration for these phases. An examination of the revolved polygon in (a) shows that $A_{C/B}^t$ is zero for these phases. Since C has no velocity, $V_{B/C} = V_B$. Velocity V_B is laid off from B and the graphical construction of Art. 5.5 is used to determine $-A_{B/C}^n$. When this vector is rotated through 180° it becomes $-A_{C/B}^n$. Since all the other vectors are reversed, this is consistent.

The acceleration space graph is shown in Fig. 6.11(a). The SHM acceleration space graph for an infinite connecting rod is a straight line.

Sometimes it is necessary to determine the acceleration of a point on the rod such as P, the center of percussion.   The line Bc' is the acceleration image of the connecting rod.   A horizontal line through P locates p'.   In Fig. 6.12, p' is located by proportion.

An offset slider crank mechanism is shown in Fig. 6.13.   It is a quick-return mechanism.   The ratio of the times for the two strokes is θ/ϕ.

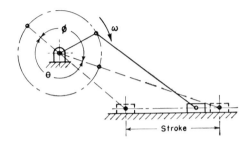

Fig. 6.13

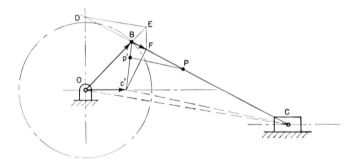

Fig. 6.14

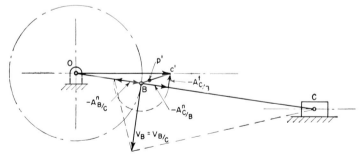

Fig. 6.15

A modified Ritterhaus construction can be used to determine accelerations in this mechanism.   In Fig. 6.14 OBD is the revolved velocity polygon.   In the construction DE is drawn parallel to OC.   The proof given above applies.   Point p' is located by drawing a line through

P parallel to Cc'. When the crank and connecting rod are collinear the construction fails. For these two phases the construction can be made as shown in Fig. 6.15. Acceleration $-A^n_{C/B}$ is determined as in Fig. 6.12, and $-A^t_{C/B}$ is perpendicular to the terminus of $-A^n_{C/B}$. Point c' must lie on the horizontal line through o. It is located as shown.

6.6. Mathematical analysis. Equations for linear and angular velocities and accelerations can be obtained by differentiating displacement equations. The slider crank, Fig. 6.16, will be used to illustrate the

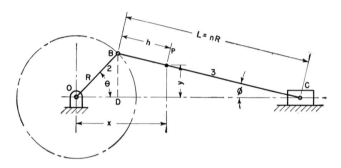

Fig. 6.16

method. Let $n = L/R$ and $m = h/L$. A relationship between θ and ϕ is

$$BD = L \sin \phi = R \sin \theta$$

$$\sin \phi = \frac{\sin \theta}{n} \qquad (6.3)$$

One of the fundamental trigonometric identities is

$$\cos \phi = (1 - \sin^2 \phi)^{\frac{1}{2}}$$

Then

$$\cos \phi = \left(1 - \frac{\sin^2 \theta}{n^2}\right)^{\frac{1}{2}}$$

This can be expressed as a binomial series

$$\left(1 - \frac{\sin^2 \theta}{n^2}\right)^{\frac{1}{2}} = 1 - \frac{1}{2}\frac{\sin^2 \theta}{n^2} - \frac{1}{2 \cdot 4}\frac{\sin^4 \theta}{n^4}$$

$$- \frac{1 \cdot 3}{2 \cdot 4 \cdot 8}\frac{\sin^6 \theta}{n^6} - \frac{1 \cdot 3 \cdot 5}{2 \cdot 4 \cdot 8 \cdot 16}\frac{\sin^8 \theta}{n^8} \cdots$$

When $n = 4$ and all terms are dropped but the first two; the maximum error in the accelerations calculations is about 0.6 per cent. Only the first two terms will be considered here. If greater accuracy is desired an additional term can be included. Then

$$\cos \phi = \frac{1}{n}\left(n - \frac{1}{2n} \sin^2 \theta\right) \qquad \text{approximately} \qquad (6.4)$$

The displacement of any point P on the connecting rod is

$$x = R \cos \theta + h \cos \phi = R \cos \theta + \frac{h}{n}\left(n - \frac{1}{2n} \sin^2 \theta\right) \tag{6.5}$$

$$y = (L - h) \sin \phi = \left(\frac{L - h}{n}\right) \sin \theta \tag{6.6}$$

Differentiating these equations with respect to time gives

$$V_P^x = \frac{dx}{dt} = -R\omega_2 \left(\sin \theta + \frac{m}{2n} 2 \sin \theta \cos \theta\right)$$

$$= -R\omega_2 \left(\sin \theta + \frac{m}{2n} \sin 2\theta\right) \tag{6.7}$$

$$V_P^y = \frac{dy}{dt} = R\omega_2(1 - m) \cos \theta \tag{6.8}$$

If the angular velocity of the crank is constant,

$$A_P^x = \frac{dV_P^x}{dt} = -R\omega_2^2\left(\cos \theta + \frac{m}{n} \cos 2\theta\right) \tag{6.9}$$

$$A_P^y = \frac{dV_P^y}{dt} = -R\omega_2^2(1 - m) \sin \theta \tag{6.10}$$

The acceleration of the piston is obtained by substituting $m = 1$ in the above equations.

$$A_c^x = -R\omega_2^2\left(\cos \theta + \frac{1}{n} \cos 2\theta\right) \tag{6.11}$$

$$A_c^y = 0 \tag{6.12}$$

It can be seen that when n is infinite the motion of the piston is simple harmonic.

From Eq. (6.3) the angular displacement of the connecting rod is

$$\phi = \sin^{-1}\left(\frac{\sin \theta}{n}\right)$$

The angular velocity of the connecting rod is

$$\omega_3 = \frac{d\phi}{dt} = \frac{\omega_2^2(1 - n^2) \sin \theta}{(n^2 - \sin^2 \theta)^{\frac{1}{2}}} \tag{6.13}$$

and the angular acceleration is

$$\alpha_3 = \frac{d\omega_3}{dt} = \frac{\omega_2^2(1 - n^2) \sin \theta}{(n^2 - \sin^2 \theta)^{\frac{3}{2}}} \tag{6.14}$$

For most mechanisms this trigonometric method becomes quite tedious.

6.7. Complex variables.* Before developing the next topic, an analytical method for determining velocities and accelerations in mechanisms, a brief review of complex variables will be given. A complex

---

* R. S. Hartenberg, "Complex Numbers and Four-Bar Linkages," *Machine Design*, March 20, 1958; C. R. Wylie, Jr., *Advanced Engineering Mathematics*, McGraw-Hill Book Co., Inc., New York, 1951, p. 291.

number is a number of the form

$$z = x + iy$$

where x and y are real numbers and i is the imaginary unit defined as $i = \sqrt{-1}$. The real and imaginary parts of a number are often denoted by the symbols $\Re(z)$ and $\Im(z)$. It is necessary to keep in mind that $\Im(z)$ is a real quantity.

The geometric representation of a complex number is shown in Fig. 6.17. Either the point P whose abscissa and ordinate are, respectively, the real and imaginary components of the given number, or the directed line segment which joins the origin to this point, represents the given complex number. When used in this manner, the Cartesian plane is referred to as the complex plane or z-plane. The length r is called the *absolute value* or *modulus* of z, and the angle θ is called the *amplitude* or *argument* of z.

Two complex numbers are equal if and only if the real and imaginary parts of the first are respectively equal to the real and imaginary parts of the second; i.e., if two complex numbers are equal, they are represented by the same point P; therefore, the x and y components of one must equal the x and y components of the other.

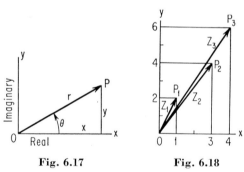

Fig. 6.17   Fig. 6.18

Addition, subtraction, and multiplication of complex numbers follow the familiar rules for real quantities, with the additional provision that in multiplication, all powers of i are to be reduced as far as possible by applying the following properties

$$i^2 = -1$$
$$i^3 = i^2 i = -i$$
$$i^4 = i^2 i^2 = 1$$

$$\cdots$$

If $z_1 = 1 + i2$ and $z_2 = 3 + i4$, then $z_3 = z_1 + z_2 = 4 + i6$. These values are shown in Fig. 6.18 as P_1, P_2, and P_3. If $z_1 = 1 + i2$ and $z_2 = 3 + i4$, then the product $z_1 z_2 = 3 + i6 + i4 + i^2 8 = -5 + i10$. These values are shown in Fig. 6.19 as P_1, P_2, and P_3.

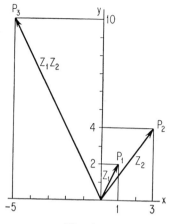

Fig. 6.19

From Fig. 6.17, it can be seen that the polar or trigonometric form of a complex number, $z = x + iy$, is

$$z = r \cos \theta + ir \sin \theta = r(\cos \theta + i \sin \theta) \qquad (6.15)$$

This can be expressed in exponential form

$$z = re^{i\theta} \qquad (6.16)$$

by using the following series

$$e^{i\theta} = 1 + i\theta - \frac{\theta^2}{2!} - \frac{i\theta^3}{3!} + \frac{\theta^4}{4!} + \frac{i\theta^5}{5!} - \frac{\theta^6}{6!} - \quad \cdots$$

$$\cos \theta = 1 - \frac{\theta^2}{2!} + \frac{\theta^4}{4!} - \frac{\theta^6}{6!} + \quad \cdots \qquad (6.17)$$

$$i \sin \theta = i\theta - \frac{i\theta^3}{3!} + \frac{i\theta^5}{5!} - \frac{i\theta^7}{7!} + \quad \cdots$$

Multiplication of a complex number by i rotates the vector that represents it 90° in a positive (CCW) direction. This can be seen in Fig. 6.20

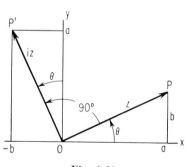

Fig. 6.20

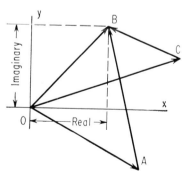

Fig. 6.21

where $z = a + ib$ is represented by OP, and $iz = ia - b$ is represented by OP'. Then

$$ire^{i\theta} = re^{i(\theta+90)} \tag{6.18}$$

Complex exponential quantities are differentiated in the usual manner, for example (remembering that $\theta_3 = \omega_3 t$)

$$\frac{d}{dt} e^{i\theta_3} = e^{i\theta_3} \frac{d}{dt} i\theta_3 = ie^{i\theta_3} \frac{d\theta_3}{dt} = i\omega_3 e^{i\theta_3} = i\dot\theta_3 e^{i\theta_3}$$

A second differentiation gives

$$\frac{d}{dt} (i\dot\theta_3 e^{i\theta_3}) = i\left(\dot\theta_3 \frac{d}{dt} e^{i\theta_3} + e^{i\theta_3} \frac{d\dot\theta_3}{dt} \right) = -\dot\theta_3^2 e^{i\theta_3} + i\ddot\theta_3 e^{i\theta_3}$$

A useful concept is shown in Fig. 6.21. If a vector OB can be expressed as either of two (or more) independent paths, e.g. OCB and OAB, then the real components of the two paths can be equated, and the imaginary components of the two paths can be equated. Obviously, all exponential terms $(e^{i\theta})$ must first be written in the trigonometric form before the separation can be made. This concept will be used in the theory shortly to be explained.

In conclusion, let it be stated again that an expression of the form $z = (r_2\dot\theta_2)(e^{i\theta_2})$ means that z (a vector in the complex plane) has length $(r_2\dot\theta_2)$ and orientation θ_2 with the real axis.

6.8. Position, velocity, and acceleration analysis by means of independent-position equations. In a recent paper* Dr. Raven presented a generalized analytical method for determining positions, velocities and accelerations in mechanisms. A position equation is a vector equation which expresses the position of a point on a mechanism as a function of the geometry of the mechanism. There are only two position equations which are mathematically independent for mechanisms other than complex mechanisms; e.g., in Fig. 6.24, the two independent-position equations are obtained by going from the fixed center O_2 to B to C, and from O_2 to O_3 to C. For two equations to be independent, there must be at least one vector not in common to the two equations. Successive differentiation of these independent-position equations for a point on a mechanism will yield independent equations for the velocity and acceleration of the point. The desired kinematic quantities may be determined from the simultaneous solution of these independent equations. Therefore, the method is called the method of independent-position equations.

Dr. Raven later developed a similar but more direct method which employs loop equations.† A loop equation is a position equation which

---

* F. H. Raven, "Velocity and Acceleration Analysis of Plane and Space Mechanisms by Means of Independent Position Equations," *Trans.* ASME, Vol. 25, 1958, pp. 1–6.

† F. H. Raven, "Position, Velocity and Acceleration Analysis and Kinematic Synthesis of Plane and Space Mechanism by a Generalized Procedure Called the Method of Independent Position Equations," L.C. Card No. 58–5833, University Microfilms, Ann Arbor, Michigan.

is obtained by expressing in complex exponential form a closed path which starts from any point in the mechanism and proceeds through the links and then back to the starting point. By independent-loop equations is meant equations which are mathematically independent. Four link-mechanisms, for example Fig. 6.24, have only one, six link-mechanisms (Fig. 6.25) have two, and eight link-mechanisms (Fig. 6.26) have three loop equations which are mathematically independent.

The independent-loop equations for a mechanism may be separated into real and imaginary components to obtain algebraic equations from which unknown position terms may be evaluated. The first derivative with respect to time of these loop equations yields velocity equations from which the velocity of any link may be determined. Similarly, the second derivative yields equations for evaluating accelerations.

To determine the position, velocity, or acceleration of any point on a mechanism, write the simplest position equation for this point and by successive differentiation obtain velocity and acceleration equations. The unknown position, velocity, and acceleration terms are evaluated from the independent-loop equations and the first and second derivatives of the loop equations.

Example 1. This method of analysis will now be demonstrated for the four bar linkage shown in Fig. 6.22. Let it be desired to determine the velocity and acceleration of the point B. Assume that O_2O_3, r_2, r_3, r_4, θ_2, $\dot{\theta}_2$, $\ddot{\theta}_2$ are known. θ_3, θ_4, θ_B can be calculated from the known geometry. The simplest position equation for point B relative to ground (a fixed pivot) is

$$r_B = r_3 e^{i\theta_3} \tag{6.19}$$

Successive differentiation of the preceding equation with respect to time yields the following equations for the velocity and acceleration of point B.

$$v_B = ir_3\dot{\theta}_3 e^{i\theta_3} = r_3\dot{\theta}_3 e^{i(\theta_3+90°)} \tag{6.20}$$
$$a_B = ir_3(i\dot{\theta}_3^2 + \ddot{\theta}_3)e^{i\theta_3} \tag{6.21}$$
$$= r_3\ddot{\theta}_3 e^{i(\theta_3+90°)} - r_3\dot{\theta}_3^2 e^{i\theta_3}$$

The loop equation for this mechanism is obtained by following the closed path from O_2 to A to B to O_3 and back to O_2. That is

$$r_2 e^{i\theta_2} + r_4 e^{i\theta_4} - r_3 e^{i\theta_3} - O_2O_3 e^{i\theta} = 0$$
or
$$r_2 e^{i\theta_2} + r_4 e^{i\theta_4} = r_3 e^{i\theta_3} + O_2O_3 e^{i\theta_1} \tag{6.22}$$

Differentiation of equation (6.22) yields

$$ir_2\dot{\theta}_2 e^{i\theta_2} + ir_4\dot{\theta}_4 e^{i\theta_4} = ir_3\dot{\theta}_3 e^{i\theta_3} \tag{6.23}$$

The physical interpretation of Eq. (6.23) is shown by the velocity polygon, Fig. 6.22(b), where it is assumed that $\dot{\theta}_2$ is positive (CCW). The velocity of A is $ir_2\dot{\theta}_2 e^{i\theta_2}$ where $r_2\dot{\theta}_2$ is the magnitude and $ie^{i\theta_2}$ or $e^{i(\theta_2+90°)}$ is the direction. The velocity of B relative to A is $ir_4\dot{\theta}_4 e^{i\theta_4}$. The velocity of B, $ir_3\dot{\theta}_3 e^{i\theta_3}$, may appear to be in the wrong direction, but it is correct because $\dot{\theta}_3$ is negative: $\dot{\theta}_2$ was chosen positive but the line of transmission, AB, lies between the fixed centers O_2 and O_3, hence, $\dot{\theta}_2$ and $\dot{\theta}_3$ have opposite signs. If a numerical value is solved for from

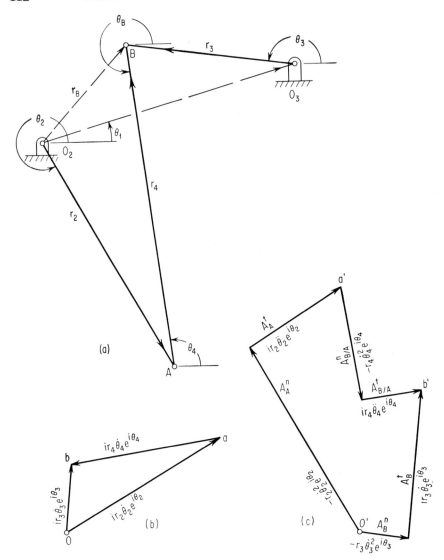

Fig. 6.22

the work that follows, with a positive $\dot{\theta}_2$ and with the configuration of Fig. 6.22(a), $\dot{\theta}_3$ will be negative.

When written in the trigonometric form Eq. (6.23) is

$$ir_2\dot{\theta}_2(\cos\theta_2 + i\sin\theta_2) + ir_4\dot{\theta}_4(\cos\theta_4 + i\sin\theta_4)$$
$$= ir_3\dot{\theta}_3(\cos\theta_3 + i\sin\theta_3) \qquad (6.24)$$

Reducing i to the power of one, the above equation becomes

$$r_2\dot{\theta}_2(i\cos\theta_2 - \sin\theta_2) + r_4\dot{\theta}_4(i\cos\theta_4 - \sin\theta_4)$$
$$= r_3\dot{\theta}_3(i\cos\theta_3 - \sin\theta_3) \qquad (6.24a)$$

The preceding equation, which contains two unknowns, can be resolved into two equations by equating the real and imaginary parts (see Fig. 6.21). After transposing so that the unknowns (which for clarity, are enclosed in brackets) appear on the left, we get

$$\Re(z), \quad r_3 \sin \theta_3 [\dot{\theta}_3] - r_4 \sin \theta_4 [\dot{\theta}_4] = r_2 \dot{\theta}_2 \sin \theta_2 \tag{6.25}$$

$$\mathscr{I}(z), \quad r_3 \cos \theta_3 [\dot{\theta}_3] - r_4 \cos \theta_4 [\dot{\theta}_4] = r_2 \dot{\theta}_2 \cos \theta_2 \tag{6.26}$$

Solving by determinants

$$\dot{\theta}_3 = \frac{\begin{vmatrix} r_2 \dot{\theta}_2 \sin \theta_2 & -r_4 \sin \theta_4 \\ r_2 \dot{\theta}_2 \cos \theta_2 & -r_4 \cos \theta_4 \end{vmatrix}}{\begin{vmatrix} r_3 \sin \theta_3 & -r_4 \sin \theta_4 \\ r_3 \cos \theta_3 & -r_4 \cos \theta_4 \end{vmatrix}} = \frac{r_2 \dot{\theta}_2 (\sin \theta_4 \cos \theta_2 - \cos \theta_4 \sin \theta_2)}{r_3 (\sin \theta_4 \cos \theta_3 - \cos \theta_4 \sin \theta_3)}$$

$$= \frac{r_2 \dot{\theta}_2 \, \sin \, (\theta_4 - \theta_2)}{r_3 \, \sin \, (\theta_4 - \theta_3)} \tag{6.27}$$

Similarly

$$\dot{\theta}_4 = \frac{r_2 r_3 \dot{\theta}_2 \begin{vmatrix} \sin \theta_3 & \sin \theta_2 \\ \cos \theta_3 & \cos \theta_2 \end{vmatrix}}{r_3 r_4 \sin \, (\theta_4 - \theta_3)} = \frac{r_2 \dot{\theta}_2 \, \sin \, (\theta_3 - \theta_2)}{r_4 \sin \, (\theta_4 - \theta_3)} \tag{6.28}$$

Substituting the expression for $\dot{\theta}_3$ in the right hand side of Eq. (6.20) gives

$$\boldsymbol{v}_B = r_2 \dot{\theta}_2 \frac{\sin \, (\theta_4 - \theta_2)}{\sin \, (\theta_4 - \theta_3)} e^{i(\theta_3 + 90°)} \tag{6.29}$$

Twice differentiating loop Eq. (6.22) with respect to time yields

$$ir_2 (i\dot{\theta}_2^2 + \ddot{\theta}_2) e^{i\theta_2} + ir_4 (i\dot{\theta}_4^2 + \ddot{\theta}_4) e^{i\theta_4} = ir_3 (i\dot{\theta}_3^2 + \ddot{\theta}_3) e^{i\theta_3} \tag{6.30}$$

Reducing the powers of i and writing each term separately gives

$$-r_2 \dot{\theta}_2^2 e^{i\theta_2} + ir_2 \ddot{\theta}_2 e^{i\theta_2} - r_4 \dot{\theta}_4^2 e^{i\theta_4} + ir_4 \ddot{\theta}_4 e^{i\theta_4} = -r_3 \dot{\theta}_3^2 e^{i\theta_3} + ir_3 \ddot{\theta}_3 e^{i\theta_3} \tag{6.31}$$

The physical interpretation of Eq. (6.31) is shown in Fig. 6.22(c). Note that the normal accelerations all have negative signs which means that they are reversed or directed toward the center from which the angle is measured. This results from multiplication by i^2 which appeared automatically in the derivation. This agrees with the earlier work in this book (Art. 2.4) where it is shown that normal accelerations are directed toward the center of rotation. The multiplying factor i rotates all tangential accelerations 90° in a positive direction (see Fig. 6.20) which makes the accelerations perpendicular to the links. If the angular acceleration $\ddot{\theta}$ is negative, the tangential acceleration vector will be reversed. The proper sign of $\ddot{\theta}$ will appear automatically when numerical calculations are made using the equations that follow.

By expressing Eq. (6.31) in trigonometric form, expanding, and reducing the powers of i, we obtain

$$ir_2 \ddot{\theta}_2 \cos \theta_2 - r_2 \ddot{\theta}_2 \sin \theta_2 - r_2 \dot{\theta}_2^2 \cos \theta_2 - ir_2 \dot{\theta}_2^2 \sin \theta_2 + ir_4 \ddot{\theta}_4 \cos \theta_4$$
$$- r_4 \ddot{\theta}_4 \sin \theta_4 - r_4 \dot{\theta}_4^2 \cos \theta_4 - r_4 i \dot{\theta}_4^2 \sin \theta_4$$
$$= ir_3 \ddot{\theta}_3 \cos \theta_3 - r_3 \ddot{\theta}_3 \sin \theta_3 - r_3 \dot{\theta}_3^2 \cos \theta_3 - ir_3 \dot{\theta}_3^2 \sin \theta_3 \tag{6.32}$$

Equating the real and imaginary parts, and transposing so that the unknowns appear on the left, we get

$\mathcal{R}(z)$, $r_3 \sin \theta_3 [\ddot{\theta}_3] - r_4 \sin \theta_4 [\ddot{\theta}_4]$

$$= r_2 \ddot{\theta}_2 \sin \theta_2 + r_2 \dot{\theta}_2^2 \cos \theta_2 + r_4 \dot{\theta}_4^2 \cos \theta_4 - r_3 \dot{\theta}_3^2 \cos \theta_3 \qquad (6.33)$$

$\mathcal{I}(z)$, $r_3 \cos \theta_3 [\ddot{\theta}_3] - r_4 \cos \theta_4 [\ddot{\theta}_4]$

$$= r_2 \ddot{\theta}_2 \cos \theta_2 - r_2 \dot{\theta}_2^2 \sin \theta_2 - r_4 \dot{\theta}_4^2 \sin \theta_4 + r_3 \dot{\theta}_3^2 \sin \theta_3 \qquad (6.34)$$

Solving by determinants

$$\ddot{\theta}_3 = \cfrac{-r_4 \begin{vmatrix} r_2\ddot{\theta}_2 \cos \theta_2 - r_2\dot{\theta}_2^2 \sin \theta_2 - r_4\dot{\theta}_4^2 \sin \theta_4 + r_3\dot{\theta}_3^2 \sin \theta_3 & \cos \theta_4 \\ r_2\ddot{\theta}_2 \sin \theta_2 + r_2\dot{\theta}_2^2 \cos \theta_2 + r_4\dot{\theta}_4^2 \cos \theta_4 - r_3\dot{\theta}_3^2 \cos \theta_3 & \sin \theta_4 \end{vmatrix}}{r_3 r_4 \begin{vmatrix} \cos \theta_3 & -\cos \theta_4 \\ \sin \theta_3 & -\sin \theta_4 \end{vmatrix}}$$

or

$$\ddot{\theta}_3 = \cfrac{\begin{aligned} r_2\ddot{\theta}_2(\sin \theta_4 \cos \theta_2 - \cos \theta_4 \sin \theta_2) - r_2\dot{\theta}_2^2(\sin \theta_4 \sin \theta_2 + \cos \theta_4 \cos \theta_2) \\ - r_4\dot{\theta}_4^2(\cos^2 \theta_4 + \sin^2 \theta_4) + r_3\dot{\theta}_3^2(\cos \theta_4 \cos \theta_3 + \sin \theta_4 \sin \theta_3) \end{aligned}}{- r_3(\cos \theta_4 \sin \theta_3 - \sin \theta_4 \cos \theta_3)}$$

or

$$\ddot{\theta}_3 = \frac{r_2\ddot{\theta}_2 \sin(\theta_4 - \theta_2) - r_2\dot{\theta}_2^2 \cos(\theta_4 - \theta_2) + r_3\dot{\theta}_3^2 \cos(\theta_4 - \theta_3) - r_4\dot{\theta}_4^2}{r_3 \sin(\theta_4 - \theta_3)} \qquad (6.35)$$

Similarly

$$\ddot{\theta}_4 = \frac{-r_2\ddot{\theta}_2 \sin(\theta_3 - \theta_2) + r_2\dot{\theta}_2^2 \cos(\theta_3 - \theta_2) + r_4\dot{\theta}_4^2 \cos(\theta_3 - \theta_4) - r_3\dot{\theta}_3^2}{r_4 \sin(\theta_3 - \theta_4)} \qquad (6.36)$$

Substitution of the value of $\ddot{\theta}_3$ from Eq. (6.35) into the right hand side of Eq. (6.21) gives

$$\mathbf{a}_B = \frac{[r_2\ddot{\theta}_2 \sin(\theta_4 - \theta_2) - r_2\dot{\theta}_2^2 \cos(\theta_4 - \theta_2) + r_3\dot{\theta}_3^2 \cos(\theta_4 - \theta_3) - r_4\dot{\theta}_4^2]}{\sin(\theta_4 - \theta_3)} e^{i(\theta_3 + 90°)} - r_3\dot{\theta}_3^2 e^{i\theta_3}$$

$$(6.37)$$

Example 2. The crank shaper mechanism, Fig. 6.23, will now be analyzed. Assuming that r_2, r_B, (O_4O_2), θ_2, $\dot{\theta}_2$, and $\ddot{\theta}_2$ are known, let it be desired to determine the position, velocity and acceleration of point B. By following the closed path O_4 to A to O_2 to O_4, the loop equation is expressed in the form

$$r_4 e^{i\theta_4} - r_2 e^{i\theta_2} - i(O_2O_4) = 0 \qquad (6.38)$$

The real and imaginary parts of this equation are

$$r_4 \cos \theta_4 = r_2 \cos \theta_2 \qquad (6.39)$$
$$r_4 \sin \theta_4 = r_2 \sin \theta_2 + O_2O_4 \qquad (6.40)$$

The unknown position term θ_4 may be evaluated by dividing the sides of Eq. (6.40) by the corresponding sides of Eq. (6.39)

$$\theta_4 = \tan^{-1}\left[\frac{r_2 \sin \theta_2 + O_2O_4}{r_2 \cos \theta_2}\right] \qquad (6.41)$$

The unknown position term r_4 may be evaluated by squaring the sides of Eqs. (6.39) and (6.40), and then adding the two equations.

$$r_4 = \sqrt{r_2^2 + 2r_2(O_2O_4) \sin \theta_2 + (O_2O_4)^2} \qquad (6.42)$$

The simplest position equation for point B is seen to be

$$\mathbf{r}_B = r_B e^{i\theta_4} \qquad (6.43)$$

Successive differentiation of Eq. (6.43) yields for the velocity and acceleration of point B

$$\boldsymbol{v}_B = \frac{d\boldsymbol{r}_B}{dt} = ir_B\dot{\theta}_4 e^{i\theta_4} = r_B\dot{\theta}_4 e^{i(\theta_4+90°)} \tag{6.44}$$

$$\boldsymbol{a}_B = \frac{d\boldsymbol{v}_B}{dt} = r_B(i\ddot{\theta}_4 - \dot{\theta}_4^2)e^{i\theta_4} \tag{6.45}$$

The first time derivative of the loop Eq. (6.38) is

$$ir_4\dot{\theta}_4 e^{i\theta_4} + \dot{r}_4 e^{i\theta_4} - ir_2\dot{\theta}_2 e^{i\theta_2} = 0 \tag{6.46}$$

Separating Eq. (6.46) into real and imaginary parts and solving for the unknown

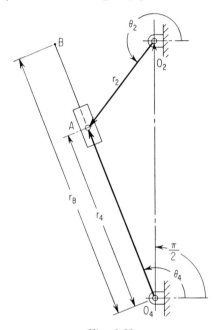

Fig. 6.23

velocity terms $\dot{\theta}_4$ and $\dot{r}_4$ yields

$$\dot{\theta}_4 = \frac{r_2\dot{\theta}_2}{r_4} \cos(\theta_4 - \theta_2) \tag{6.47}$$

$$\dot{r}_4 = r_2\dot{\theta}_2 \sin(\theta_4 - \theta_2) \tag{6.48}$$

Thus, the velocity of point B is

$$\boldsymbol{v}_B = \frac{r_B r_2\dot{\theta}_2}{r_4} \cos(\theta_4 - \theta_2)\ e^{i(\theta_4+90°)} \tag{6.49}$$

In a similar manner, the acceleration of point B may be expressed as

$$\boldsymbol{a}_B = \frac{r_B}{r_4}[r_2\ddot{\theta}_2 \cos(\theta_4 - \theta_2) + r_2\dot{\theta}_2^2 \sin(\theta_4 - \theta_2) - 2\dot{r}_4\dot{\theta}_4]e^{i(\theta_4+90°)} - r_B\dot{\theta}_4^2 e^{i\theta_4}$$

$$\tag{6.50}$$

It should be noticed that the Coriolis component of acceleration $2\dot{r}_4\dot{\theta}_4$ is automatically included.

When applying this method to direct contact mechanisms, the path to follow in going from one member to another is that of the radii of curvature of the surfaces at the point of contact. In the discussion of equivalent linkages, it was shown that for position, velocity and acceleration analysis, these radii of curvature may be considered to remain constant for an incremental motion of the members.

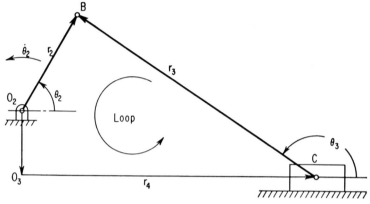

Fig. 6.24

Three more mechanisms will be considered briefly to further illustrate the method. The loop equation for the offset slider crank, Fig. 6.24, is

$$r_2e^{i\theta_2} = (O_2O_3)e^{-i\,90°} + r_4 + r_3e^{i\theta_3} \qquad (6.51)$$

Differentiation yields

$$i\dot{\theta}_2r_2e^{i\theta_2} = \dot{r}_4 + ir_3\dot{\theta}_3e^{i\theta_3} \qquad (6.52)$$

The preceding equation may be solved for the two unknown velocity terms $\dot{\theta}_3$ and $\dot{r}_4$, the velocity of the slider. The next derivative would yield equations for determining the unknown accelerations $\ddot{\theta}_3$ and $\ddot{r}_4$.

A six link mechanism has two loop equations. For Fig. 6.25, the equations are

Loop 1:

$$r_2e^{i\theta_2} = (O_2O_6) + r_6'e^{i\theta_6} + r_5e^{i\theta_5} \qquad (6.53)$$

Loop 2:

$$r_5e^{i\theta_5} + r_3e^{i\theta_3} = r_6e^{i\theta_6} + r_4e^{i\theta_4} \qquad (6.54)$$

Differentiation yields

$$ir_2\dot{\theta}_2e^{i\theta_2} = ir_6'\dot{\theta}_6e^{i\theta_6} + ir_5\dot{\theta}_5e^{i\theta_5} \qquad (6.55)$$

$$ir_5\dot{\theta}_5e^{i\theta_5} + ir_3\dot{\theta}_3e^{i\theta_3} = ir_6\dot{\theta}_6e^{i\theta_6} + ir_4\dot{\theta}_4e^{i\theta_4} \qquad (6.56)$$

Four equations may be obtained from the two preceding equations by separating them into real and imaginary parts. Then, by the use of determinants, any of the unknown velocities $\dot{\theta}_3$, $\dot{\theta}_4$, $\dot{\theta}_5$, or $\dot{\theta}_6$ may be found.

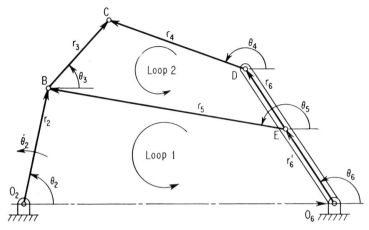

Fig. 6.25

An eight link mechanism has three loop equations.   For Fig. 6.26, the equations are

Loop 1:

$$r_2 e^{i\theta_2} + r_3' e^{i\theta_3} = (O_2 O_5) + r_5 e^{i\theta_5} + r_4 e^{i\theta_4} \tag{6.57}$$

Loop 2:

$$r_5 e^{i\theta_5} + r_4 e^{i\theta_4} + r_3 e^{i\theta_3} = r_5' e^{i(\theta_5 + 180°)} + r_6 e^{i\theta_6} + r_7 e^{i\theta_7} \tag{6.58}$$

Loop 3:

$$r_5' e^{i(\theta_5 + 180°)} + r_6 e^{i\theta_6} = (O_5 O_8) + r_8 e^{i\theta_8} + r_7' e^{i\theta_7}$$

By differentiating the above equations, and separating the real and imaginary components, six equations are obtained from which any

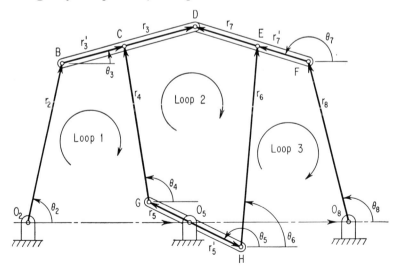

Fig. 6.26

of the six unknown velocities $\dot{\theta}_3$, $\dot{\theta}_4$, $\dot{\theta}_5$, $\dot{\theta}_6$, $\dot{\theta}_7$, or $\dot{\theta}_8$, may be found by determinants.

From these examples it can be seen that mathematical analysis may be tedious. For most purposes, a graphical analysis has sufficient accuracy and is less time consuming. However, with the high speed computers now available, it may be desirable at times to use the mathematical approach. Once an equation has been derived for a mechanism, it is valid for any phase and for any proportion of the lengths of the various links. The method, described in Art. 6.6, of writing a trigonometric displacement equation and then differentiating twice gets out of hand because of the long equations; few of the terms can be cancelled or combined. When complex numbers are used, many terms can be cancelled or combined which prevents the work from becoming unwieldy, even for complex mechanisms. Raven's method of independent-position equations employs a powerful basic concept, and can be used for synthesis as will be shown in the chapter on cams.

In another method,* the velocity and acceleration equations are written in vector form as though one were going to make a graphical solution. These vectors are then written as complex numbers and a mathematical solution is made. Often this requires less time than to obtain the equations by differentiation as described above.

6.9. Finite difference calculations in kinematic analysis.† From Art. 6.1, it should be evident that graphical differentiation may not be sufficiently accurate for some purposes. If the displacement-time data is accurate, finite-difference equations may be used to obtain derivatives that are equally accurate. In the work that follows, finite-difference expressions will be derived and then applied to a specific problem.

The Cartesian coordinates (x,y) of any point in a mechanism may be expressed in terms of the angular coordinate θ of the driving link, or directly in terms of the time coordinate t, for a prescribed angular velocity of the driving link; e.g., Fig. 6.27 may be the displacement-time graph

* G. H. Martin, and M. F. Spotts, "An Application of Complex Geometry to Relative Velocities and Accelerations in Mechanisms," *Trans.* ASME, Vol. 79, 1957, pp. 687–693.

† This article is based largely on two research reports by B. W. Shaffer and I. Krause, prepared for the Department of Mechanical Engineering, New York University. "The Kinematic Analysis of a Specific Point in a Mechanism by the Use of Finite Difference Expressions," November, 1957; and "Refinement of Finite Difference Calculations in Kinematic Analysis," March, 1959. Other references are "Development of a High Speed Indexing Mechanism," by Ray C. Johnson, *Machine Design*, September, 4, 1958; "The Dynamic Analysis and Design of Relatively Flexible Cam Mechanisms Having More than One Degree of Freedom," by Ray C. Johnson, *Trans.* ASME, Paper No. 58–A–192. "Numerical Methods in Engineering," by M. G. Salvadori and M. Baron, Prentice-Hall, Inc., Englewood Cliffs, N. J., 1952. "Introduction to Numerical Analysis," by F. B. Hildebrand, McGraw-Hill Book Co., Inc., New York, 1956.

for the follower, Fig. 6.28.   The functions $x(t)$ and $y(t)$ are continuous and so are the derivatives.   One may, therefore, write Taylor's series for $y(t)$* either in the form

$$y(t + \Delta t) = y(t) + (\Delta t) \frac{dy(t)}{dt} + \frac{(\Delta t)^2}{2!} \frac{d^2 y(t)}{dt^2} + \frac{(\Delta t)^3}{3!} \frac{d^3 y(t)}{dt^3} + \cdots$$

(6.59)

or in the form

$$y(t - \Delta t) = y(t) - (\Delta t) \frac{dy(t)}{dt} + \frac{(\Delta t)^2}{2!} \frac{d^2 y(t)}{dt^2} - \frac{(\Delta t)^3}{3!} \frac{d^3 y(t)}{dt^3} + \cdots$$

(6.60)

for the purposes of comparing the values of the function at t and $t + \Delta t$, or t and $t - \Delta t$ respectively.

For a given mechanism, the function $y(t)$ is known either algebraically or numerically.   In either case, numerical values of the function may be determined at uniform time intervals, h time units apart, as indicated in Fig. 6.27.

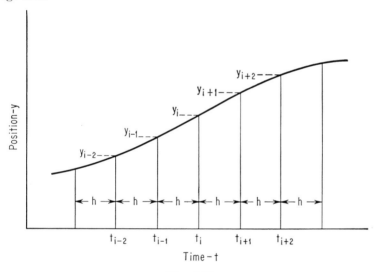

Fig. 6.27

It is convenient in the analysis to follow, to study the displacement-time curve one point at a time.   The procedure is facilitated by denoting the particular time to be investigated by t_i and by denoting the corresponding space coordinate by y_i.   Similarly, the time "stations" to the left of t_i are labeled t_{i-1}, t_{i-2}, ... and those to the right of t_i are labeled t_{i+1}, t_{i+2}, ...   The corresponding space coordinates are denoted by y_{i-1}, y_{i-2}, ... and y_{i+1}, y_{i+2}, ... respectively.

---

* Analogous expressions may be written for $x(t)$.   The resulting finite difference expressions are identical except that x and y are interchanged.

With this notation, and with the time interval Δt set equal to h, Eq. (6.59) may be written

$$y_{i+1} = y_i + h\, y_i' + \frac{h^2}{2!}\, y_i'' \tag{6.61}$$

while Eq. (6.60) may be written

$$y_{i-1} = y_i - h\, y_i' + \frac{h^2}{2!}\, y_i'' \tag{6.62}$$

where the higher order terms have been neglected and the primes indicate differentiation with respect to time. Subtraction of Eq. (6.62) from Eq. (6.61) leads to

$$y_i' = \frac{y_{i+1} - y_{i-1}}{2h} \tag{6.63}$$

whereas their addition leads to

$$y_i'' = \frac{y_{i-1} - 2y_i + y_{i+1}}{h^2} \tag{6.64}$$

In view of the basic definition for the velocity component, $v_y = dy/dt$, Eq. (6.63) is called the first central difference expression for the velocity at the time $t = t_i$. From a geometric point of view, y_i' is equal to the slope of a line drawn from y_{i-1} to y_{i+1} in Fig. 6.27. Similarly, in view of the basic definition for the acceleration component, $a_y = d^2y/dt^2$, Eq. (6.64) is called the first central difference expression for acceleration at the instant under investigation. These two equations permit the evaluation of velocity and acceleration of a point in terms of its positions h time units before, h time units after, and at the instant t_i.

The previous equations were derived by neglecting all terms in Taylor's series that contain derivatives that are higher than the second order. If some of these higher derivative terms are retained, one may develop expressions for velocity and acceleration which are more accurate than those previously derived. For example, by including the third and fourth derivative terms in Eqs. (6.59) and (6.60), the Taylor's series, when written in terms of the current notation, with Δt replaced by h, become

$$y_{i+1} = y_i + h\, y_i' + \frac{h^2}{2!}\, y_i'' + \frac{h^3}{3!}\, y_i''' + \frac{h^4}{4!}\, y_i^{iv} \tag{6.65}$$

and

$$y_{i-1} = y_i - h\, y_i' + \frac{h^2}{2!}\, y_i'' - \frac{h^3}{3!}\, y_i''' + \frac{h^4}{4!}\, y_i^{iv} \tag{6.66}$$

Subtraction of Eq. (6.66) from Eq. (6.65) gives

$$y_{i+1} - y_{i-1} = 2h\, y_i' + \frac{2h^3}{3!}\, y_i''' \tag{6.67}$$

If the original Taylor's series are rewritten in terms of the current notation, but with Δt now replaced by $2h$, Eqs. (6.59) and (6.60) become

$$y_{i+2} = y_i + (2h)y_i' + \frac{(2h)^2}{2!}\, y_i'' + \frac{(2h)^3}{3!}\, y_i''' + \frac{(2h)^4}{4!}\, y_i^{iv} \qquad (6.68)$$

and

$$y_{i-2} = y_i - (2h)y_i' + \frac{(2h)^2}{2!}\, y_i'' - \frac{(2h)^3}{3!}\, y_i''' + \frac{(2h)^4}{4!}\, y_i^{iv} \qquad (6.69)$$

where, in keeping with the current notation, $y(t + 2h) = y_{i+2}$ and $y(t - 2h) = y_{i-2}$. The difference between Eqs. (6.68) and (6.69) is

$$y_{i+2} - y_{i-2} = 4 h\, y_i' + 2\,\frac{(2h)^3}{3!}\, y_i''' \qquad (6.70)$$

Equation (6.70) is subtracted from Eq. (6.67) after it has been multiplied by 8, giving

$$y_i' = \frac{y_{i-2} - 8y_{i-1} + 8y_{i+1} - y_{i+2}}{12h} \qquad (6.71)$$

The sum of Eqs. (6.68) and (6.69) is subtracted from 16 times the sum of Eqs. (6.65) and (6.66), giving

$$y_i'' = \frac{-y_{i-2} + 16y_{i-1} - 30y_i + 16y_{i+1} - y_{i+2}}{12h^2} \qquad (6.72)$$

In view of the physical meaning of dy/dt and d^2y/dt^2, the last two equations describe the velocity and acceleration of a point in a mechanism. They were obtained by including terms in Taylor's series that are of higher order than those retained in the earlier derivations. Thus Eq. (6.71) is called the second central difference expression for velocity, and Eq. (6.72) is called the second central difference expression for acceleration at the instant $t = t_i$. These finite difference expressions require information concerning the position of the point up to $2h$ time units from the instant under consideration.

It is also possible to derive a finite difference expression for the third derivative of displacement with respect to time. If Eqs. (6.67) and (6.70) are solved simultaneously for y_i''', it is found that

$$y_i''' = \frac{-y_{i-2} + 2y_{i-1} - 2y_{i+1} + y_{i+2}}{2h^3} \qquad (6.73)$$

Equation (6.73) is the first central difference approximation for d^3y/dt^3, which is sometimes called the pulse, or jerk.

If the fifth and sixth derivative terms are included in Eqs. (6.59), (6.60), (6.65), (6.66), (6.68), and (6.69); and Eq. (6.59) and (6.60) are rewritten in terms of the current notation with Δt replaced by $3h$, then the second difference approximation for the third derivative may be derived. When these six equations are solved for y_i''', one finds that

$$y_i''' = \frac{y_{i-3} - 8y_{i-2} + 13y_{i-1} - 13y_{i+1} + 8y_{i+2} - y_{i+3}}{8h^3} \qquad (6.74)$$

If the same six equations were used to solve for y_i' and y_i'', the resulting expressions would be the third central difference approximations of velocity and acceleration.

A specific problem will now be analyzed kinematically by using the first and second central difference expressions. The results will then be compared with those obtained from an exact solution. This approach is used to demonstrate the application of the finite difference expressions and to observe the accuracy that is obtained.

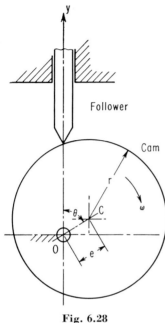

Consider the circular plate cam and follower shown in Fig. 6.28. The cam, of radius r, is rotated about the axis O which is a distance e from the geometric center C.

The y axis is chosen so that it originates at the center of rotation of the cam and is parallel to the direction of motion of the follower. The angular position of the cam, represented by θ, is measured clockwise from the y axis to the line OC. From geometric considerations, one may describe the position of the tip of the follower in terms of the physical dimensions of the cam and its angular position θ as

Fig. 6.28

$$y = e \cos \theta + r \sqrt{1 - \left(\frac{e}{r} \sin \theta\right)^2} \quad (6.75)$$

The velocity of the follower is the first derivative of Eq. (6.75) with respect to time. Since the angular velocity, $\omega = d\theta/dt$,

$$v_y = \frac{dy}{dt} = -e\omega \left[\sin \theta + \frac{e \sin 2\theta}{2r \sqrt{1 - \left(\frac{e}{r} \sin \theta\right)^2}} \right] \quad (6.76)$$

The acceleration of the follower is the second derivative of Eq. (6.75) with respect to time. If ω is specified as constant, $d\omega/dt = 0$ and

$$a_y = \frac{d^2y}{dt^2} = -e\omega^2 \left\{ \cos \theta + \frac{\left[\frac{e}{r} - \left(\frac{e}{r}\right)^3\right] \cos 2\theta + \left(\frac{e}{r}\right)^3 \cos^4 \theta}{\left[1 - \left(\frac{e}{r} \sin \theta\right)^2\right]^{3/2}} \right\} \quad (6.77)$$

The pulse of the follower is the third derivative of Eq. (6.75) with respect to time. Thus

$$p = \frac{d^3y}{dt^3} = e\omega^3 \left\{ \sin \theta + \frac{2A \sin 2\theta}{\left[1 - \left(\frac{e}{r} \sin \theta\right)^2\right]^3} \right\} \quad (6.78)$$

where $A = \left[1 - \left(\dfrac{e}{r}\sin\theta\right)^2\right]^{3/2}\left[\left(\dfrac{e}{r} - \left[\dfrac{e}{r}\right]^3\right) + \left(\dfrac{e}{r}\right)^3\cos^2\theta\right]$

$- \left[\left(\dfrac{e}{r} - \left[\dfrac{e}{r}\right]^3\right)\cos 2\theta + \left(\dfrac{e}{r}\right)^3\cos^4\theta\right]$

$\left[3\left(\dfrac{e}{2r}\right)^2\left(1 - \left[\dfrac{e}{r}\sin\theta\right]^2\right)^{1/2}\right]$

For purposes of a specific analysis, the cam shown in Fig. 6.28, is assumed to have an eccentricity e equal to 0.6 in., a radius r equal to 1.6 in., and an angular velocity ω equal to 100 radians per second. The displacement, velocity, acceleration, and pulse of the follower may be found by substituting the appropriate dimensions into Eqs. (6.75), (6.76), (6.77), and (6.78), respectively.

This was done for every 15° of rotation and the results appear in Table 6.1. The results are tabulated only for the first 180° of rotation, because of the symmetry of the problem.

One may also calculate the velocity, acceleration, and pulse of the follower by substituting the displacement-time data of Table 6.1 into appropriate finite-difference expressions derived earlier. For example, the velocity, acceleration, and pulse at $\theta = 15°$ may be calculated by designating y_i as the position of the follower at $\theta = 15°$; while $y_{i-3}, y_{i-2}, y_{i-1}, y_{i+1}, y_{i+2}$, and y_{i+3} correspond to its position at $\theta = -30°, \theta = -15°, \theta = 0°, \theta = 30°, \theta = 45°$, and $\theta = 60°$, respectively. Thus, according to the data of Table 6.1,

$$y_{i-3} = 2.0912 \text{ in.} \qquad y_{i-1} = 2.2000 \text{ in.} \qquad y_{i+2} = 1.9670 \text{ in.}$$
$$y_{i-2} = 2.1720 \text{ in.} \qquad y_i = 2.1720 \text{ in.} \qquad y_{i+3} = 1.8133 \text{ in.} \qquad (6.79)$$
$$y_{i+1} = 2.0912 \text{ in.}$$

When the station i corresponds to $\theta = 15°$, notice that the numerical values of y_{i-2} and y_i are equal because of the symmetry of the problem.

According to the first central difference approximation, Eq. (6.63), the velocity of the follower is -20.779 ips, when the displacements are prescribed by Eqs. (6.79) and $h = 0.00261799$ sec. According to Eq. (6.71), which is the second central difference approximation, the follower velocity at $\theta = 15°$ is -21.180 ips. These values have also been tabulated in Table 6.1 and compare favorably with the exact value of -21.181 ips.

Similarly, the acceleration of the follower may also be found by using the finite difference expressions derived earlier. When the numerical values of Eqs. (6.79) are introduced into Eq. (6.64), the first central difference approximation for acceleration of the follower at $\theta = 15°$ is found to be -7703.7 ips^2; whereas, from Eq. (6.72), the second central difference approximation of the follower acceleration is found to be -7779.0 ips^2. As before, these approximations are close to the exact value of -7773.4 ips^2.

TABLE 6.1

Position of cam, θ degrees	Position of follower, y inches	VELOCITY			ACCELERATION			PULSE × 10⁻⁶		
		1st central difference in./sec	2nd central difference in./sec	Exact method in./sec	1st central difference in./sec²	2nd central difference in./sec²	Exact method in./sec²	1st central difference in./sec³	2nd central difference in./sec³	Exact method in./sec³
0	2.2000	0.000	0.000	0.000	−8170.5	−8248.4	−8250.0	0.00000	0.00000	0.00000
15	2.1720	−20.779	−21.180	−21.181	−7703.7	−7779.0	−7773.4	0.35110	0.36434	0.36031
30	2.0912	−39.152	−39.893	−39.919	−6332.2	−6386.9	−6404.0	0.64926	0.67434	0.67388
45	1.9670	−53.075	−54.043	−54.094	−4304.1	−4335.7	−4330.9	0.84711	0.87985	0.88897
60	1.8133	−61.192	−62.236	−62.263	−1896.7	−1894.3	−1880.7	0.91398	0.95508	0.95452
75	1.6466	−63.044	−63.977	−63.990	48.2	52.2	51.3	0.81645	0.84989	0.84603
90	1.4832	−59.301	−59.970	−60.000	2378.2	2439.0	2427.2	0.58517	0.59214	0.60000
105	1.3361	−51.547	−51.920	−51.921	3545.4	3597.7	3619.0	0.32602	0.31488	0.31309
120	1.2133	−41.559	−41.686	−41.660	4085.3	4126.6	4119.3	0.11146	0.08987	0.08741
135	1.1185	−30.806	−30.787	−30.759	4129.0	4143.6	4154.5	−0.01672	−0.03831	−0.04043
150	1.0520	−20.168	−20.101	−20.081	3997.7	4001.4	3938.3	−0.05852	−0.07245	−0.07388
165	1.0129	−9.931	−9.880	−9.879	3822.6	3812.9	3817.7	−0.04458	−0.05225	−0.04972
180	1.0000	0.000	0.000	0.000	3764.2	3754.6	3750.0	0.00000	0.00000	0.00000

In a like manner, the pulse of the follower may be approximated by means of Eq. (6.73) or Eq. (6.74).   Substitution of the values of Eqs. (6.79) into Eq. (6.73) yields the first central difference approximation of the pulse at $\theta = 15°$, as 0.35110×10^6 ips^3.   Equation (6.74) shows that the second central difference approximation of the pulse is 0.36434×10^6 ips^3.   The exact pulse at $\theta = 15°$ is equal to 0.36031×10^6 ips^3. The results of similar calculations for velocity, acceleration, and pulse are listed in Table 6.1 for 15° intervals of cam rotation.

Even though the results obtained from a first central difference calculation are reasonably close to exact numerical values, the errors can be reduced.   One method is to reduce the time interval initially used. A second method, demonstrated earlier, calls for the inclusion of higher order terms of the Taylor's series.

It has been shown that the finite-difference expressions developed previously may be used to evaluate numerically the corresponding velocity-time, acceleration-time, and pulse-time relations from a position-time curve for a point on a mechanism.   Two expressions, representing a first and second approximation, were presented for velocity, acceleration, and pulse.

When the finite-difference expressions are applied to a specific cam mechanism and the results are compared with those obtained from the exact solution, it is found that the first central difference expressions lead to numerical results that are reasonable for engineering studies, whereas the second central difference expressions lead to even closer agreement.   In a practical case, where the exact solution is not known in advance, closeness of the results obtained by using the first and second order finite-difference expressions indicates relative accuracy of the numerical results and convergence to the exact solution.   In cases where the numerical results are not sufficiently accurate, they may be improved by including still higher order terms in the Taylor series expansion by using smaller time intervals, or by extrapolating previous calculations.

It is significant to observe from the data listed in Table 6.1 that the results found by using finite-difference expressions are in close agreement with results found by using analytical expressions, obtained by successive differentiation of the displacement-time relation, even though crank-angle intervals as large as 15° were used.   Obviously, one need not resort to infinitesimal increments in order to obtain reasonable numerical results.

A number of additional concepts are described in texts dealing with the finite-difference method.   One is concerned with finite-difference expressions written entirely in terms of stations in advance of the one under investigation.   They are known as the forward finite-difference expressions.   Another is concerned with finite-difference expressions written entirely in terms of stations behind the one under investigation.

They are known as backward finite difference expressions. Also, the restriction of equally spaced stations may be removed so that finite difference expression can be written in terms of unequally spaced stations. It is not uncommon for cam contours to be made of sections that are expressed by several functions; e.g., a cam contour may be composed of circular arcs and straight lines. There may be discontinuities in the second and third derivatives where the sections join. For these cases, the values of the discontinuities can be determined accurately by treating each section separately and using forward and backward finite difference expressions, which may be developed in a manner analogous to the present derivation.

The term for the third derivative, called *jerk* or *pulse* in the above discussion, has not been agreed upon. Shaffer prefers to call it *third derivative*, while Wolford and Hall, and Carter use the term *second-acceleration*. The effect of pulse on the dynamic characteristics of mechanisms is not known. However, future investigations of the type made by Mercer and Holowenko should lead to an understanding of it.*

PROBLEMS

6.1. (a) Plot the velocity-space graph for the slider of Fig. P 6.1 (see Fig. 6.5). The mechanism is to be drawn one-half size. Use 30° intervals for θ. Calculate the velocity scale.

(b) Plot the velocity-time graph. Let the velocity scale be the same as in part (a) and let the time axis be 6 in. long (see Fig. 6.6). Calculate the time scale.

(c) Determine the acceleration-time graph using graphical differentiation. Let the horizontal leg of the tangent triangle be 1 in. Calculate the acceleration scale.

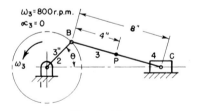
Fig. P 6.1

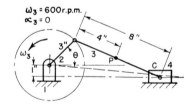
Fig. P 6.2

6.2. Same as Prob. 1, except Fig. P 6.2 is to be used.

6.3. Plot the polar-velocity graph for the slider of Fig. P 6.1 (see Fig. 6.8).

* J. C. Wolford, and A. S. Hall, Jr., "Second-Acceleration Analysis of Plane Mechanisms," ASME Paper No. 57–A–52. W. J. Carter, "Second-Acceleration in Four-Bar Mechanisms as Related to Rotopole Motion," *Trans.* ASME, Vol. 80, 1958, p. 293. S. Mercer, Jr. and A. R. Holowenko, "Dynamic Characteristics of Cam Forms Calculated by the Digital Computer," *Trans.* ASME, Vol. 80, 1958, p. 1695.

6.4. Same as Prob. 6.3 except Fig. P 6.2 is to be used.

6.5. Plot the polar-velocity graph for point C, Fig. P 6.5. Indicate the velocity scale used.

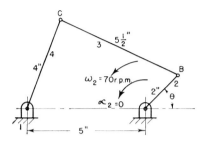

Fig. P 6.5

6.6. The center distance of driver and follower of a Geneva stop mechanism is to be 3 in. The driver is to rotate 5 times for each revolution of the follower. The driving pin is to enter the slot tangentially so that there will be no impact loading.

(a) Draw a Geneva stop mechanism that meets these requirements.

(b) Plot the angular velocity graph for the stop member for one-fifth revolution. The time axis is to be 3 in. long and is to be divided into 6 equal time spaces. Use the method of Art. 6.4. The angular velocity of the driver is to be represented by a line $1\frac{1}{4}$ in. long. The speed of the driver is 140 rpm. Calculate the angular velocity scale.

6.7. Plot the angular velocity graph for member 4 of Fig. P 6.5. Use 30° intervals for θ. Apply the method of Art. 6.4. The angular velocity of member 2 is to be represented by a line 2 in. long, and the time axis is to be 3 in. long. Calculate the angular velocity scale and the time scale.

6.8. Plot the angular velocity graph for member 3, Fig. P 6.5. Indicate the scale used. The time axis is to be 6 in. long and 30° intervals for θ are used. The revolved polygon method can be used to obtain $V_{B/C}$ for each phase and the values plotted; $\omega_{3/1} = V_{B/C}/BC$. Since BC is a constant, the $V_{B/C}$ graph will represent the $\omega_{3/1}$ graph if the scale for it is calculated.

6.9. Determine the velocity and acceleration of slider C, Fig. P 6.1, for 45° intervals of θ. Draw the mechanism one-half size and use the Ritterhaus construction.

6.10. Same as Prob. 9, but applied to Fig. P 6.2.

6.11. Plot the angular acceleration graph for the connecting rod of Fig. P 6.1. Use 45° intervals for θ. Here $A^t_{C/B}$ can be taken from the Ritterhaus construction for each phase and plotted; $\alpha_{3/1} = A^t_{C/B}/CB$. Since CB is a constant, the $A^t_{C/B}$ graph will represent $\alpha_{3/1}$ if the scale for it is calculated.

6.12. Same as Prob. 11, but applied to Fig. P 6.2.

6.13. Using analytical methods, calculate the velocity and acceleration of the slider, Fig. P 6.1, for $\theta = 0, 45°, 90°, 180°$.

CHAPTER 7

Cams

7.1. Introductory. A cam is a direct-contact machine element so formed that its prescribed motion imparts a prescribed motion to a follower. Within reasonable limits the motions of cam and follower can be arbitrarily chosen and the cam profile made to fit these conditions. Usually the cam rotates with uniform angular velocity.

Fig. 7.1. The cams assembled on the shaft actuate and control most of the mechanical action of the Linotype. (Courtesy of Mergenthaler Linotype Co.)

The previous chapters in this book deal largely with determination of motions of assumed linkages. Kinematic synthesis is the reverse of this; that is, the motion is assumed and the mechanism to give this motion is then determined. When pin-connected links are used it is often difficult or impossible to obtain the desired motion. In many cases satisfactory approximations can be obtained. Cam design is an example of a case where kinematic synthesis can be easily applied.

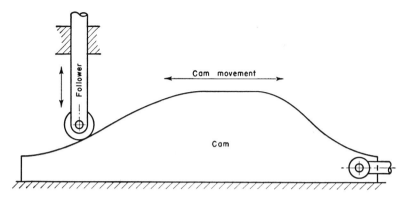

Fig. 7.2. Translation cam with reciprocating roller follower.

7.2. Classification. Most cams fall into one of the three major classifications.

1. Disk cams
2. Translation cams
3. Cylindrical cams

These types are illustrated in the pages that follow.

7.3. Displacement diagrams. The displacement-time relationship of the follower governs the shape of the cam profile. This relationship is chosen to fulfill the requirements of the machine in which the cam mechanism is to be used. In many applications, as for example, the internal combustion engine valve cam, considerable latitude can be taken in choosing the type of motion. Four common types of motion are listed below.

1. Constant acceleration
2. Modified constant velocity
3. Simple harmonic
4. Cycloidal

These will be considered in detail.

7.4. Constant acceleration. A motion of constant or uniform acceleration is sometimes called gravity motion or parabolic motion. The equation of motion is

$$ s = \frac{1}{2} A t^2 \tag{7.1} $$

This is Eq. (2.14) with an initial velocity of zero. When A is the acceleration of gravity this is the equation of motion of a freely falling body that has started from rest. The graph of this equation is a parabola. For equal time intervals the distances traveled will be in the ratio 1, 3, 5, 7, 9, . . . The total distance traveled after each time interval will be 1, 4, 9, 16, 25, . . . The method of constructing a displacement-time diagram for this motion will be illustrated with an example.

A follower is to move radially outward 1 in. with constant acceleration while the cam turns through 90°. (This can be any type of disk cam with reciprocating follower, as for example that of Fig. 7.9.) During the next 90° of cam rotation the follower is to continue to move outward with constant deceleration and is to have zero velocity at the end of this time. The follower is to return with constant acceleration and deceleration during the next 150° of cam rotation. The follower dwells or rests during the remaining 30° of cam rotation. The graph is shown in Fig.

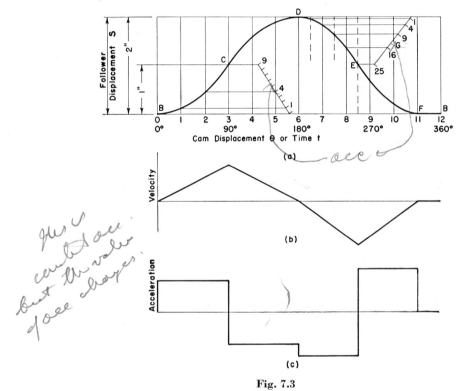

Fig. 7.3

7.3(a). It is assumed that the cam rotates with constant angular velocity. Equal angular displacements can then be represented by equal time intervals. The abscissa represents one revolution of the cam. Each division represents the time required for the cam to turn through 30°. The first portion of the curve is a plot of Eq. (7.1), starting with $t = 0$ and $s = 0$. It starts at B with a horizontal tangent and terminates at C. This curve can be constructed by drawing any line between the time axis and a horizontal line through C that can be conveniently divided into 9 equal lengths. Points 1, 4, and 9 are projected as shown. The curve CD is constructed in the same way. The two curves BC and CD have a common tangent at C. This results from equal distances moved during acceleration and deceleration in equal time intervals.

handwritten: $V = \text{1st deriv } S$. $a \ V = \dfrac{dS}{dt}$ then $a = \dfrac{dV}{dt}$

The follower returns from D to E in $2\frac{1}{2}$ time intervals. For convenience the intervals 6–7 and 7–8 are divided to give a total of 5 equal lengths. Points 1, 4, 9, and 25 are projected as shown. Curve EF is constructed in the same manner. Here FB represents a dwell.

The velocity and acceleration graphs are shown at (b) and (c). The maximum acceleration occurs between D and F. Assuming that the cam is rotating 100 rpm the acceleration can be determined as follows. The distance traveled from D to E is $\frac{1}{12}$ ft. The corresponding time is

handwritten: fraction of 1 rev   for D to E.

handwritten: time for 1 rev.

$$\frac{2.5}{12} \times \frac{60}{100} = 0.125 \quad \text{sec}$$

handwritten: for $s = \frac{1}{2} A t^2$

$$A = \frac{2S}{t^2} = \frac{2 \times \frac{1}{12}}{(0.125)^2} = 10.66 \ \text{fps}^2$$

The maximum velocity occurs midway between points 8 and 9. Its value is

handwritten: diff. $s = \frac{1}{2} A t^2$ + get $V = A t$

$$V = At = 10.66 \times 0.125 = 1.333 \quad \text{fps}$$

7.5. Modified constant velocity. The displacement, velocity, and acceleration diagrams for a follower having constant outward velocity for one-half revolution of the cam, constant return velocity for 150°, and dwell for 30° are shown in Fig. 7.4. Theoretically the velocity changes instantaneously, causing an infinite acceleration. This is of course impossible; the parts would deform and reduce the acceleration to a finite value. Except at low speeds there would be impact loading and large forces. This type of motion should be avoided if possible. Part

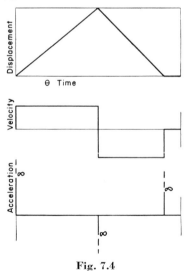

Fig. 7.4

of the follower motion can be constant if the follower is brought up to speed and then brought to a stop over a period of time. This motion is called modified constant velocity. The construction of a displacement-time diagram for this type of motion will be illustrated with an example.

A follower is to move outward 2 in. It is to be constantly accelerated for 60°, then move with uniform velocity for 30°, then decelerate for 90° of the cam rotation. The return motion is to be constant acceleration for 60° and constant deceleration for 90°. The follower is to dwell

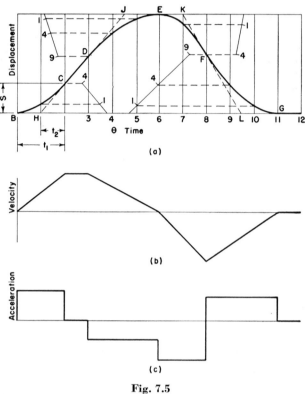

Fig. 7.5

for the remaining 30°. The displacement, velocity, and acceleration graphs are shown in Fig. 7.5. Here BC represents constant acceleration. A terminal velocity V is attained at C, and CD is a continuation of this terminal velocity. Here DE is constant deceleration. Points C and D are located on a straight line through H and J, the mid-points of the acceleration and deceleration periods. This results from the fact that a point moving with constant velocity V through a distance S requires only half as much time as a point starting from rest and accelerating uniformly through the same distance and attaining the same velocity. This can be shown as follows: HC represents uniform velocity; the equation of motion is

$$S = V t_2$$

and for BC,

$$S = \frac{1}{2} A t_1^2$$

The final velocity is

$$V = At_1$$

These three equations give

$$\tfrac{1}{2}At_1^2 = At_1t_2 \qquad \text{or} \qquad \tfrac{1}{2}t_1 = t_2$$

For the return motion, F is located by drawing a line through K and L, the mid-points of the acceleration and deceleration periods.

7.6. Simple harmonic motion. This motion was discussed in Art. 2.5. The method of constructing a SHM (simple harmonic motion) graph will be illustrated with an example. A follower is to move outward 2 in. with SHM while the cam turns through one-half revolution. The follower is to return with SHM during the next 150° and then dwell for 30°. The displacement, velocity, and acceleration graphs are shown in Fig. 7.6. Use is made of the fact that the projection on the diameter,

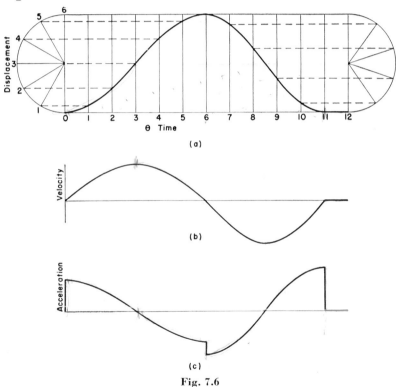

Fig. 7.6

of a point moving with constant speed on a circle, is harmonic motion. A semicircle is drawn on the left end of Fig. 7.6(a). It is divided into 6 equal sectors corresponding to the 6 equal time intervals on the time axis. The points on the semicircle are projected as shown to determine the curve. The follower returns in 5 time intervals. The semicircle on the right is divided into 5 equal sectors corresponding to these time intervals.

The maximum acceleration occurs at the beginning and end of the return stroke. It can be determined as follows. Assume that the speed of the cam is 100 rpm. The time for the return stroke is

$$\frac{60}{100} \times \frac{5}{12} = 0.25 \quad \text{sec}$$

During this time the imaginary point that is used for projection moves around the semicircle, or π radians. The angular velocity of this point is

$$\omega = \frac{\pi}{0.25} = 4\pi \quad \text{radians per sec}$$

The acceleration is

$$A = r\omega^2 \cos \theta = \tfrac{1}{12}(4\pi)^2 = 13.2 \quad \text{fps}^2$$

7.7. Cycloidal motion. * Cycloidal motion is defined by the equation

$$s = S \frac{\theta}{\theta_0} - \frac{S}{2\pi} \sin \frac{2\pi\theta}{\theta_0} \tag{7.2}$$

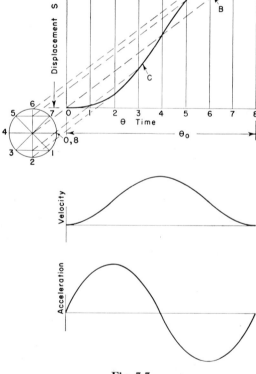

Fig. 7.7

* J. A. Hrones, "An Analysis of the Dynamic Forces in a Cam-Drive System," Paper 47-A-46, *Trans. ASME*, 1948.

where θ_0 is the angle turned through by the cam corresponding to the total displacement S, and θ is any intermediate angle corresponding to a displacement s. Curve C in Fig. 7.7 is the displacement graph that is obtained from this equation. The curve can be obtained graphically. The broken line B represents the first term in Eq. (7.2). The construction for the second term is similar to that for harmonic motion. The displacements are superimposed on line B. The radius of the circle shown at the left is $S/2\pi$. It is divided into sectors corresponding to the intervals on the time axis. The points on the circumference are projected to the vertical centerline of the circle and then parallel to line B, to the corresponding lines on the time axis. The resulting curve is C.

7.8. Selection of motion. Some of the factors that must be considered in selecting a motion are functional requirements, speed, mass of moving parts, external loads, elasticity of parts, and cost of manufacture. When operating speeds are low, selection of the motion is usually not critical. All types of motion cannot be used at high speeds. The finite instantaneous changes in acceleration may lead to vibration and noise. Harmonic motion has a higher peak acceleration for a given lift in a given time than a motion of uniform acceleration and deceleration. It can be used for higher speeds if the outward and return motions each equal 180° of cam rotation. When this is not true the acceleration graph is discontinuous, as shown in Fig. 7.6. Cycloidal motion has a higher peak acceleration than harmonic motion but there are no discontinuities in the acceleration graph.

In the above examples deformation of the parts was not considered. Deformations are always present and sometimes they may be large. *Actually in a large radial aircraft engine at take-off speed, the sum of the forces due to inertia, valve-spring force, and gas pressure may be a ton or more, resulting in deflections of the order of $\frac{1}{8}$ in. at the valve.* A method has been developed for determining a motion that compensates for deflections and produces smooth action at high speeds.[*]

7.9. Cam profile determinations. After the displacement diagram and type of follower are chosen to fulfill the requirements of the machine, the cam profile is determined. To simplify the work inversion is used. Instead of a fixed frame and a rotating cam the cam is fixed and the frame is rotated in such a manner that the relative motions of the parts are unchanged. When this concept is grasped cam layout becomes very simple. Several examples will be considered. The technique used by the author in some of the examples is not necessarily the only way of determining the cam profiles. The reader can probably develop variations.

7.10. Disk cam with reciprocating knife-edge follower. This type of cam and follower is shown in Fig. 7.8. The displacement graph

---

[*] W. M. Dudley, "New Methods in Valve Cam Design," *SAE Quart. Trans.*, January, 1948, Vol. 2, No. 1, p. 19.

for one revolution of the cam is shown. The diagram is divided into 12
equal time intervals and the cam is divided into 12 corresponding equal
angles. The displacements for the 12 positions are projected on the
centerline of the follower as 0′, 1′, 2′, 3′, etc. This is called the displacement scale. The distance from the point of the follower in its lowest
position to the center of the cam is the radius of the base circle. When
the cam is rotated clockwise the follower is to move according to the
displacement scale. When the cam turns clockwise 2 spaces, the edge

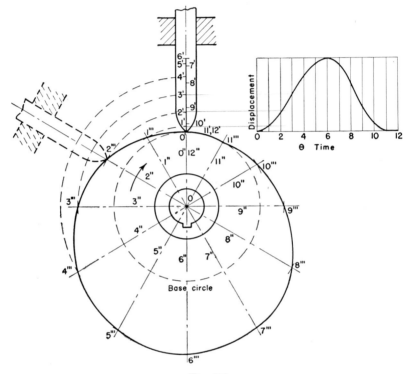

Fig. 7.8

of the follower is to be pushed to position 2′. To produce the same relative motion with the cam fixed the frame is rotated CCW 2 spaces and
the edge of the follower is moved radially out a distance 0′2′. This
locates point 2‴ a point on the cam profile. Points 1‴, 3‴, 4‴, etc.
are determined in the same manner. A smooth curve through these
points is the cam profile. For greater accuracy more points should be
located for drawing the profile.

Knife-edge followers are subject to excessive wear and are not practical in most applications.

7.11. Disk cam with reciprocating roller follower. This type of
cam and follower is shown in Fig. 7.9(a). The follower is to move radially

according to the scale indicated on the centerline.   The lowest point on
the scale, $0'$, is at the center of the roller, and $0'0$ is the radius of the base
circle.   The centers of the roller for the other positions, $1'''$, $2'''$, $3'''$,
etc. are determined as in the previous example.   A smooth curve through
these points is the pitch profile of the cam.   Arcs with radii equal to the
roller radius are struck from these points.   The envelope of these arcs is
the cam profile.   It is necessary to determine first the pitch profile,
because contact between cam and follower is not on the radial line through

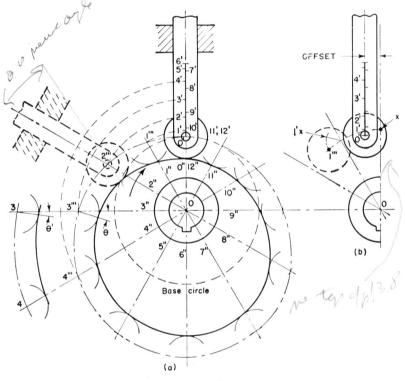

Fig. 7.9

the center of the roller except during periods of dwell.   When the follower is moving, contact is shifted to one side or the other.   This results
in a pressure angle shown as θ for position $3'''$.   The resultant force
between cam and roller, neglecting friction, will lie along the common
normal.   This produces an undesirable side force on the follower that
tends to cause it to bind in its guide.   The pressure angle can be reduced
by increasing the radius of the base circle.   This is shown at the left
of the figure.   Then θ is reduced to θ'.   This is because the follower
movement is produced by a greater length of cam profile; 3–4 is greater
than $3'''$–$4'''$.

In Fig. 7.9(b) the follower is shown in an offset position. The cam profile is determined as before, with one additional construction for each roller center. This is shown for position 1. An arc with 0 as the center and radius of 01′ is drawn locating point x. The offset 1′x is used to locate 1‴ as shown.

7.12. Disk cam with reciprocating flat-faced follower. This is shown in Fig. 7.10. The cam is to turn clockwise and move the follower

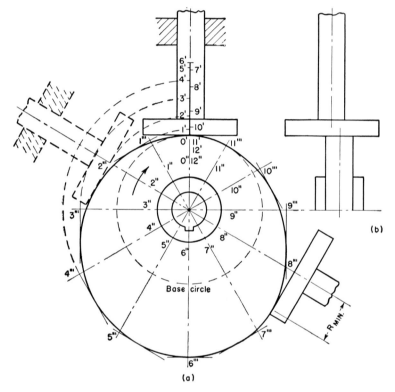

Fig. 7.10

according to the scale on its centerline. Points 1‴, 2‴, 3‴, etc. are determined as in the previous examples. At each of these points a line normal to the radial line is drawn. The envelope of these lines is the desired cam contour.

The diameter of the flat face must be of sufficient size to reach the point of contact in all phases. This is determined by inspection. In phase 8 the point of contact is farthest from the radial line. This is indicated R minimum. The flat face should be made a little larger.

A portion of the side view of the cam and follower is shown at (b). A small offset as shown is often used to produce rotation of the follower. This results in more uniform wear.

7.13. Disk cam with oscillating flat-faced follower. This mechanism is shown in Fig. 7.11. The cam is to turn clockwise and the follower is to oscillate according to the scale indicated. An angular scale can be used but it is usually more convenient to work with arc lengths that represent the corresponding angular values. The flat face extended is tangent to a circle of radius r with center at $0'''$. The construction for phase 3 (90° CW rotation of the cam) is shown. Point $3'''$ is located by

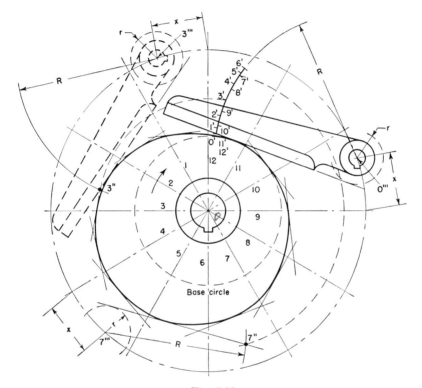

Fig. 7.11

any convenient means 90° CCW from $0'''$. Point $3''$ is the intersection of arc of radius $03'$ with 0 as the center and the arc of radius R with $3'''$ as the center. A line through $3''$ tangent to the circle of radius r with center at $3'''$ is the correct position for the follower face. The construction for position 7 is also shown.

7.14. Disk cam with two followers. The base circle of a cam with primary and secondary followers is shown in Fig. 7.12. The offset is too large to use a single follower as was done in Fig. 7.9. The scale for the required motion of the secondary follower is shown on the centerline as $0'$, $1'$, $2'$, etc. This scale is transferred to the primary follower on any convenient arc with O as the center. The construction for phases 0, 5,

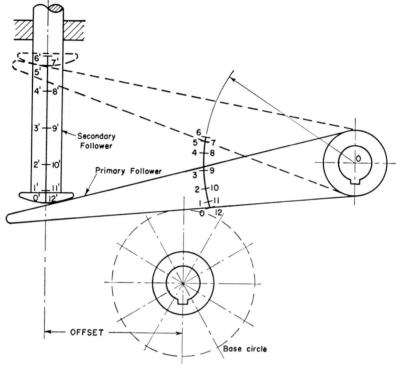

Fig. 7.12

and 7 are shown.   The cam profile is then determined from the primary follower as in the previous example.

7.15. Design limitations.   The usual procedure in cam design is to assume the displacement scale, the type of follower, and the base circle. These assumptions are not always compatible.   When this is the case, modification of one or more of the assumptions will usually lead to a practical solution.

In Fig. 7.13(a) the assumptions produced the pitch profile with a point at B.   It can be seen that the working profile will not force the roller along the pitch contour to the point B.   The center of the roller will follow the dotted path shown.   The desired motion can be approached by making the base circle larger or by making the diameter of the roller smaller.

In (b) the reciprocating flat-faced follower is to move according to the scale indicated.   The radius of the base circle is R_1.   The follower face is drawn in the different positions $1''$, $2''$, $3''$, etc.   It can be seen that a smooth curve cannot be drawn tangent to all these, since $3''$ lies beyond the intersection of $2''$ and $4''$.   When the radius of the base circle is increased to R_2 the new positions $2'''$, $3'''$, $4'''$ are satisfactory.

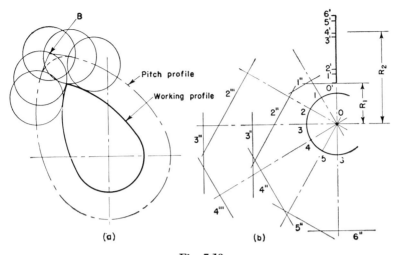

Fig. 7.13

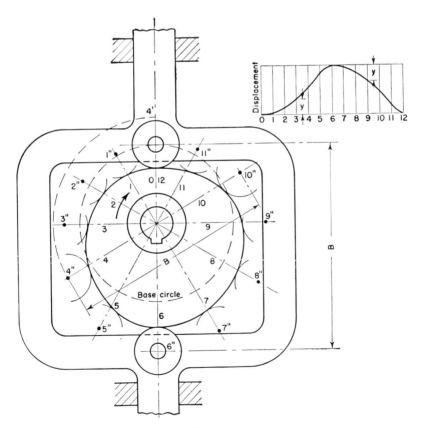

Fig. 7.14

7.16. Positive return cams. In the previous examples the return motion of the follower was not positive. An external force such as a spring force is required to maintain contact between cam and follower during portions of the cycle. Abnormal conditions such as lack of lubrication or spring failure may occur and the follower may not return. In some applications this would do no damage. In applications where damage would result, mechanical restraint should be introduced for the entire cycle.

A constant diameter cam is shown in Fig. 7.14. The two rollers produce constraint over the entire cycle. This type of cam requires that the outward and return motions be the same. The outward motion is according to the given displacement graph, points 0 to 6. The cam profile for this motion is determined in the usual manner. Distance B

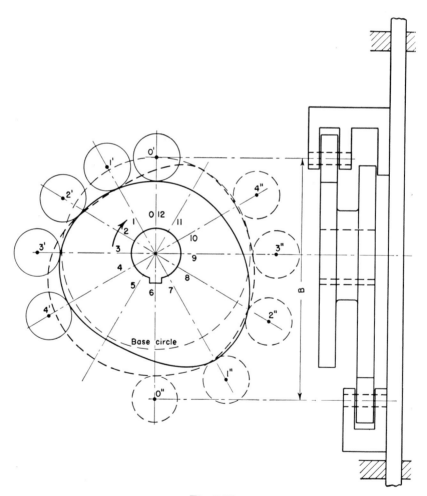

Fig. 7.15

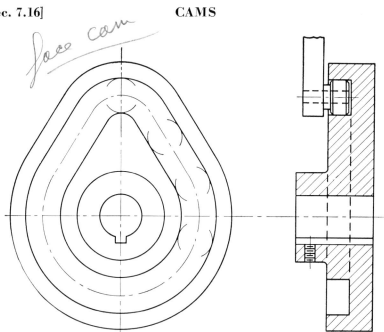

face cam

Fig. 7.16

is equal to the sum of the base circle diameter and the total displacement.

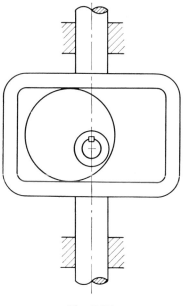

Fig. 7.17

Centers 7″, 8″, 9″, etc. are located by making $1''7'' = 2''8'' = 3''9''$, etc. $= B$. This construction produces a return motion that is the same as the outward motion.

If the outward and return motions are to be different, two cams must be used as shown in Fig. 7.15. The entire profile of the cam shown solid is determined in the usual manner. The second cam, shown by a broken line, is determined by letting $0'0'' = 1'1'' = 2'2''$, etc. $= B$, a constant.

Another type of positive return cam is shown in Fig. 7.16. The roller follower is constrained to move in the groove. This mechanism has an undesirable feature in that each time the roller changes contact from one side of the groove to the other its direction of rotation is reversed.

The eccentric cam shown in Fig. 7.17 produces constrained simple harmonic motion.

7.17. Auxiliary linkages. The maximum angular displacement of an oscillating follower is usually about 45°. A larger angular motion can be obtained with an auxiliary linkage. One type is shown in Fig. 7.18(a). The assumed ϕ scale is transferred to the primary follower 3.

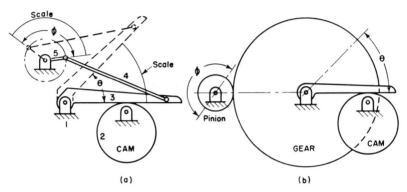

Fig. 7.18

The cam profile is determined from this. A greater displacement ratio can be obtained with gears as shown at (b).

7.18. Automotive cams. A typical automotive valve cam for use with a flat-faced follower is shown in Fig. 7.19. It is symmetrical about the vertical centerline. Portions BC, CD, and EF are circular arcs of

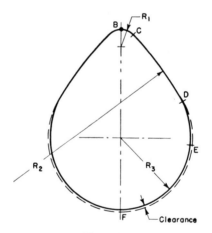

Fig. 7.19

radii R_1, R_2, and R_3, respectively. The portion of the profile from D to E is called the ramp. The radial distance of this curve from the center of the cam increases at a uniform rate from E to D. For the average cam this increase is about 0.0006 in. per degree. This produces a slow lift and closes the gap between the follower and the valve stem. When hydraulic valve lifters are used the clearance and ramp are unnecessary. When hydraulic lifters are not used the clearance is necessary to allow for inaccuracies in adjustment and unequal expansion of the engine parts. A hydraulic valve lifter automatically adjusts itself for these conditions.

Under ideal conditions the valve lift begins at *D*. The follower motion consists of portions of harmonic motion cycles. The acceleration graph is discontinuous. This type of valve cam is not always satisfactory at high speeds.

7.19. Cylindrical cams. Cylindrical cams are made by machining grooves in a cylinder, Fig. 7.20, or by fastening guide strips on the outside

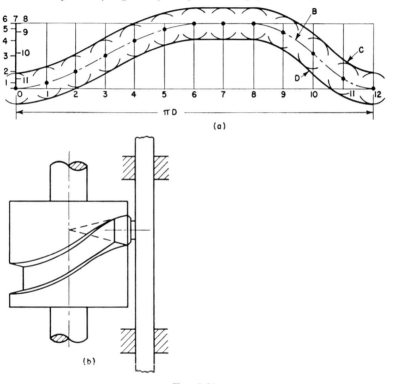

Fig. 7.20

of a cylinder, Fig. 7.22. The cam in Fig. 7.20 drives a reciprocating roller follower. If the roller is a cylinder it will not have rolling contact with the side of the groove. If the roller is a frustum of a cone with the apex on the axis of the cam, it will have rolling contact with the side of the groove during periods of dwell, e.g., when the groove is circular, and approximate rolling when the groove is a helix. (Rolling cones will be considered in the next chapter.)

When the cam in Fig. 7.20 turns one revolution it is to move the follower according to the displacement graph *B*. The displacement scale is drawn full size and the length of the time axis is equal to the circumference of the cam cylinder. Curves C and D are obtained by drawing arcs equal in radius to that of the roller. If this diagram is wrapped around the cylinder it can be used as a template for scribing lines to

Fig. 7.21. Fay automatic lathe. (Courtesy of Jones & Lamson Machine Co.)

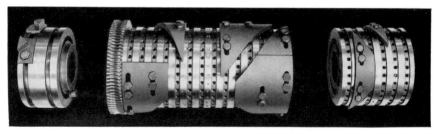

Fig. 7.22. (Courtesy of Jones & Lamson Machine Co.)

outline the groove that is to be cut. Cams are usually made in a different manner as shown in Fig. 7.23. In this illustration the groove is being cut with a conical milling cutter. Rotation of the disk cam or former shown at the lower left produces a vertical motion of the head that carries the cutter. Rotation of the former and the cam blank are coordinated

Fig. 7.23. Cam milling machine. (Courtesy of Rowbottom Machine Co.)

through a gear train. The profile of the former is designated to produce the required groove for the particular cam being cut.

7.20. Coordinated cams. Each of the cams in Fig. 7.1 is designed to produce specific movements in the Linotype machine. The coordination of these movements was considered in the determination of each displacement diagram. The cams are assembled with the correct angular relationship to produce the correct sequence of motions throughout the machine.

This is also true of the cylindrical cams on the Fay automatic lathe, Fig. 7.21. This lathe is completely automatic. The operator places the work in the machine and pulls the starting lever. All necessary operations are performed automatically, including stopping the lathe when the part is finished. A set of cams must be designed for each product that is to be machined. The cams are easily attached to the drums by means of capscrews.

If a point on a follower is to move according to arbitrarily chosen vertical and horizontal scales two cams must be used. An example is shown in Fig. 7.24. Two cams are to move the pen so that it writes the word "Jets." Points 0, 1, 2, 3, etc. are selected to outline the word.

The two cams can then be laid out simultaneously by using the methods of the previous examples. Another method is to construct the mechanism except for the cams. Circular disks of cardboard, wood, or sheet metal are placed on the cam axis. When the pen is placed on a numbered point the disks are turned to the corresponding displacement and points

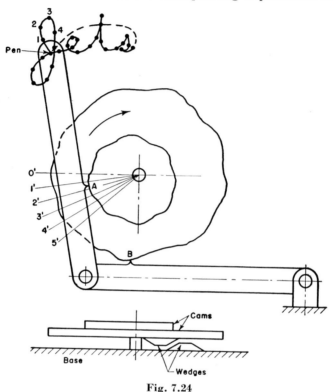

Fig. 7.24

A and B marked. The arm carrying the pen can be lifted from the paper for those portions of the word shown dotted by fastening wedges on the under surface of the cam and the base.

7.21. Analytical design of disk cams by independent-position equations. * Independent-position equations can be used to obtain general equations for the cam parameters for any cam system regardless of the type of motion of the follower. These equations completely specify the position of a point on a cam or its follower as a function of the geometry of the system and the desired motion. The point of most interest in the design of a cam is the center of curvature of the follower at the point of contact between the cam and its follower. This point

---

* F. H. Raven, "Analytical Design of Disk Cams and Three-Dimensional Cams by Independent Position Equations," *Trans. ASME*, Vol. 26, Series E, No. 1, March, 1959 pp. 18–24.

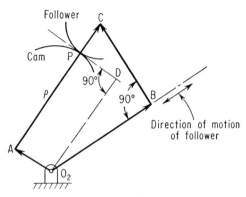

Fig. 7.25

has only two position equations which are mathematically independent; i.e., only two equations can be written that have at least one vector not in common. By successive differentiation of the independent-position equations for this point with respect to the angle of rotation of the cam, we obtain information from which the desired unknown cam parameters may be obtained.

Diagrams for the two basic types of plate cams are shown in Figs. 7.25 and 7.26. The following no-menclature is used:

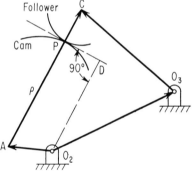

P = point of contact between cam and follower

A = center of curvature of cam contour at point P

C = center of curvature of follower at point P

ρ = vector from A to P to C

O_2 = center of rotation of cam

O_3 = center of rotation of oscillating follower

Fig. 7.26

The first independent-position equation for C, the point of interest, is obtained by writing the sum of the vectors O_2A and APC. Point A was chosen as part of the path for convenience, and also for obtaining an equation for the radius of curvature at all points on the cam contour. The second independent-position equation for the cam mechanism with reciprocating follower is the vector sum of O_2B and BC, and for an oscillating follower is the vector sum of O_2O_3 and O_3C. For the case of a straight-sided cam, point A has no significance. Thus, let point D be the intersection of the straight side and the line drawn through O_2 perpendicular to this side. The first independent position equation will then be the vector sum O_2D plus DP plus PC.

7.22. Disk cam with flat-faced follower. For the case of the flat-faced follower, Fig. 7.27, point C lies at infinity and therefore has no significance. Point P then becomes the point of interest and is substituted for C in the foregoing procedure. For convenience in writing, the symbols r, ρ, R and l will represent the vectors shown in Fig. 7.27.

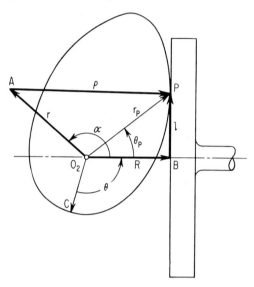

Fig. 7.27

Determine the equation for the cam contour, the equation for the required length of the follower face l, and the equation for the radius of curvature ρ, for the condition that the displacement of the follower from the initial position of the cam (i. e., at $\theta = 0$), satisfies the following equation:

$$R = C + f(\theta) \qquad (7.3)$$

where C is the minimum radius of the cam, and $f(\theta)$ represents the desired displacement of the follower as a function of the angular displacement θ of the cam. In Fig. 7.27 the cam has been turned clockwise through the angle θ from the initial position.

The first independent-position equation for the point of contact P is obtained by traveling the path from O_2 to A to P.

$$\boldsymbol{r}_p = re^{i\alpha} + \rho \qquad (7.4)$$

The second independent-position equation is obtained by going from O_2 to B to P.

$$\boldsymbol{r}_p = R + il \qquad (7.5)$$

By equating the right-hand sides of Eqs. (7.4) and (7.5), and writing the terms in trigonometric form, we obtain

$$R + il = r \cos \alpha + ir \sin \alpha + \rho$$

This equation is then separated into real and imaginary parts

$$R = r \cos \alpha + \rho \qquad (7.6)$$
$$l = r \sin \alpha \qquad (7.7)$$

Substitution of $R = C + f(\theta)$ into Eq. (7.6) and differentiation with respect to θ, gives

$$\frac{dR}{d\theta} = \frac{d}{d\theta}[C + f(\theta)] = f'(\theta) = -r \sin \alpha \frac{d\alpha}{d\theta} \qquad (7.8)$$

For an infinitesimal rotation of the cam, ρ may be considered to remain constant. Thus point A, the center of curvature of the cam at the point of contact, and r may be regarded as fixed to the cam for an incremental rotation $d\theta$. This is true because the circle with center at A and radius ρ (the osculating circle) has the same first and second derivatives as those of the cam contour at P; i. e., when only the first two derivatives are involved, the analysis at the point on a curve can be made using the osculating circle at that point. Therefore the magnitude of $d\alpha$ is equal to $d\theta$; and since α decreases as θ increases, it follows that

$$\frac{d\alpha}{d\theta} = -1$$

Substitution of the foregoing into Eq. (7.8) gives

$$f'(\theta) = r \sin \alpha \qquad (7.9)$$

From Eqs. (7.7) and (7.9), we can write

$$l = f'(\theta) \qquad (7.10)$$

From Fig. 7.27, it can be seen that the equation for the cam contour, measured from the initial position, may be written as follows,

$$r_p e^{i(\theta + \theta_p)} = (R^2 + l^2)^{1/2} e^{i\left[\theta + \tan^{-1}\frac{l}{R}\right]}$$
$$= \{R^2 + [f'(\theta)]^2\}^{1/2} e^{i\left[\theta + \tan^{-1}\frac{f'(\theta)}{R}\right]} \qquad (7.11)$$

The equation for ρ (the radius of the osculating circle) may be obtained by taking the second derivative of Eq. (7.6) with respect to θ, and substituting this result back into Eq. (7.6) to eliminate the $\cos \alpha$ term. This is shown below.

$$R = C + f(\theta) = r \cos \alpha + \rho$$
$$f''(\theta) = -r \cos \alpha$$
$$\rho = R + f''(\theta) \qquad (7.12)$$

To avoid a sharp point in the cam contour, ρ must be greater than zero.

A general design chart can be made to facilitate the solution of a particular type of cam-design problem. This will be illustrated with an example.

A flat-faced follower is to move out with uniform acceleration and deceleration, dwell, and return with simple harmonic motion in accord-

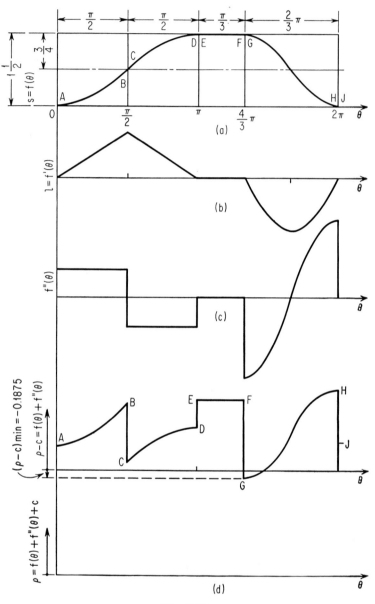

Fig. 7.28

ance with the diagram shown in Fig. 7.28(a). To keep the surface stress on the cam within the allowable limit, assume that the minimum radius, ρ_{min}, of the cam contour must be at least 2 in. Determine the value of the base radius C of the cam such that the foregoing conditions are satisfied.

The equations for $f(\theta)$, $f'(\theta)$, and $f''(\theta)$ which are determined from the required motion are shown in Table 7.1. For constant acceleration, the basic equation for displacement s as a function of θ is

$$s = f(\theta) = K\theta^2 \tag{7.13}$$

TABLE 7.1

	$f(\theta)$	$f'(\theta)$	$f''(\theta)$
Constant acceleration	$\dfrac{3\theta^2}{\pi^2}$	$\dfrac{6\theta}{\pi^2}$	$\dfrac{6}{\pi^2}$
Constant deceleration	$1\tfrac{1}{2} - \dfrac{3}{\pi^2}(\pi - \theta)^2$	$\dfrac{6}{\pi^2}(\pi - \theta)$	$-\dfrac{6}{\pi^2}$
Dwell	$1\tfrac{1}{2}$	0	0
Simple harmonic motion	$\tfrac{3}{4} + \tfrac{3}{4}\cos\left(\tfrac{3}{2}\theta - 2\pi\right)$	$-\tfrac{9}{8}\sin\left(\tfrac{3}{2}\theta - 2\pi\right)$	$-\tfrac{27}{16}\cos\left(\tfrac{3}{2}\theta - 2\pi\right)$

The first boundary condition, $s = 0$ when $\theta = 0$, is satisfied by any value of K. For the second boundary condition, $s = \dfrac{3}{4}$ in. when $\theta = \dfrac{\pi}{2}$ radians, the value of K is $\dfrac{3}{\pi^2}$.

For the return motion, it might appear that the following equation is correct

$$s = \frac{3}{4} + \frac{3}{4}\cos\left(\theta - \frac{4}{3}\pi\right)$$

The first boundary condition, $s = 1\tfrac{1}{2}$ when $\theta = \dfrac{4}{3}\pi$ is satisfied but the second one is not. Observe that the return curve, Fig. 7.28(a), which occupies $\dfrac{2}{3}\pi$ radians on the θ axis, is one-half cycle of a cosine curve. To obtain the correct equation it is necessary to multiply the angle by $\dfrac{3}{2}$ giving

$$s = \frac{3}{4} + \frac{3}{4}\cos\left(\frac{3}{2}\theta - 2\pi\right) \tag{7.14}$$

This equation now satisfies the second boundary condition, $s = 0$ when $\theta = 2\pi$, as well as the first.

In the design chart, Fig. 7.29, $f(\theta)$ is the abscissa, and $f''(\theta)$ is the ordinate. The values of $f(\theta)$ and $f''(\theta)$ for given values of θ on this generalized graph from a closed path, A to B to C ... to J, since the follower starts from its initial positions, moves through a complete cycle, and returns to the initial position; i.e., $f(\theta) = f(2\pi)$ and $f''(\theta) = f''(2\pi)$. The value of ρ can be determined from the equation

$$\rho = R + f''(\theta) = C + f(\theta) + f''(\theta) \qquad (7.15)$$

or $\qquad\qquad \rho - C = f(\theta) + f''(\theta) \qquad\qquad\qquad (7.16)$

Because the base radius C is a constant $(\rho - C)_{\min}$ can be used to obtain $\rho_{\min}$. In this example it is desired to determine the value of the

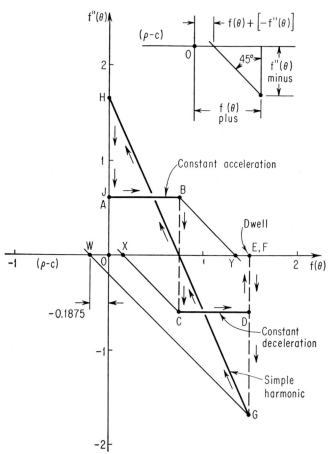

Fig. 7.29

base radius C of the cam when $\rho_{\min} = 2$ in. The value of θ for the $\rho_{\min}$ condition is not obvious from Eq. (7.15) or (7.16), but it is obvious on the design chart, Fig. 7.29. The algebraic sum, $f(\theta) + f''(\theta)$, may be obtained by drawing a line with slope of -1 through the desired value on the closed curve. The intersection of this line with the abscissa gives the value $(\rho - C)$; i.e., the numbers on the abscissa also represent the value $(\rho - C)$. See the construction at the upper right of Fig. 7.29.

An examination of Fig. 7.29 shows that the minimum value of ρ occurs at the beginning of the return motion where $\theta = \frac{4}{3}\pi$. The value of $(\rho - C)$ can be determined graphically as shown by point W, or it can be calculated from Eq. (7.16)

$$\rho_{\min} - C = f(\theta) + f''(\theta) = 1.5 - \frac{27}{16} = -0.1875 \text{ in.}$$

then $C = 0.1875 + \rho_{\min} = 2.1875$ in.

The minimum radius may not be the critical value if a large load occurs at some other point on the cam contour. It may be necessary to establish different minimum values of ρ at several points, which means that the largest value of C determined from these calculations would be used. In this example, at the end of the constant acceleration period, the value of $(\rho - C)$ is 1.356 in. (point Y), and $\rho = 3.543$ in. At the beginning of the deceleration period, the value of $(\rho - C)$ is 0.144 in. (point X), and $\rho = 2.331$ in.

It is also necessary to determine the maximum value of l which becomes the minimum permissible radius of the flat-faced follower. From Eq. (7.10) it can be seen that l is maximum when the velocity of the follower is maximum. In this example the maximum velocity occurs at the middle of the return stroke, $\theta = \frac{5}{3}\pi$. The maximum value of l is then

$$l = f'(\theta) = -\frac{9}{4}\sin\left(\frac{3}{2}\theta - 2\pi\right) = -\frac{9}{4}\sin\left(\frac{3}{2} \times \frac{5}{3}\pi - 2\pi\right) = -2.25 \text{ in.}$$

Another type of design chart is shown in Fig. 7.28. The $(\rho\text{-}C)$ graph shown at (d) is obtained by adding the displacement graph (a) and the acceleration graph (c). The value of l may be obtained from the velocity graph (b). The ρ graph shown at (d) is obtained by dropping the θ axis as shown.

7.23. Disk cam with offset roller follower. A cam of this type is shown in Fig. 7.30 where the offset is measured by the distance h. Note that ϕ is chosen so that it represents the pressure angle. The distance R is the desired displacement of the follower and is given by the equation

$$R = R_0 + f(\theta) \tag{7.17}$$

where $f(\theta)$ is the desired displacement of the follower with respect to the reference position R_0. For the case shown, $R = R_0$ when $\theta = 0$.

One independent-position equation for point C, the center of the roller, is obtained by going from O_2 to A to C

$$\mathbf{r}_c = re^{i\alpha} + \rho e^{i\phi} = r\cos\alpha + ir\sin\alpha + \rho\cos\phi + i\rho\sin\phi \tag{7.18}$$

The other independent-position equation is found by going from O_2 to B to C.

$$\mathbf{r}_c = R + ih \tag{7.19}$$

Equating the right-hand sides of Eqs. (7.18) and (7.19) and separating the real and imaginary components, we find that

$$R = r \cos \alpha + \rho \cos \phi \qquad (7.20)$$
$$h = r \sin \alpha + \rho \sin \phi \qquad (7.21)$$

By substituting $R = R_0 + f(\theta)$ into Eq. (7.20), and differentiating Eqs. (7.20) and (7.21) with respect to θ, we obtain

$$\frac{dR}{d\theta} = \frac{d}{d\theta}[R_0 + f(\theta)] = f'(\theta) = -r \sin \alpha \frac{d\alpha}{d\theta} - \rho \sin \phi \frac{d\phi}{d\theta}$$

$$0 = r \cos \alpha \frac{d\alpha}{d\theta} + \rho \cos \phi \frac{d\phi}{d\theta}$$

For an incremental change in θ, the point A may be considered as a fixed point on the cam. This leads to the result that $d\alpha/d\theta = -1$.

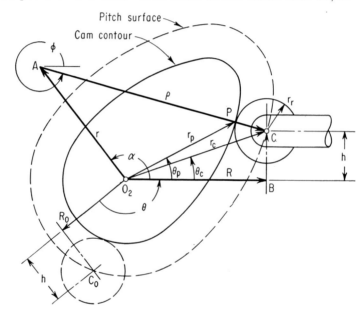

Fig. 7.30

Substitution of this into the foregoing equations gives

$$f'(\theta) = r \sin \alpha - \rho \sin \phi \frac{d\phi}{d\theta} \qquad (7.22)$$

$$0 = -r \cos \alpha + \rho \cos \phi \frac{d\phi}{d\theta} \qquad (7.23)$$

Elimination of $d\phi/d\theta$ from the above equations gives

$$f'(\theta) = r \sin \alpha - r \tan \phi \cos \alpha \qquad (7.24)$$

The unknown α and r terms are eliminated from Eq. (7.24) by means of Eqs. (7.20) and (7.21), giving

R= radius of Bose circle + displacement of follower at a given pt.

$$f'(\theta) = (h - \rho \sin \phi) - \tan \phi (R - \rho \cos \phi)$$
$$= h - R \tan \phi$$

Therefore

$$\tan \phi = \frac{h - f'(\theta)}{R} \tag{7.25}$$

For the case of a radial roller follower, there is no offset; thus h becomes zero in Eq. (7.25).

Having determined the pressure angle ϕ by means of Eq. (7.25) we may evaluate the following equation for point P

$$r_P = r_P e^{i\phi_P} = R + ih - r_r e^{i\phi} \tag{7.26}$$

To measure the point P from the reference station of the cam, it is necessary to rotate r_P through the angle θ. Thus the general equation for a point on the cam contour with respect to the reference position of the cam is

$$r_P e^{i(\theta + \theta_P)} = [R + ih - r_r e^{i\phi}] e^{i\theta}$$
$$= (A^2 + B^2)^{1/2} e^{i(\theta + \tan^{-1} B/A)} \tag{7.27}$$

where
$$A = R - r_r \cos \phi$$
$$B = h - r_r \sin \phi$$

To determine the radius of curvature ρ, first differentiate Eq. (7.25) with respect to θ. Thus

$$\frac{R}{\cos^2 \phi} \frac{d\phi}{d\theta} + \tan \phi \frac{dR}{d\theta} = -f''(\theta) \tag{7.28}$$

But $\frac{dR}{d\theta} = f'(\theta)$ because $f(\theta) = R - R_0$.

Hence

$$\frac{R}{\cos^2 \phi} \frac{d\phi}{d\theta} + \tan \phi f'(\theta) = -f''(\theta) \tag{7.29}$$

Using Eq. (7.23) to eliminate $d\phi/d\theta$, Eq. (7.20) to eliminate $r \cos \alpha$, Eq. (7.25) to eliminate $f'(\theta)$, and finally multiplying numerator and denominator by R, we may write

$$\rho = \frac{R^3 \dfrac{1}{\cos^3 \phi}}{\dfrac{R^2}{\cos^2 \phi} - Rh \tan \phi + R^2 \tan^2 \phi - Rf''(\theta)} \tag{7.30}$$

But

$$\frac{1}{\cos^3 \phi} = \sec^3 \phi = (\sec^2 \phi)^{3/2} = (1 + \tan^2 \phi)^{3/2}$$

Hence

$$\rho = \frac{(R^2 + R^2 \tan^2 \phi)^{3/2}}{(R^2 + 2R^2 \tan^2 \phi - Rh \tan \phi) - Rf''(\theta)} \tag{7.31}$$

Using

$$\tan \phi = \frac{h - f'(\theta)}{R} \quad \text{and} \quad \tan^2 \phi = \frac{[h - f'(\theta)]^2}{R^2}$$

we can write

$$\rho = \frac{\{[h - f'(\theta)]^2 + R^2\}^{3/2}}{R^2 + [h - f'(\theta)] \{2[h - f'(\theta)] - h\} - R[f''(\theta)]} \tag{7.32}$$

Undercutting of the cam occurs whenever the magnitude of ρ is less than the radius of the roller.

Equation (7.31) may also be written in the nondimensional form

$$\frac{\rho}{R} = \frac{[\tan^2 \phi + 1]^{3/2}}{1 + \tan \phi \left[2 \tan \phi - \dfrac{h}{R}\right] - \dfrac{f''(\theta)}{R}} \tag{7.33}$$

Equation (7.32) and (7.33) are further simplified for the case of a radial roller follower in which there is no offset; i.e., $h = 0$.

7.24. Disk cam with offset oscillating flat-faced follower. A disk cam with an offset, oscillating, flat-faced follower is shown in Fig. 7.31. The required length of the follower is indicated by the variable distance l, and the offset of the follower from its center of rotation is designated by the fixed length h. Let it be desired that the angular displacement β of the follower be a function of the angular displacement θ of the cam according to the equation

$$\beta = \beta_0 + f(\theta) \tag{7.34}$$

where $f(\theta)$ is the variation in the angular displacement of the follower from its reference position β_0.

From Fig. 7.31 it can be seen that the independent position equations for the point of contact may be written as follows

$$r_P = re^{i\alpha} + \rho e^{i(\beta-90)} = a + ib + he^{i(\beta+90)} + le^{i\beta} \tag{7.35}$$

Separation of Eq. (7.35) into its real and imaginary components yields

$$a + l \cos \beta = r \cos \alpha + (\rho + h) \sin \beta \tag{7.36}$$

$$b + l \sin \beta = r \sin \alpha - (\rho + h) \cos \beta \tag{7.37}$$

By differentiating Eqs. (7.36) and (7.37) with respect to θ, remembering that A is the center of the oscillating circle which means that for incremental rotations r and ρ are constants, and noting that

$$\frac{d\alpha}{d\theta} = -1 \quad \text{and} \quad \frac{d\beta}{d\theta} = \frac{d[\beta_0 + f(\theta)]}{d\theta} = f'(\theta)$$

we find that

$$-lf'(\theta) \sin \beta + \cos \beta \frac{dl}{d\theta} = r \sin \alpha + (\rho + h)f'(\theta) \cos \beta \tag{7.38}$$

$$lf'(\theta) \cos \beta + \sin \beta \frac{dl}{d\theta} = -r \sin \alpha + (\rho + h)f'(\theta) \sin \beta \tag{7.39}$$

Multiply Eq. (7.38) by $-\sin \beta$, and Eq. (7.39) by $\cos \beta$, then add the two equations to obtain the following expression for the follower length

$$lf'(\theta) = -r[\sin \alpha \sin \beta + \cos \alpha \cos \beta] \tag{7.40}$$

The unknown $\sin \alpha$ and $\cos \alpha$ terms in the preceding equation may be eliminated by substitution from Eqs. (7.36) and (7.37), giving

$$l = \frac{-(a \cos \beta + b \sin \beta)}{1 + f'(\theta)} \tag{7.41}$$

Having evaluated l by means of Eq. (7.41), we may then determine

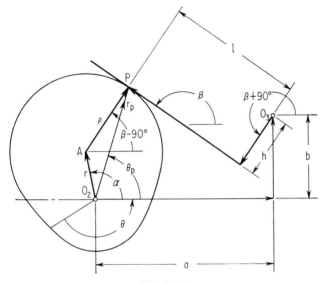

Fig. 7.31

the coordinates of the cam contour at point P from the following equation

$$r_P e^{i(\theta + \theta_P)} = [a + ib + (l + ih)e^{i\beta}]e^{i\theta}$$
$$= (A^2 + B^2)^{1/2} e^{i[\theta + \tan^{-1} B/A]} \tag{7.42}$$

where
$$A = a + l \cos \beta - h \sin \beta$$
$$B = b + l \sin \beta + h \cos \beta$$

To determine the radius of curvature ρ, first differentiate Eq. (7.41) with respect to θ, then use the relation $d\beta/d\theta = f'(\theta)$.

$$[1 + f'(\theta)]\frac{dl}{d\theta} + lf''(\theta) = f'(\theta)[a \sin \beta - b \cos \beta] \tag{7.43}$$

Eliminating $dl/d\theta$ from the preceding equation by means of Eq. (7.38), and then eliminating the resulting $r \sin \alpha$ term by use of Eq. (7.37), we obtain

$$1 + f'(\theta)] \left\{ \rho[1 + f'(\theta)] + h[1 + f'(\theta)] + l[1 + f'(\theta)]\frac{\sin \beta}{\cos \beta} \right.$$
$$\left. + \frac{b}{\cos \beta} \right\} + lf''(\theta) = f'(\theta)[a \sin \beta - b \cos \beta] \tag{7.44}$$

Eliminate l in the third term by the use of Eq. (7.41), and arrange as follows

$$(\rho + h)[1 + f'(\theta)]^2 - \left(a \sin \beta + \frac{b \sin^2 \beta}{\cos \beta}\right)[1 + f'(\theta)] + \frac{b[1 + f'(\theta)]}{\cos \beta}$$
$$+ lf''(\theta) = f'(\theta)[a \sin \beta - b \cos \beta] \qquad (7.45)$$

After replacing $\sin^2 \beta$ with $(1 - \cos^2 \beta)$, we can finally write

$$\rho = \frac{[1 + 2f'(\theta)][a \sin \beta - b \cos \beta] - lf''(\theta)}{[1 + f'(\theta)]^2} - h \qquad (7.46)$$

The value of ρ should be greater than zero.

7.25. Disk cam with oscillating roller follower. A disk cam with oscillating roller follower is shown in Fig. 7.32. The angular displacement β of the follower is given by the equation

$$\beta = \beta_0 + f(\theta) \qquad (7.47)$$

where $f(\theta)$ is the desired angular displacement of the follower from the reference position β_0.

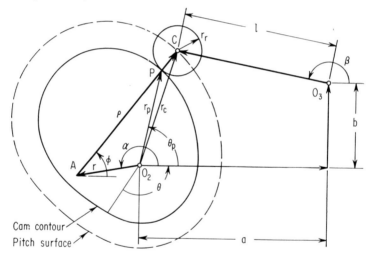

Fig. 7.32

The independent-position equations for the point C are

$$\mathbf{r}_c = re^{i\alpha} + \rho e^{i\phi} = a + ib + le^{i\beta} \qquad (7.48)$$

Separating Eq. (7.48) into its real and imaginary components yields

$$r \cos \alpha + \rho \cos \phi = a + l \cos \beta \qquad (7.49)$$
$$r \sin \alpha + \rho \sin \phi = b + l \sin \beta \qquad (7.50)$$

Differentiating Eqs. (7.49) and (7.50) with respect to θ, and noting as before that

$$\frac{d\alpha}{d\theta} = -1 \qquad \text{and} \qquad \frac{d\beta}{d\theta} = f'(\theta)$$

we find

$$r \sin \alpha - \rho \sin \phi \frac{d\phi}{d\theta} = -lf'(\theta) \sin \beta \tag{7.51}$$

$$-r \cos \alpha + \rho \cos \phi \frac{d\phi}{d\theta} = lf'(\theta) \cos \beta \tag{7.52}$$

Eliminating $d\phi/d\theta$ from Eqs. (7.51) and (7.52), and eliminating the α term by means of Eqs. (7.49) and (7.50), we obtain the following equation for $\tan \phi$

$$\tan \phi = \frac{D}{C} \tag{7.53}$$

where

$$C = [1 + f'(\theta)]l \cos \beta + a$$
$$D = [1 + f'(\theta)]l \sin \beta + b$$

From Fig. 7.32, it may be seen that the equation for the cam contour is

$$r_P e^{i(\theta + \theta_P)} = [a + ib + le^{i\beta} - r_r e^{i\phi}]e^{i\theta}$$
$$= (A^2 + B^2)^{1/2} e^{i(\theta + \tan^{-1} B/A)} \tag{7.54}$$

where

$$A = a + l \cos \beta - r_r \cos \phi$$
$$B = b + l \sin \beta - r_r \sin \phi$$

The radius of curvature ρ is obtained by differentiating Eq. (7.53) with respect to θ and eliminating unknown terms. Thus

$$\rho = \frac{[C^2 + D^2]^{3/2}}{(C^2 + D^2)[1 + f'(\theta)] - (aC + bD)f'(\theta) + (a \sin \beta - b \cos \beta)lf''(\theta)} \tag{7.55}$$

To avoid undercutting, it is necessary that the magnitude of ρ be greater than the radius of the roller. It should be noticed that either a or b may be made equal to zero in the foregoing expressions by proper selection of the initial cam position.

7.26. Closure. The above discussion of Raven's method of cam design can be summarized as follows. The first derivative of the equations yields information for obtaining the cam contour, pressure angle or length of contact of the follower for any position of the cam; and the second derivative yields information for obtaining the radius of curvature of the cam surface at the point of contact between the cam and follower. It should be noted that the two independent position equations for the center of curvature of the follower are actually the loop equation for the cam and follower mechanism. Raven's method of cam design is, then, really a special application of his general theory described in Art. 6.9.

Cams have been widely used for many years, and there is a large body of literature pertaining to them. Carver and Quinn were among the first to develop analytical design methods. Rothbart's modern book includes comprehensive treatments of both theory and application.*

PROBLEMS

7.1. In this problem various types of displacement time graphs are to be constructed. The displacements are to be $1\frac{1}{4}$ in. and 30° intervals are to be used. In some cases it will be necessary to divide some of the 30° intervals into smaller units. The motions are arbitrarily chosen to give practice in plotting these types of graphs.

(a) Outward, constant acceleration 75° and constant deceleration 75°, dwell 60°, return, constant acceleration 60° and constant deceleration 60°, dwell 30°.

(b) Outward, constant acceleration 30°, constant velocity 90°, constant deceleration 60°, return, constant acceleration 120°, and constant deceleration 60°.

(c) Outward, constant acceleration 60°, constant velocity 60°, constant deceleration 30°, dwell 30°, return, constant acceleration 60°, and constant deceleration 120°.

(d) Outward, constant acceleration 60°, constant velocity 30°, constant deceleration 90°, dwell 30°, return SHM 150°.

(e) Outward, SHM 120°, dwell 30°, return, SHM 180°, dwell 30°.

(f) Outward motion $\frac{3}{4}$ in. SHM 60°, dwell in this position 30°, remainder of outward motion SHM 90°, return SHM 150°, dwell 30°.

(g) Outward, cycloidal 180°, dwell 30°, return cycloidal 120°, dwell 30°.

(h) Outward, cycloidal 210°, return, cycloidal 150°.

7.2. Determine the maximum velocity and acceleration of the follower in feet and seconds during the outward and during the return motion for:

(a) Prob. 7.1(a).   Speed of cam 350 rpm.
(b) Prob. 7.1(b).   Speed of cam 600 rpm.
(c) Prob. 7.1(c).   Speed of cam 400 rpm.
(d) Prob. 7.1(d).   Speed of cam 700 rpm.
(e) Prob. 7.1(e).   Speed of cam 650 rpm.
(f) Prob. 7.1(f).   Speed of cam 850 rpm.

7.3. (a) Differentiate Eq. (7.2) and obtain equations for velocity and accelerations of the follower.

(b) Same as Prob. 7.2 but applied to Prob. 7.1(g). Speed of cam is 600 rpm.

(c) Same as Prob. 7.2 but applied to Prob. 7.1(h). Speed of cam is 400 rpm.

7.4. In this problem cam contours are to be laid out graphically, using methods described in the book. The type of follower is indicated by specifying Figs. P 7.1, P 7.2, P 7.3, P 7.4, or P 7.5. The follower motion is indicated by specifying Prob. 7.1(a), (b), (c), (e), or (f). The direction of the cam is indicated

---

* W. B. Carver and B. E. Quinn, "An Analytical Method of Cam Design," *Mechanical Engineering*, August, 1945; H. A. Rothbart, "Cams, Design, Dynamics and Accuracy," John Wiley & Sons, Inc., New York, 1956.

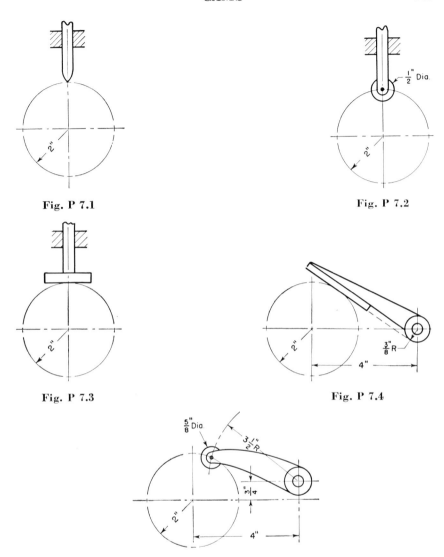

Fig. P 7.1

Fig. P 7.2

Fig. P 7.3

Fig. P 7.4

Fig. P 7.5

as CW (clockwise) or CCW (counterclockwise). Oscillating follower displacement scales are to be laid off on an arc of $3\frac{1}{2}$-in. radius unless otherwise specified.

(a) Fig. 7.1, Prob. 7.1(a), CW.

(b) Fig. P 7.1, Prob. 7.1(b), CCW.

(c) Fig. P 7.1, Prob. 7.1(a), CW, follower offset $\frac{1}{2}$ in. to the left.

(d) Fig. P 7.2, Prob. 7.1(a), CW. Determine the maximum pressure angle.

(e) Fig. P 7.2, Prob. 7.1(a), CW, follower offset $\frac{1}{2}$ in. to the right. Determine the maximum pressure angle.

(f) Fig. P 7.2, Prob. 7.1(b), CCW.

(g) Fig. P 7.2, Prob. 7.1(c), CW.

(h) Fig. P 7.3, Prob. 7.1(a), CW.

(i) Fig. P 7.3, Prob. 7.1(a), CCW.

(j) Fig. P 7.3, Prob. 7.1(b) CW.

(k) Fig. P 7.3, Prob. 7.1(e), CCW.

(l) Fig. P 7.4, Prob. 7.1(a), CW.

(m) Fig. P 7.4, Prob. 7.1(a), CCW, the follower to oscillate through an angle of 15°.

(n) Fig. P 7.4, Prob. 7.1(b), CW.

(o) Fig. P 7.4, Prob. 7.1(f), CCW.

(p) Fig. P 7.5, Prob. 7.1(a), CW.

(q) Fig. P 7.5, Prob. 7.1(a), CCW, the follower to oscillate through an angle of 20°.

(r) Fig. P 7.5, Prob. 7.1(e), CW.

(s) Fig. P 7.5, Prob. 7.1(f), CW.

(t) Fig. P 7.5, Prob. 7.1(b), CCW, the follower to oscillate through an angle of 20°.

7.5. Lay out the contour of a positive return cam that is similar to Fig. 7.14. Here B is 4 in. and the roller diameters are $\frac{3}{4}$ in. The displacement is 1 in., and the outward motion is constant acceleration 60°, constant deceleration 90°, dwell 30°. The cam rotates CCW.

7.6. Lay out the contour of a positive return cam that is similar to Fig. 7.15. Here B is $4\frac{1}{2}$ in. and the roller diameters are $\frac{3}{4}$ in. The displacement scale is that of Prob. 7.1(a). The cam rotates CCW.

7.7. A disk cam is to move a flat-faced follower with the following motion; outward 1.25 in. with SHM during 90° of cam rotation, dwell for 90° of cam rotation, return with constant acceleration and deceleration during 180° of cam rotation. The minimum radius of curvature of the cam is to be 1.5 in. Construct the design chart, and determine C, the minimum radius of the cam.

7.8. A disk cam is to move a flat-faced follower with the following motion; outward with constant acceleration for $\pi/4$ radians of cam rotation, constant velocity for $\pi/2$ radians of cam rotation, constant deceleration for $\pi/4$ radians of cam rotation, dwell for $\pi/4$ radians of cam rotation, then return with cycloidal motion in $\frac{3}{4}\pi$ radians of cam rotation. The total displacement is 3 in. The minimum radius of curvature of the cam is to be 2 in. Construct the design chart and determine C, the minimum radius of the cam.

CHAPTER 8

Rolling Contact

8.1. Introductory. A study of bodies having rolling contact is of value for several reasons. Rolling bodies are used to transmit power and produce desired motions; they are used in machine elements such as ball and roller bearings; an understanding of rolling bodies is necessary for the development of the theory of gearing.

8.2. Conditions of pure rolling. In Art. 2.16 it was shown that rolling contact exists when the point of contact lies on the line of centers of the two bodies. When the centers of rotation of the two bodies are fixed it is obvious that the sum of the contact radii is constant. When pure rolling exists there is no slipping, the lengths of arcs making contact in any interval of time must therefore be equal. It was shown in Art. 3.8 that the point of contact is the instant center of the two bodies.

8.3. Rolling cylinders. A cylinder or ball rolling on a plane is the simplest type of rolling contact (Fig. 8.1). The plane can be considered

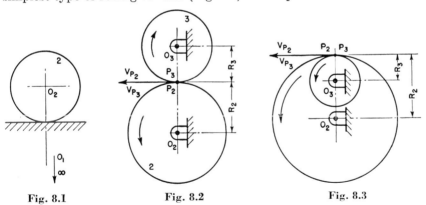

| Fig. 8.1 | Fig. 8.2 | Fig. 8.3 |

a cylinder with its center at infinity. When cylinder 2 is rotated once, it moves over the plane a distance equal to its circumference. Rolling external cylinders are shown in Fig. 8.2 and an external and internal cylinder in Fig. 8.3.

In Fig. 2.24 rolling contact exists for the phase shown. When 2 is turning CCW there is a component of motion along the common normal

in the direction of the follower.   In Figs. 8.2 and 8.3 the common normal
lies along the line of centers.   The direction of motion of the point of
contact in the driver is along the common tangent.   Positive driving
does not exist; force is transmitted by means of friction.   In some applications this is undesirable and in others desirable.   Friction wheels could
not be used to drive the camshaft of an automobile engine.   In some
cases where overloading of a machine is possible, friction wheels or other
friction drives can be used as safety devices.   The friction drive is
designed to slip before any of the machine parts are damaged.

Large forces can be transmitted by means of rolling friction drives.
The force that is required to move a freight train is transmitted through
rolling friction of steel on steel.   In general, rolling friction drives are
not used to transmit large forces because of high bearing loads that are
present in this type of drive.

In Art. 2.16 it was shown that for bodies having rolling contact the
angular velocity ratio of driver and follower is inversely as the contact
radii.

$$\frac{\omega_2}{\omega_3} = \frac{R_3}{R_2} \tag{8.1}$$

If the center distance and angular velocity ratio are known, the radii of
the cylinders can be found as follows.   If the cylinders are to rotate in
opposite directions, external cylinders must be used (Fig. 8.2) then

$$R_2 + R_3 = O_2O_3$$
$$R_3 = O_2O_3 - R_2$$

Substituting this in Eq. (8.1) gives

$$\frac{\omega_2}{\omega_3} = \frac{O_2O_3 - R_2}{R_2} = \frac{O_2O_3}{R_2} - 1$$

$$R_2 = \frac{O_2O_3}{1 + \omega_2/\omega_3} \tag{8.2}$$

If the cylinders are to rotate in the same direction an internal and an
external cylinder must be used (Fig. 8.3).   Following the procedure for
external cylinder gives

$$R_2 = \frac{O_2O_3}{1 - \omega_2/\omega_3} \tag{8.3}$$

8.4. Rolling cones.   Cones can be used to transmit motion between
shafts with intersecting axes.   In Fig. 8.4 the frusta of two cones are
shown connecting shafts that intersect at an angle ϕ.   The cones have
a common apex at D.   If there is pure rolling contact at P the angular
velocity ratio will be

$$\frac{\omega_2}{\omega_3} = \frac{PC}{PB}$$

Rolling will occur at all other points of contact P' on the line of contact since, from similar triangles,

$$\frac{P'C'}{P'B'} = \frac{PC}{PB}$$

If the cones do not have a common apex the above relationship does not hold. A common apex is therefore a necessary requirement for rolling.

Cylinders can be considered cones with a common apex at infinity.

The most common problem is to design a pair of cones to transmit motion between shafts that intersect at a specified angle at a specified angular velocity ratio. For the case of external cones, Fig. 8.4, the directions of rotation of the shafts have an opposite sense.

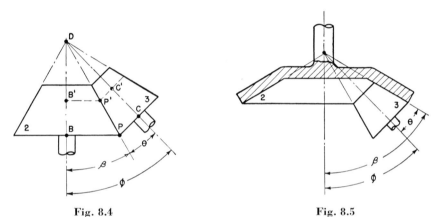

Fig. 8.4   Fig. 8.5

The cone angles β and θ can be expressed as

$$\sin \beta = \frac{BP}{PD} \quad \text{and} \quad \sin \theta = \frac{PC}{PD}$$

Then

$$\frac{\sin \beta}{\sin \theta} = \frac{BP}{PC} = \frac{\omega_3}{\omega_2} = \frac{\sin (\phi - \theta)}{\sin \theta}$$

This can be written in the form

$$\frac{\sin \phi \cos \theta - \cos \phi \sin \theta}{\sin \theta} = \frac{\omega_3}{\omega_2}$$

Dividing numerator and denominator by $\cos \theta$ and solving for $\tan \theta$ gives

$$\tan \theta = \frac{\sin \phi}{\omega_3/\omega_2 + \cos \phi} \tag{8.4}$$

If the directions of rotation of the shafts are to have the same sense an internal and an external cone must be used (Fig. 8.5). For this case the relationship is

$$\tan \theta = \frac{\sin \phi}{\omega_3/\omega_2 - \cos \phi} \tag{8.5}$$

The cone angles can also be determined graphically.   In Fig. 8.6
external cones are to be made such that

$$\frac{\omega_3}{\omega_2} = \frac{3}{2}$$

Distances DF of three units and DE of two units are laid off on the respective cone axes, and P is located at the intersection of lines through E

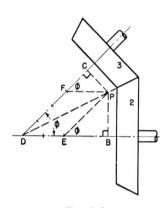

Fig. 8.6

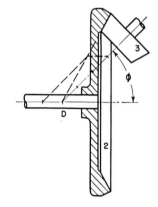

Fig. 8.7

and F parallel to the axes.   The construction can be proved as follows.
Triangles EPB and FCP are similar.   Then

$$\frac{\omega_3}{\omega_2} = \frac{PB}{PC} = \frac{EP}{FP} = \frac{DF}{DE}$$

The contact radii PB and PC are therefore correctly proportioned.

The construction for an internal and external cone of ratio of $\dfrac{\omega_3}{\omega_2} = \dfrac{3}{1}$
is shown in Fig. 8.7.

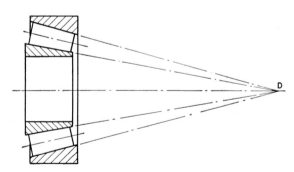

Fig. 8.8

Tapered roller bearings, Fig. 8.8, turn with rolling contact.   Each
point in a set of rolling cones remains a constant distance from the
common apex, and therefore moves on the surface of a sphere.

8.5. Hyperboloids. Two hyperboloids are shown in Fig. 8.9. Hyperboloid 2 is generated by rotating line A-A about axis B-B. The distance R_2 and angle ϕ are held constant during rotation. Hyperboloid 3 is generated by rotating line A-A about axis C-C; R_3 and θ are held constant. The minimum circles of radii R_2 and R_3 are called gorge circles. It can be shown that if the hyperboloids are to fit together with contact along A-A as shown in Fig. 8.9, these radii must be proportional to the tangents of the angles made by line A-A with the axes, i.e.,

$$\frac{R_2}{R_3} = \frac{\tan \phi}{\tan \theta} \tag{8.6}$$

The pitch surfaces of hypoid gears are portions of hyperboloids. Pairs of rolling hyperboloids are used in steel mills for straightening rods and tubing.

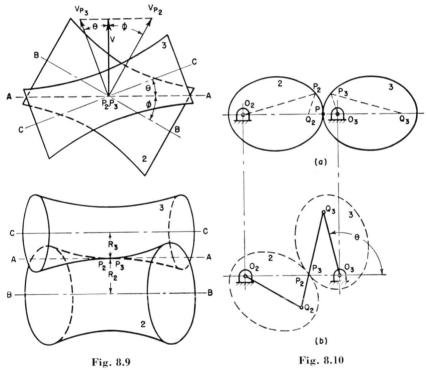

Fig. 8.9   Fig. 8.10

8.6. Rolling ellipses. Two equal ellipses if initially placed together as shown in Fig. 8.10(a) will roll together; O_2, Q_2, O_3, and Q_3 are foci. The center distance O_2O_3 is equal to the major axis of each ellipse. One of the properties of an ellipse is that the sum of the distances from any point on the circumference to the foci is equal to the major axis. Since the two ellipses are equal, $O_2P_2 + P_2Q_2 = O_3P_3 + P_3Q_3 =$ major axis $= O_2O_3$.

If the points P_2 and P_3 are chosen such that the elliptical arcs PP_2 and PP_3 are equal, then from the symmetry of the figure

$$O_2P_2 = P_3Q_3 \quad \text{and} \quad P_2Q_2 = P_3O_3$$

Hence
$$O_2P_2 + P_3O_3 = O_2O_3$$

The conditions for pure rolling are therefore satisfied.

At (b) the ellipses are shown with 3 displaced through angle θ. If the ellipses are replaced with the linkage $O_3Q_3Q_2O_2$, links O_3Q_3 and O_2Q_2 will have the same relative motion as the ellipses. This is true since $Q_2P_2 + P_3Q_3$ is a constant and link Q_2Q_3 always intersects the line of centers at the point where the ellipses are in contact.

8.7. General case of rolling curves. The general case can be considered in three ways depending on the requirements:

1. The angular displacement relationship is chosen for one cycle.
2. The angular velocity relationship is chosen for one cycle.
3. For a finite number of points in the cycle both the displacement and velocity relationships are chosen.

These cases will be considered separately.

1. Angular Displacement Relationship. An example will be used to illustrate this method for determining the contours of rolling bodies. An assumed displacement curve is shown in Fig. 8.11, and the rolling curves are shown in Fig. 8.12. The θ axis represents the displacement of member 3 and the ϕ axis represents the displacement of member 2. Both axes are 360° in length so that rotations can be continuous. Points 0 to 7 were chosen for plotting. The corresponding displacements θ_1, θ_2, θ_3, . . . , ϕ_1, ϕ_2, ϕ_3, . . . were measured and laid off in Fig. 8.12. The lengths of the radii are determined from the relationships

$$r_0 + R_0 = r_1 + R_1 = r_2 + R_2 = \ . \ . \ . \ = O_2O_3$$

and $r_0/R_0 = $ slope at point 0, $r_1/R_1 = $ slope at point 1, etc. These latter relationships come from the angular velocity ratio theorem, and from the fact that the slope of the displacement curve at a point is the angular velocity ratio of the two bodies when their displacements correspond to this point. The driver usually rotates with constant angular velocity. Even when this is not true one of the axes can be considered a time axis, since an angular velocity ratio is desired. It is necessary that the two displacement scales be equal. The slope at point 0 is 72°. In the original drawing $O_2O_3 = 4$ in.

$$\tan 72° = 3.08 = \frac{r_0}{R_0}, \qquad R_0 + r_0 = 4 \text{ in.}$$

$$r_0 = 3.02 \text{ in.}, \qquad R_0 = 0.98 \text{ in.}$$

The curve in Fig. 8.11 is made up of two circular arcs and a straight line. The slopes at 0 and 7 are equal. The straight-line portion represents uniform velocity. The corresponding rolling curves are therefore circles. The second derivative at points 0, 3, and 4 are discontinuous. This produces discontinuities in the slopes of the rolling curves at the corresponding points. For smooth operations the second derivatives should be continuous.

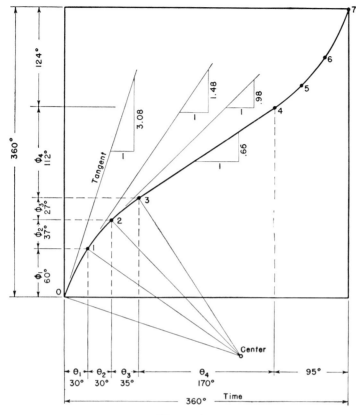

Fig. 8.11

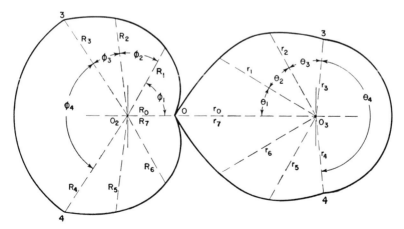

Fig. 8.12

The example above was done graphically.   For most purposes many
more points must be taken and the work done analytically.   The method
is theoretically correct and errors of calculation are not cumulative.

The following example will be solved analytically, but only a few points will be used. It is desired to design rolling curves to satisfy the displacement relationship given by Eq. (8.7), where θ is to vary from 0 degrees to 100 degrees. The graph of this equation is plotted in Fig. 8.13.

$$\phi = 4.75[(0.03\ \theta + 2)^2 - 4] \tag{8.7}$$

The derivative of Eq. (8.7) is

$$\frac{d\phi}{d\theta} = 0.285\ (0.03\ \theta + 2) \tag{8.8}$$

The ϕ values in Table 8.1 are determined from Eq. (8.7) by assuming θ values, and the $d\phi/d\theta$ values are determined from Eq. (8.8) in the same manner. From the discussion of the previous example, we may write

$$R + r = O_2O_3 \tag{8.9}$$

We also know that

$$\text{slope} = \frac{d\phi}{d\theta} = \frac{r}{R} \tag{8.10}$$

By eliminating r from Eqs. (8.9) and (8.10) we obtain

$$R = \frac{O_2O_3}{1 + \dfrac{d\phi}{d\theta}} \tag{8.11}$$

It should now be evident that Eq. (8.2) for rolling circles is a special case of Eq. (8.11); i.e., in Eq. (8.2), $\omega_2/\omega_3 = d\phi/d\theta =$ constant. The R values in Table 8.1 are for the assumed value $O_2O_3 = 1$ in. The rolling curves are constructed in Fig. 8.14.

TABLE 8.1

	θ	ϕ	$\dfrac{d\phi}{d\theta}$	R	r
0	0	0	0.57	0.64	0.36
1	25	16.9	0.78	0.56	0.40
2	50	39.2	1.00	0.50	0.50
3	75	66.8	1.21	0.45	0.55
4	100	100.0	1.43	0.41	0.59

2. Angular Velocity Relationship. When this method is used, the curve for the velocity relationship is chosen and the displacements are determined from this. The space that would be required to describe this method is more than is justified in a book of this type. The method is described elsewhere.* The pitch surfaces for the gears shown in Fig. 9.59 were determined by this method.

* H. E. Golber, "Rollcurve Gears," *Trans. ASME*, 1939, 61:223.

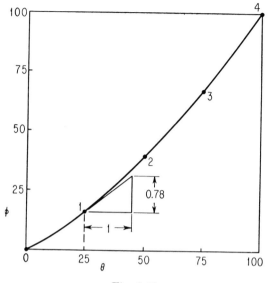

Fig. 8.13

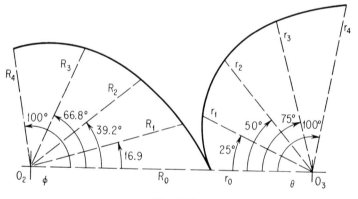

Fig. 8.14

3. Displacement and Velocity for a Finite Number of Points. This method is similar to that of type one. In Fig. 8.15, points 0, 1, 2, and 3 and the indicated slopes represent the displacement and velocity requirements. It is necessary to pass a curve through the points with the required slopes or to fit separate curves between the points. The method of type one is then applied to determine the rolling curves.

Methods for determining arc length and for machining the rolling bodies are described in the references given below.*†

* H. E. Golber, "Rollcurve Gears," *Trans. ASME,* 1939, 61:223.
† Lockenvitz, Oliphint, Wilde, and Young, "Noncircular Cams and Gears," *Machine Design,* May, 1952.

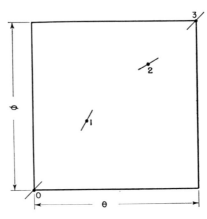

Fig. 8.15

In years past, the published work on rolling contact has been limited and scattered. After making a thorough survey of the available material, Mr. Uno Olsson added his own research and published a book (in English).* Anyone wishing to pursue the subject of rolling contact should consult this book.

PROBLEMS

8.1. Power is to be transmitted from one shaft to a parallel shaft. The shafts are 14 in. apart and they are to turn in opposite directions with an angular velocity ratio of 1.5. Determine the diameters of the cylinders.

8.2. Same as Prob. 8.1 except shafts are to turn in the same direction.

8.3. Same as Prob. 8.1 except the center distance is 7 in. and the angular velocity ratio is 1.25.

8.4. Same as Prob. 8.3 except shafts are to turn in the same direction.

8.5. The axes of two shafts intersect at 60°. Power is to be transmitted from one shaft to the other by means of rolling cones. The angular velocity ratio is 3 and the directional sense is to be opposite. The maximum diameter of the larger cone is to be 10 in. Determine the cone angles β and θ and the maximum diameter of smaller cone. Use graphical methods.

8.6. Same as Prob. 8.5 but the rotational sense is the same.

8.7. Same as Prob. 8.5 except analytical methods are to be used.

8.8. Same as Prob. 8.6 except analytical methods are to be used.

8.9. The axes of two shafts intersect at 45°. Power is to be transmitted from one shaft to the other by means of rolling cones. The angular velocity

---

* U. Olsson, "Non-Circular Cylindrical Gears," *Mechanical Engineering Series* Vol. 2, No. 10, 1953, Acta Polytechnica, Stockholm, Sweden.

ratio is 2.5 and the directional sense is to be opposite. The maximum diameter of the larger cone is to be 7 in. Determine the cone angles β and θ and the maximum diameter of the smaller cone. Use graphical methods.

8.10. Same as Prob. 8.9 except the rotational sense is to be the same.

8.11. Same as Prob. 8.9 except the analytical methods are to be used.

8.12. Same as Prob. 8.10 except analytical methods are to be used.

8.13. A displacement graph for two rolling bodies is shown in Fig. P 8.13. It consists of two equal circular arcs. The axes of the rolling bodies are to be 3 in. apart.
  (a) Construct the rolling curves graphically for 30° intervals of θ.
  (b) Using analytical methods calculate ϕ, R, and r for the position $\theta = 60°$.

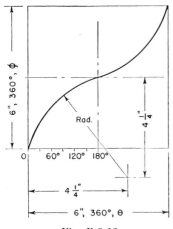

Fig. P 8.13

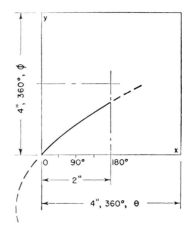

Fig. P 8.14

8.14. A portion of a displacement graph for two rolling bodies is shown in Fig. 8.14. Its equation is a parabola, $y^2 + 4y - 4x = 0$. The axes of the rolling bodies are to be 3 in. apart. Using analytical methods calculate ϕ, R, and r for positions corresponding to $\theta = 0, 45, 90, 135, 180°$. Plot the rolling curves.

8.15. Construct rolling curves that have an angular displacement relationship that is given by the equation

$$\phi = \frac{160}{(0.9397)(57.3)} \sin \frac{\theta}{2}$$

where ϕ and θ are in radians. If ϕ and θ are expressed in degrees the relationship is

$$\phi = \frac{160}{0.9397} \sin \frac{\theta}{2}$$

θ is to vary from 0 deg to 140 deg, and the center distance is to be 3 in. Make a table of values, similar to Table 8.1, for 20 deg intervals of θ.

CHAPTER 9

Gearing

9.1. History. It is believed that toothed gears were used as early as 350 B.C. Ctesibius in 150 B.C. used spur and bevel gears in his water-clocks. The Trojan Column, erected in Rome in 114 A.D., contains sculptured gears. Drawings of Leonardo da Vinci include spur, bevel, and worm gears. All these gears were of the "cog wheel" variety. Even if they could have been made accurately according to the designer's ideas they would not have run smoothly.

A Danish astronomer, Olaf Roemer, in 1674, first offered a theory of correct tooth shapes. He proposed the use of cycloidal teeth. A Frenchman, Philippe de Lahaire, in 1695, proposed the use of involute profiles.

Figure 9.1 is from *Mechanic-Powers*.* This illustrates the method of determining a tooth profile to operate with a pin gear. Circle *POB*

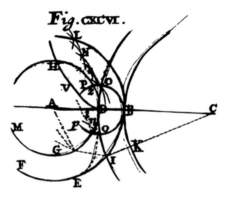

Fig. 9.1

is a pin on the wheel with center at *A*, and *HVD* is an epicycloid obtained by rolling circle *HDGM* on the circle with radius *CI*. The tooth profile on the gear with center at *C* is obtained by drawing arcs of radius equal to the pin radius, using the epicycloid as the locus of the centers. The

* Mandy and Moxon, *Mechanic-Powers*, London, 1696.

176

envelope of these arcs *ONL* is the tooth profile. This is theoretically correct. Note that inversion was used to obtain the tooth profile.

The authors also suggest that the pin be made in the form of a roller on a smaller pin so that the contacting teeth have rolling instead of sliding friction. This is described by the authors.

Behold here a particular conſtruction for the Teeth of Wheels of a great Engin, where the faces which rencounter themſelves or meet, are made ſo that they touch one another without rubing or wearing, and what remains is only made on the Axis, or Pivot.

The conſtruction of theſe Teeth is the ſame as thoſe of the firſt Example of the 6th. Propoſition, but the Application is different: In the 6th. Propoſition the circular Tooth propoſed is ſtayed firmly by the Wheel; but in thoſe here that is a little wheel which is movable about its centre D, on an axle-tree, or pin, placed at the end of the Radius A D; there will be then no other fretting, or wearing, in this Engin, than that of the little wheel B Z P on its axis; for the circumference will apply it ſelf every way, without fretting, or wearing, on the Curve of the other Tooth O N L.

Theory was of little use until accurate methods were developed for machining the gears. In 1864 Joseph R. Brown invented the formed milling cutter that could be sharpened by grinding without changing the shape of the cutting faces. In 1884 Hugo Bilgram invented the generating method for cutting teeth. This is the principal method used today.

9.2. Introductory. Power transmission by means of rolling bodies was discussed in Chapter 8. It was shown that rolling bodies of circular cross section do not have positive transmission. Motion transmitted by gears is equivalent to that of rolling bodies but is positive. Comparing pairs of members of the same size, gears will transmit much larger torques than rolling members. *Gears* are machine elements that transmit motion by means of successively engaging teeth.* Spur gears and their equivalent cylindrical friction surfaces are shown in Fig. 9.2. Bevel gears and their equivalent conical friction surfaces are shown in Fig. 9.3. Other types of gears are shown in the pages that follow. Most gears are circular, and the angular velocity ratio of driver and follower is constant. The discussion of noncircular gears will be confined to the last article in this chapter.

* Extracted from *American Standard Gear Nomenclature* (ASA B6.10-1950), with the permission of the publishers, The American Society of Mechanical Engineers, 29 West 39th Street, New York 18, New York. All definitions in italics are taken from this source.

Gearing is a large subject. The design of many gear drives requires the work of experts. The author's aim is to present the fundamental concepts of the theory of gears and to indicate some of the practical aspects that must always be considered when a machine element is to

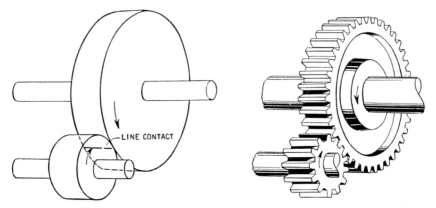

Fig. 9.2.   (Courtesy of Socony-Vacuum Oil Co.)

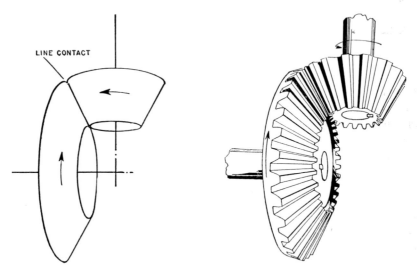

Fig. 9.3.   (Courtesy of Socony-Vacuum Oil Co.)

be produced in physical form. An understanding of this chapter should be an adequate background for further study in the works of Buckingham* and the writings of others.

9.3. Classification.   Gears can be classified according to the relationship of their axes. Any two lines in space must fall into one of the

---

* Buckingham, Earl, *Analytical Mechanics of Gears* and *Spur Gears*, New York: McGraw-Hill Book Co., Inc.

three relationships listed below. The gears that are used with each one are listed.

             Parallel axes:
                 Straight spur, stepped, parallel helical

             Intersecting axes:
                 Straight bevel, spiral bevel, face

             Nonparallel nonintersecting axes:
                 Crossed helical, worm, face, hypoid

Each of these types will be discussed.

9.4. Fundamental law of gearing. Gear design may be considered a special case of cam design. In Art. 2.12 it was shown that the angular velocity ratio of driver and follower is inversely as the segments cut by the common normal on the line of centers. In Fig. 9.4 the common normal intersects the line of centers at P. If the angular velocity ratio of 2 and 3 is to be constant, the common normal must pass through P for all phases. The angular velocity ratio will then be equivalent to that of rolling circles of radii O_3P and O_2P. These imaginary circles are called pitch circles. The fundamental law of gearing for circular gears is: *the common normal at the point of contact of the teeth must pass through a fixed point on the line of centers.* This is point P, the pitch point.

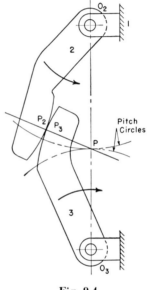

Fig. 9.4

Within reasonable limits one tooth profile can be arbitrarily chosen and the mating profile determined to fulfill the fundamental law. Any pair of teeth that fulfill the law are called conjugate teeth. For practical reasons to be discussed later, involute profiles are usually used.

9.5. Nomenclature. *Spur gears are cylindrical in form and operate on parallel axes. Their teeth are straight and parallel to the axes.* Spur gears are the simplest type of gears and will be discussed first. Much of the theory pertaining to them is basic to all gears. Some of the nomenclature given below is indicated in Fig. 9.5.

The circular pitch p is the distance along the pitch circle or pitch line between corresponding profiles of adjacent teeth.

The addendum a is the height by which a tooth projects beyond the pitch circle or pitch line; also the radial distance between the pitch circle and the addendum circle.

The dedendum b is the depth of a tooth space below the pitch circle or pitch line; also the radial distance between the pitch circle and the root circle.

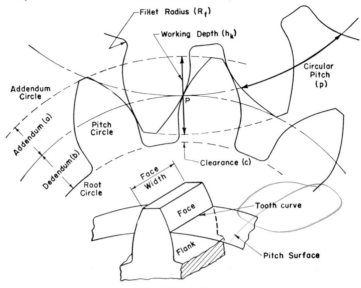

Fig. 9.5

The clearance *c* is the amount by which the dedendum in a given gear exceeds the addendum of its mating gear.

The working depth h_k is the depth of engagement of two gears, that is, the sum of their addendums.

The whole depth h_t is the total depth of a tooth space, equal to addendum plus dedendum, also equal to working depth plus clearance.

The backlash *B* is the amount by which the width of a tooth space exceeds the thickness of the engaging tooth on the pitch circles.

The diametral pitch P_d is the ratio of the number of teeth to the number of inches in the pitch diameter. There is a fixed relation between diametral pitch P_d and circular pitch *p*, namely, $p = \pi/P_d$. Let *N* be the number of teeth and *D* the diameter of the pitch circle; then

$$p = \frac{\pi D}{N} \quad \text{and} \quad P_d = \frac{N}{D} \quad \text{giving} \quad p = \frac{\pi}{P_d} \qquad (9.1)$$

Some of the standard diametral pitches are shown in Fig. 9.6.

The module *m* (inch) is the ratio of the pitch diameter in inches to the number of teeth. It is the reciprocal of the diametral pitch.

The fillet curve is the concave portion of the tooth profile where it joins the bottom of the tooth space.

The fillet radius r_f is the radius of the fillet curve at the base of the gear tooth. In generated teeth, this radius is an approximate radius of curvature.

The gear ratio m_G is the ratio of the larger to the smaller number of teeth in a pair of gears.

A pinion is a gear with a small number of teeth. Of two gears that run together, the one with the smaller number of teeth is called the pinion.

Fig. 9.6.   (Courtesy of Barber–Colman Co.)

A tooth curve is a general term for the curve of intersection of a tooth surface and its pitch surface.   The tooth curve of a straight tooth is a straight line.

9.6. Involute gear teeth.   The involute of a circle is the curve described by the end of a thread as it is unwound from a stationary cylinder.   This is illustrated in Fig. 9.7.   The end of the thread D traces an involute.   The direction of the motion of the end D at any instant is perpendicular to the thread, hence the normal at any point of an involute is tangent to the circle from which it was derived.

In Fig. 9.8 a plate R is attached to the cylinder, and the cylinder is allowed to rotate.   If the end of the thread is moved in the direction indicated, any point D on the thread will trace an involute on the plate. This is merely an inversion of Fig. 9.7.

Two cylinders and a connecting thread *BCDEF* are shown in Fig. 9.9.   If cylinder 3 is rotated counterclockwise, the thread will act as a belt and cause clockwise rotation of cylinder 2.   The thread will always

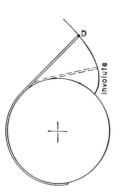

Fig. 9.7

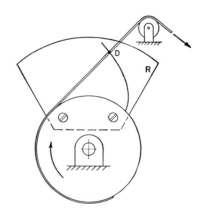

Fig. 9.8

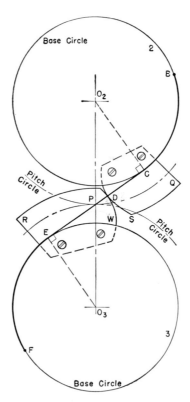

Fig. 9.9

pass through the fixed point P on the centerline. Plates Q and R are fastened to the cylinders. As movement takes place any point D will simultaneously trace involutes W and S on plates R and Q. If the plates are cut along the involutes they can serve as teeth. If cylinder 2 is rotated CW, profile S will push on profile W, causing cylinder 3 to rotate. The point of contact D and the common normal will always lie on the line CE. The fundamental law is fulfilled.

The base circle is the circle from which the involute tooth profiles are derived. Triangles O_3EP and O_2CP are similar; hence

$$\frac{O_3E}{O_2C} = \frac{O_3P}{O_2P}$$

The angular velocity ratio is also inversely as the base circle radii.

9.7. Construction of the involute. A method of constructing an involute is shown in Fig. 9.10(a). Assume that the involute is to originate from point B. Equal arc lengths B-1, 1-2, 2-3, 3-4 are stepped off. Perpendiculars are erected to the radii at 1, 2, 3, and 4. Lengths 1a, 2b, 3c, 4d are made equal to the corresponding arc lengths. Then $Babcd$ is the desired involute.

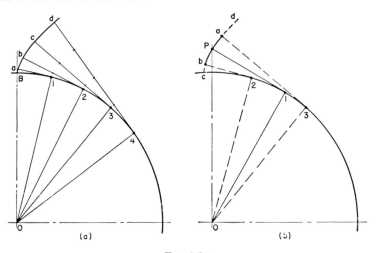

Fig. 9.10

An approximate construction is shown at (b). Assume that the involute is to pass through point P. A line is drawn through P tangent to the circle. With 1 as a center, an arc aPb is drawn. A line through b is tangent to the circle at 2. With 2 as a center, arc bc is drawn. Arc ad is drawn with 3 as a center. The more centers that are used the more accurate is the involute.

9.8. Involute gear tooth action. Portions of a pair of involute gears are shown in Fig. 9.11. The gear with center at O_2 is driving in a CW direction. The terminology and relationships that are necessary for an understanding of gear tooth action are listed below. Line EC is the line of transmission or line of action. Angle ϕ is called the angle of obliquity or the pressure angle. From triangle O_2CP the radius of the base circle in terms of the pitch circle is

$$R_b = R_p \cos \phi \qquad (9.2)$$

It was shown that the point of contact of involute gear teeth lies on the line of action EC. In this case the first point of contact is K. It is the point on the line of action nearest C that can be reached by a tooth on 3. It is the intersection of the addendum circle of gear 3 and the line CE. Similarly L is the last point of contact, and KL is called the path of contact.

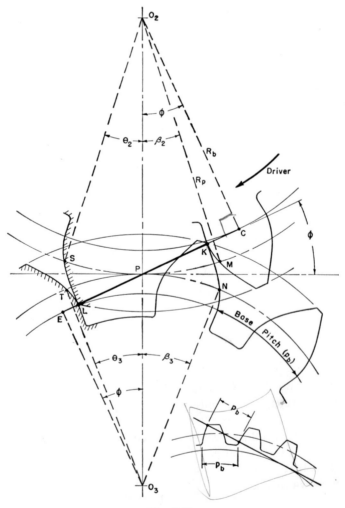

Fig. 9.11

The *arc of action* is the arc of the pitch circle through which a tooth profile moves from the beginning to the end of contact with a mating profile. This is shown as MS for gear 2 and NT for gear 3.   The arc of action can be divided into MP, the arc of approach, and PS, the arc of recess. The corresponding angles β_2 and θ_2 are, respectively, the angles of approach and recess.   Arc MP is equal to NP, and PS is equal to PT because of rolling of the pitch circles.   Angle β_2 is not equal to β_3, and θ_2 is not equal to θ_3 except for the case of equal gears.   It has been found from practice that gear tooth action is smoother in recess than in approach.

The *base pitch p_b* in an involute gear is the pitch on the base circle or along the line of action.   Corresponding sides of involute gear teeth are parallel curves, and the base pitch is the constant and fundamental distance between them along a common normal in the plane of rotation.   This is shown at the lower right of Fig. 9.11.   The base pitch can be determined by dividing the circumference of the base circle by the number of teeth. The relationship between the circular and base pitch using Eq. (9.2) is

$$p_b = p \cos \phi \qquad (9.3)$$

The *contact ratio* (m_c) is the ratio of the arc of action to the circular pitch, and sometimes is thought of as an average number of teeth in contact. For involute gears, the contact ratio is obtained most directly as the ratio of the length of action to the base pitch.   The length of action is the path of contact KL.   The contact ratio is KL/p_b.   In order that action be continuous it is necessary that the ratio be at least unity.   For smooth action it should be at least 1.4.   This means that during 40 per cent of the time two pairs of teeth are in contact.

When the teeth are in contact at P, pure rolling exists.   At all other points there is both rolling and sliding.   The sliding component can be determined by the method of Art. 2.11 or of Prob. 3.25.

9.9. Involute rack and pinion.   Portions of rack and pinion are shown in Fig. 9.12.   A rack can be thought of as a portion of a gear of infinite radius.   The infinite pitch circle of the rack is called the pitch line.   The line of action is tangent to the base circle at infinity; hence the radius of curvature of a tooth profile is infinite.

9.10. Involute interference.   In Fig. 9.12 the addendum a of the rack was chosen so that the first point of contact would coincide with C, the point of tangency of the line of action with the base circle of the pinion.   The involute profile of the pinion tooth begins on the base circle.   The portion of the profile inside the base circle is shown as a radial line.   An involute tooth profile can not exist inside the base circle. Then PC is the maximum length of contact in approach.   The maximum rack addendum that should be used in this case is a.   In order to see the effect of a longer addendum it is shown as a'.   When the teeth are in contact at C the additional portion of the rack face will lie along the radial flank of the pinion. When the pitch circle of the pinion and the pitch line of the rack are rolled to the right there will be interference, as shown by the broken line profiles. In order that the fundamental law be fulfilled and that the teeth mesh it is necessary to remove part of the pinion teeth as shown at the right. This undercutting weakens the teeth

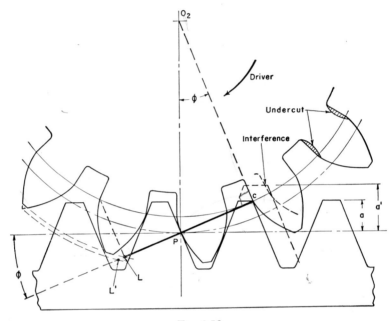

Fig. 9.12

and removes part of the involute profile, which shortens the path of contact.

There can be no interference due to a large addendum on the pinion, the point of tangency is at infinity. The maximum length of path in recess is PL', which is obtained with a pointed pinion tooth.

If a rack will mesh with a pinion without interference, any external gear having the same addendum as the rack will also mesh with the pinion without interference. This can be seen from Fig. 9.12. The addendum circle of any finite gear will intersect PC to the left of C.

9.11. Determination of contact ratio. The contact ratio can be determined semigraphically for any pair of involute gears (Fig. 9.13). The pitch circles, addendum circles, and pressure angle are known. This is sufficient for determining the length of the path of contact KL. This divided by the base pitch gives the contact ratio. The lengths of LP and PK can be calculated, using the trigonometric relationships included in the next article.

9.12. Checking for interference. Any pair of involute gears can be checked for interference by the method of Fig. 9.13(a). If either K or L falls beyond the limits C and E, there is interference.

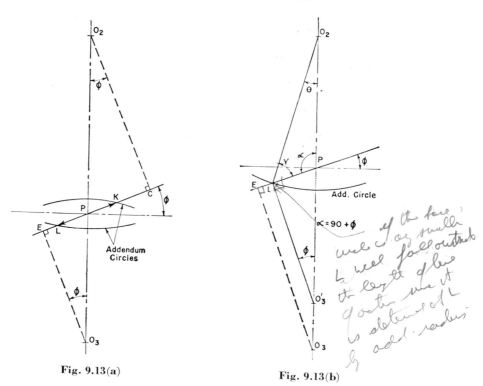

Fig. 9.13(a)   Fig. 9.13(b)

Sometimes it is required to find the smallest pinion that will mesh with a given gear without interference. In Fig. 9.13(b), O_2P is the pitch radius, O_2L the addendum circle radius, and ϕ the pressure angle of the given gear. Line LO_3' drawn perpendicular to LP at point L is the radius of the base circle of the smallest pinion that will mesh without interference. Any larger pinion of base radius EO_3 will not have interference. The pitch radius PO_3' can be calculated using the following relationships for the solution of oblique triangles.

$$\gamma = \sin^{-1}\frac{PO_2 \sin \alpha}{O_2L} \tag{9.4}$$

$$\theta = 180 - (\alpha + \gamma) \tag{9.5}$$

$$LP = \frac{O_2L \sin \theta}{\sin \alpha} \tag{9.6}$$

$$PO_3' = \frac{LP}{\sin \phi} \tag{9.7}$$

9.13. Internal gears.   External involute gears have convex profiles. As the number of teeth increases, the profiles approach an infinite radius of curvature and reach this condition for the rack. The profiles of internal gears are concave. As the number of teeth is increased the profiles approach a straight line. The rack is the limiting case for both external and internal gears. The basic theory is the same for both types of gears.

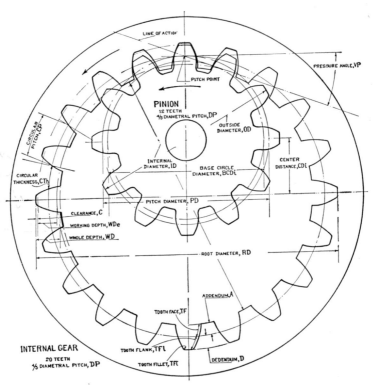

Fig. 9.14.   (Courtesy of The Fellows Gear Shaper Co.)

An internal gear and pinion is shown in Fig. 9.14. This drive is more compact than an external gear drive. The concave-convex contact facilitates lubrication and reduces the contact stress.

The location of the interference point is shown in Fig. 9.15. The line of action is tangent to the gear base circle at L and to the pinion base circle at K. An involute profile for the gear can begin at L. The pinion involute cannot begin until K is reached. This is then the first possible point of contact, and the maximum addendum of the gear is as indicated. The length of path PM' in recess is limited only by the pinion tooth coming to a point.

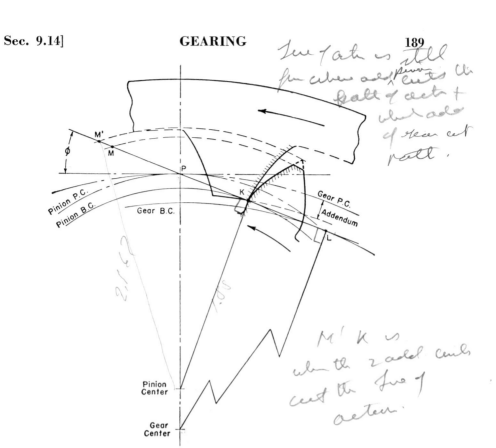

[handwritten margin notes: "line of action is still ... for either addendum cuts the ... half of action + what adds ... of rear cut path."]

[handwritten notes lower right: "M' K is when the z added cuts the line of action."]

Fig. 9.15

9.14. Interchangeable gear-tooth forms. A set of gears is said to be interchangeable when any two of the set will mesh and fulfill the fundamental law. Obviously a watch gear will not mesh with an automobile transmission gear. The gears must have the same pitch. Two gears will not mesh if the addendum of one is greater than the dedendum of the other. There is one basic requirement pertaining to tooth profiles for interchangeable gears. *Gears of a set that are conjugate to a basic rack will be interchangeable if the rack tooth profile is symmetrical in relation to the pitch point. When this condition is met, it follows that the path of contact will be symmetrical in relation to the pitch point.*

First it will be proved that a symmetrical rack tooth produces a symmetrical path of contact. In Fig. 9.16, $E P F$ is a rack tooth that is symmetrical about the pitch point, and $G P H$ is a conjugate pinion tooth. The pinion and rack are moved until contact is made at point A whose location is indicated by the distances x and y. Since these are conjugate teeth, the fundamental law is fulfilled, and the common normal at A passes through P. Now choose a point D on the rack profile that is a distance y below the centerline of the rack. Because of symmetry of the rack teeth, the tangent and normal at D will have the same slopes as at A. To fulfill the fundamental law, it is necessary to move the rack tooth to the right until the normal passes through P.   Then D is located by the distances x and y.   Points A and D are therefore symmetrically located with respect to P.   In a similar manner it can be shown that for any point B there is a corresponding symmetrically placed point C.   Therefore, the

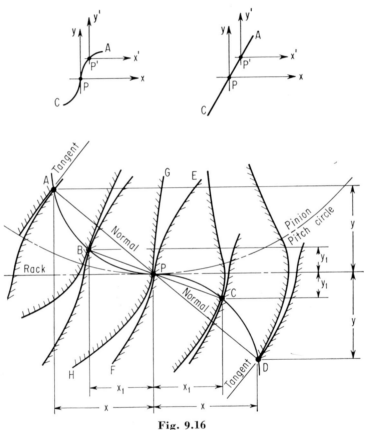

Fig. 9.16

path of contact, $A\ B\ P\ C\ D$, is symmetrically located in relation to the pitch point.

It will now be shown that gears conjugate to a rack with a symmetrical tooth profile will be conjugate to each other.   In Fig. 9.17(a) a pinion is shown in mesh with a rack having a symmetrical path of contact and profile.   The point of contact is K.   At (b) the same basic rack is meshed with another pinion.   The point of contact K was chosen the same distance x from the centerline.   From symmetry, y in (b) is equal to y in (a).   Parts (a) and (b) are superimposed at (c).   The racks and paths of contact coincide and the two pinion teeth are in contact at K. This will be true for any distance x that is chosen.   Hence the pinions

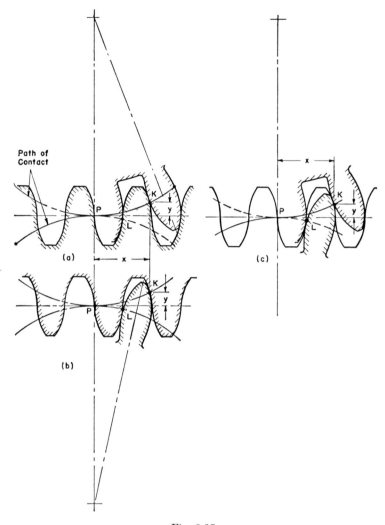

Fig. 9.17

are conjugate. If there is no backlash there will also be contact at L. If the tooth thickness of the rack is equal to the tooth space, measured on the pitch line (except an allowance for backlash), and the dedendum is greater than the addendum, all secondary requirements for interchangeability are met.

9.15. Cycloidal gears have been used in the past but are seldom used today. In order to obtain a more thorough understanding of gear tooth action it is desirable to consider at least one form in addition to the involute. This justifies a brief study of cycloidal gears.

A cycloidal rack tooth profile is shown in Fig. 9.18(a). Generating circle 2 is tangent to the pitch line at the pitch point P. When this circle is rolled to the right the point that was originally in contact with the pitch point generates a cycloid. In a similar manner generating circle 3 generates the remainder of the tooth profile when it is rolled to the left.

A cycloidal tooth profile is shown in Fig. 9.18(b). It is generated by rolling circle 2 to the right on the outside of the pitch circle and circle 3 to the left on the inside of the pitch circle.

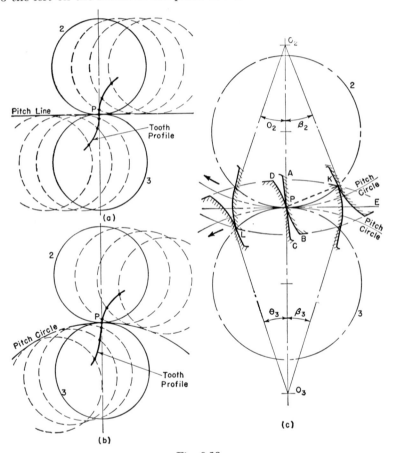

Fig. 9.18

In Fig. 9.18(c) the generating circles 2 and 3 are rolled on the pitch circles of the two gears. Points on these generating circles will generate or trace cycloidal tooth profiles on the two gears. When circle 2 is rolled to the left on the inside of the pitch circle of gear 2, point P on circle 2 will trace the profile PA. When circle 3 is rolled to the right on the outside of the pitch circle of gear 2, point P on circle 3 will trace the profile PB. Profiles PD and PC are traced in a similar manner by rolling circle 2 and 3 on the pitch circle of gear 3.

A pair of teeth are shown in mesh at K, the first point of contact. It can be shown that cycloidal teeth fulfill the fundamental law of gear tooth action as follows. Point K on circle 2 may be considered a generating point. Circle 2 and the pitch circles of the two gears are tangent at P. If these three circles are rolled together point P will be their instant center. The direction of motion of point K as a point in 2, tracing simultaneously the two tooth profiles, will be perpendicular to KP. Therefore KP is the common normal of the two profiles. This will be true for any position. The reverse curve KPL, composed of portions of the two generating circles, is the path of contact.

The angle KPE is the pressure angle for the first point of contact. This angle changes with the position of the meshing teeth and is zero when contact is at the pitch point.

It follows from the previous article that the generating circles must be of the same size if the path of contact is to be symmetrical and the gears are to be interchangeable.

9.16. Advantages of involute teeth. The extensive use of involute spur gear teeth is the result of distinct advantages of this type compared with all other types. It was shown in Art. 9.9 that tooth profiles of an involute rack are straight. Cutting tools and grinding wheels having straight sides are used in the production of gears and cutters. This makes the production of accurate involute gears more economical than the production of other types.

The radius of curvature of a cycloidal tooth profile is zero at the pitch circle. For this reason it is difficult to machine accurately the portion of the profile near the pitch circle. The radius of curvature of an involute is zero at the base circle. By controlling the length of path of contact this portion can be eliminated from the active portion of the profile.

One of the principal advantages of involute gears is that they fulfill the fundamental law of gearing regardless of the center distance between the axes. In Fig. 9.19 a pair of teeth are shown in contact at h. The angular velocity ratio is $O_3P \div O_2P$. When center O_3 is moved to O_3' the tooth contact is at h'. The common normal to the teeth at h' is tangent to the base circles and intersects the line of centers at P'. Triangles O_2PC and O_3EP are similar. Triangles $O_2P'C'$ and $O_3'E'P'$ are similar; hence

$$\frac{E'O_3'}{C'O_2} = \frac{O_3'P'}{O_2P'} \quad \text{and} \quad \frac{EO_3}{CO_2} = \frac{O_3P}{O_2P}$$

But

$$O_2C = O_2C'' \quad \text{and} \quad O_3E = O_3'E'$$

Hence

$$\frac{O_3P}{O_2P} = \frac{O_3'P'}{O_2P'}$$

The angular velocity ratio is not changed. An increase in the center distance increases the backlash and pressure angle and decreases the length of path of contact but the fundamental law is fulfilled.

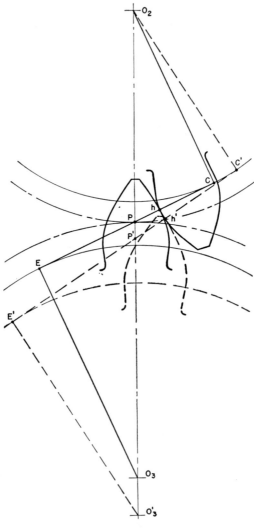

Fig. 9.19

The base circle is built into an involute gear. It is one of the necessary specifications. An involute gear has no pitch circle until it is meshed with another gear. When a pitch circle is used in specifying a gear it must be associated with a definite pressure angle. This in effect specifies the base circle.

Where the gears are to be cut with formed milling cutters, the number of cutters required to cover the range from the smallest pinion to a rack is less than for cycloidal profiles. This results from a smaller change in curvature over the range.

9.17. Summary of involute-curve properties. The previous discussion of involute teeth should be sufficient for an understanding of each of the following properties.*

1. The shape of the involute curve is dependent only upon the size of the base circle.

2. If one involute, rotating at a uniform rate of motion, acts against another involute, it will transmit a uniform angular motion to the second regardless of the distance between the centers of the two base circles.

3. The rate of motion transmitted from one involute to another depends only on the relative sizes of the base circles of the two involutes. This rate of motion is in inverse proportion to the sizes of the two base circles.

4. The common tangent to the two base circles is both the path of contact and the line of action. In other words, the two involutes will make contact with each other only along this common tangent to the two base circles.

5. The path of contact of an involute is a straight line. Any point on this line may therefore be taken as a pitch point, and the path of contact will remain symmetrical in relation to this pitch point. This can be seen at the upper right of Fig. 9.16 where the straight line $A P B$ is symmetrical about the pitch point P. The line $A B$ will also be symmetrical about any other pitch point P' chosen on this line. This is not true for any other curve as shown at the upper left of Fig. 9.16. Thus, the involute is the only tooth form that is not sensitive to center distance.

6. The intersection of the common tangent to the two base circles with their common center line establishes the radii of the pitch circles of the mating involutes. No involute has a pitch circle until it is brought into contact with another involute, or with a straight line constrained to move in a fixed direction.

7. The pitch diameters of two involutes acting together are directly proportional to the diameters of their base circles.

8. The pressure angle of two involutes acting together is the angle between the common tangent to the two base circles and a line perpendicular to their common center line. No involute has a pressure angle until it is brought into contact with another involute, or with a straight line constrained to move in a fixed direction.

9. The form of the basic rack of the involute is a straight line. The pressure angle of an involute acting against such a rack is the angle between the line of action and a line representing the direction in which this rack moves.

* E. Buckingham, *Analytical Mechanics of Gears*, McGraw-Hill Book Co., Inc., 1949.

10. The pitch radius of an involute acting against a straight-line rack form is the length of the radial line, perpendicular to the direction of motion of the rack, measured from the center of the base circle to its point of intersection with the line of action.

9.18. Standard interchangeable tooth forms. For reasons of economy standard tooth forms have been adopted to meet various requirements. All gear designs are compromises. The tooth form chosen is the one that is most satisfactory when all conditions, functional and economic, are considered. The standard forms are described below.

The $14\frac{1}{2}°$ Composite System. This tooth form came into use when both cycloidal and involute gears were in use. The basic rack is shown in Fig. 9.20. The central portion of the tooth is involute and the remainder

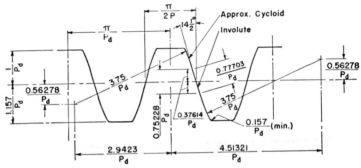

Fig. 9.20

is segmental. It is sometimes said that these portions are cycloidal because of the close approximation. The segmental form (circular arc) can be produced accurately with less difficulty than the cycloidal form. The rack tooth is symmetrical with respect to the pitch point, and gears conjugate to this rack will be interchangeable.

These gears must operate on fixed center distances. A change in center distance would cause a segmental curve on one tooth to be in contact with an involute curve on the other tooth and would produce incorrect tooth action. Only involute curves have the property of operating correctly with any center distance. Interference and under-cutting of small pinions is avoided in this system.

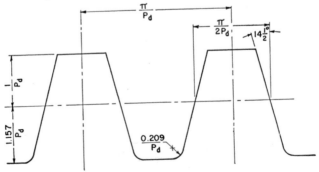

Fig. 9.21

The 14½° Full Depth System. The basic rack tooth for this system is shown in Fig. 9.21. Two 23-tooth pinions are the smallest pair of equal gears that will have the desired minimum contact ratio of 1.4. The smallest pinion that will mesh with a rack without interference has 32 teeth. This system is usually used for gears having a large number of teeth, 40 to 50 and larger.

The 20° Full Depth System. The basic rack is shown in Fig. 9.22. This system is suitable for gears having smaller numbers of teeth than

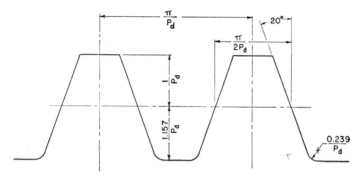

Fig. 9.22

are permitted with the 14½° systems. Two 14-tooth pinions will have a contact ratio of 1.415. The smallest pinion that will mesh with a rack without interference has 18 teeth. In general this is the best system for gears having small numbers of teeth.

The 20° Stub System. The basic rack for this system is shown in Fig. 9.23. This tooth form was introduced to meet the needs of gears having small tooth numbers and requiring high beam strength. A load

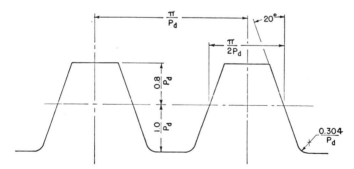

Fig. 9.23

on the end of a stub tooth does not produce as high a stress at the fillet as the same load on a longer tooth. Some of this advantage is lost since fewer pairs of teeth are in contact. Two 12-tooth pinions have a contact ratio of 1.185. A pinion and gear having 27 and 30 teeth have a contact ratio of 1.351. Gears of this system with small numbers of teeth do not

have the desired minimum ratio of 1.4.   For equal smoothness of operation these gears must be more accurately machined than gears having
a greater contact ratio.

The 20° Fellows Stub Tooth Systems are similar to the 20° stub system
described above but the tooth proportions are not the same for all sizes
of teeth.   The pitch designations are: 3/4, 4/5, 5/7, 6/8, 7/9, 8/10, 9/11,
and 12/14.   The numerator is the diametral pitch, the addendum is
unity divided by the denominator, and the clearance is 0.25 divided by
the denominator.   For a gear of diametral pitch 5 the addendum is $\frac{1}{7}$ in.
and the clearance is 0.25/7 in.

9.19. Parallel helical involute gears.   A stepped gear, Fig. 9.24,
consists of two or more gears fastened together as shown.   Each is
advanced relative to the adjacent one by an amount equal to the circular
pitch divided by the number of gears.   When accurately made, these
gears are more quiet and smooth in action than conventional spur gears.
Theoretically most gears run perfectly.   Actually there are always
inaccuracies in the teeth and deflections due to loads.   This results in
impact loading and noise.   If the masses of the parts that meet with
impact are reduced, the noise is less.   In stepped gears the masses are
reduced.   There is also a greater variety of contact.

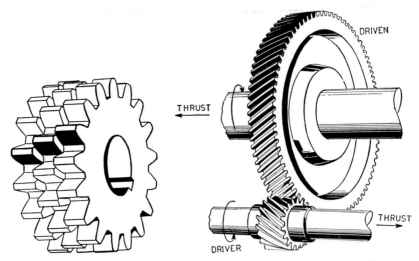

Fig. 9.24.   (Courtesy of So-
cony Vacuum Oil Co.)

Fig. 9.25.   (Courtesy of Socony-Vacuum
Oil Co.)

Parallel helical gears, Fig. 9.25, are much more widely used than
stepped gears.   These gears can be thought of as stepped gears with
infinite numbers of parts.   A more basic way of considering these gears
is shown in Fig. 9.26.   A thin flat tape lying in the plane of action is used
to connect the base cylinders of the gears.   When the base cylinders
are rotated, the diagonal lines on the tape generate the teeth of both

gears simultaneously. The line of contact of a pair of mating teeth lies along one of these lines as it moves in the plane of action. When the tape wraps around a base cylinder the diagonal generating lines become helices.

The helix angle ψ is the angle between any helix and an element of its cylinder. In helical gears and worms, it is the pitch diameter unless otherwise specified.

The lead angle λ is the complement of the helix angle.

The lead l is the axial advance of a helix for one complete turn, as in the threads of cylindrical worms and teeth of helical gears. If the base cylinder

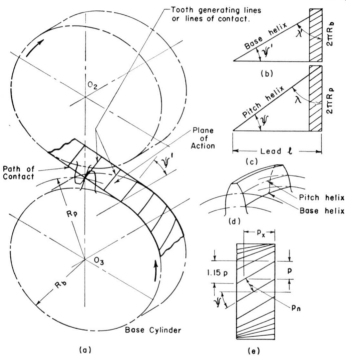

Fig. 9.26

is opened up and laid flat, the helix will appear as in Fig. 9.26(b). The helix on the pitch cylinder will appear as in (c). The relationship between the helix angles on the base and pitch cylinders is obtained from the equations

$$\tan \psi' = \frac{2\pi R_b}{l}$$

$$\tan \psi = \frac{2\pi R_p}{l}$$

and Eq. (9.2) $$R_b = R_p \cos \phi$$

giving $$\tan \psi' = \tan \psi \cos \phi \tag{9.8}$$

Parallel helical gear tooth contact is progressive. Instead of the teeth coming into contact along the entire face width, contact starts at a point on the edge and progresses across the tooth, resulting in diagonal straight-line contact. These gears have less impact loading and can be run at higher speeds than gears having straight teeth.

To gain the full advantage of helical teeth it is recommended that the tooth advance corresponding to the face width be at least 15 per cent greater than the circular pitch. This is shown at (e). Under this condition at least one pair of teeth will always be in contact at the pitch point, and the contact ratio will always be sufficiently large.

The normal circular pitch p_n is the circular pitch in the normal plane, and also the length of arc along the normal helix between helical teeth or threads.

The axial pitch p_x is the circular pitch in the axial plane and in the pitch surface between corresponding sides of adjacent teeth, in helical gears and worms.

A disadvantage of helical gears is that they produce axial thrust as shown in Fig. 9.25. This is usually not serious. If ball or tapered roller bearings are used to carry the radial load, they will usually carry the thrust also.

The designation of the hand of a helical gear is the same as that used for screws. A screw has a right-hand thread if, when held in front of an observer and turned clockwise, it moves away from the observer. In Fig 9.25 the pinion is right-hand and the gear left-hand.

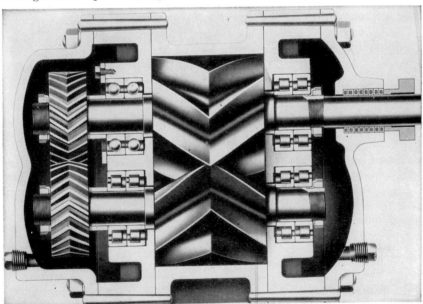

Fig. 9.27. (Courtesy of Warren Steam Pump Co.)

Thrust is eliminated in herringbone gears. They are equivalent to two helical gears of opposite hand placed side by side. The gears at the left of the pump in Fig. 9.27 are herringbone gears. The pump impellers are also herringbone gears. Pumps that are made to move fluids having lubricating qualities do not require the separate gear drive shown on the left.

9.20. Crossed helical involute gears. Crossed helical gears are used to transmit power between nonparallel, nonintersecting axes (Fig. 9.28). A pair of parallel helical gears are of opposite hand and equal helix angles. They have line contact and there is no sliding along the

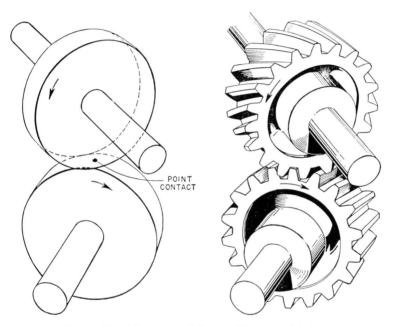

Fig. 9.28.   (Courtesy of Socony-Vacuum Oil Co.)

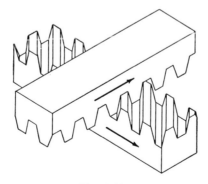

Fig. 9.29

elements of the teeth. The individual gears of a crossed helical pair are the same as parallel helical gears. When helical gears are meshed on nonparallel, nonintersecting axes, the tooth action is different. There is point contact and sliding along the elements of the teeth. Crossed helical gears are usually of the same hand and the helix angles need not be the same. A study of the action of the basic racks, Fig. 9.29, will aid in visualizing the tooth action of crossed helical gears.

In Fig. 9.30 gears 2 and 3 connect axes 2-2 and 3-3. Angles ψ_2 and ψ_3 are the helix angles of gears 2 and 3. The teeth are in contact at

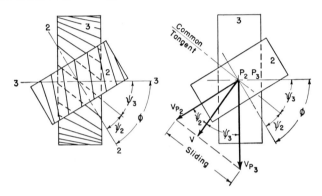

Fig. 9.30

P_2P_3. Velocity V_{p_3} is the velocity of P_3, and V_{p_2} is the velocity of P_2. These two velocities must have a common component V along the common normal. The normal circular pitches of the two gears must be equal; the circular pitches will be unequal if the helix angles are unequal.

Because of point contact, the power that can be transmitted is less than for other types of the same size having line contact. These gears are not sensitive to center distance changes. As a result of point contact the angular relationship of the axes can be changed slightly without loss of theoretically correct conjugate tooth action. When these gears are not loaded above their capacity they are generally quieter and more satisfactory than any other type of gear drive.

As with all gears, the angular velocity ratio is inversely as the number of teeth. The angular velocity ratio will be inversely as the pitch diameters only when the helix angles are equal.

Each gear of a helical pair has two distinct pitch surfaces: a pitch cylinder and a pitch plane. This is discussed in Buckingham's *Analytical Mechanics of Gears*.

9.21. Production of straight and helical spur gears.

Milling. The method of milling gears is shown in Fig. 9.31. The profiles of the milling cutter faces are that of the tooth space to be cut. A tooth space is machined by passing the gear blank across the rotating

Fig. 9.31. (Courtesy of Barber-Colman Co.)

cutter. The gear is then indexed and another tooth space is cut. Milling cutters can be sharpened by grinding the faces without changing the cutting profiles. The shapes of gear teeth vary with the number of teeth. Theoretically a different cutter should be used for each number of teeth. In practice it has been found that for a single pitch a set of 15 cutters is sufficient for cutting all gears having numbers of teeth from 12 to a rack.

Fellows Gear Shaper. The generating process is used in cutting gears on a Fellows gear shaper. The principle is illustrated in Fig. 9.32.

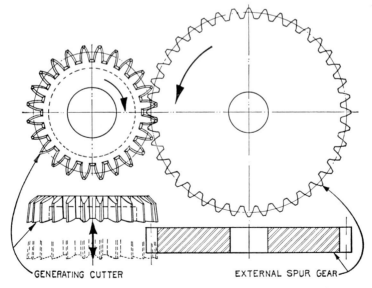

GENERATING CUTTER   EXTERNAL SPUR GEAR

Fig. 9.32. (Courtesy of The Fellows Gear Shaper Co.)

The cutting edges of the cutter are in the form of a spur gear with addendums long enough to produce the required clearance.   The cutting of a gear is started by feeding the gear blank into the reciprocating cutter until the desired depth is reached.   While the cutter continues to reciprocate, the gear blank and cutter are both rotated a small amount after each cutting stroke with a motion that is equivalent to the rolling of the pitch circles.   The manner in which a cutter tooth generates conjugate profiles is shown in Fig. 9.33.

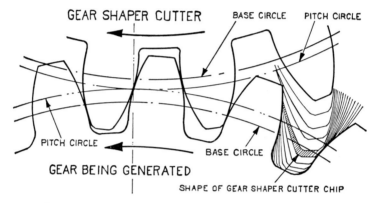

GEAR SHAPER CUTTER   BASE CIRCLE   PITCH CIRCLE

PITCH CIRCLE   BASE CIRCLE

GEAR BEING GENERATED

SHAPE OF GEAR SHAPER CUTTER CHIP

Fig. 9.33.   (Courtesy of The Fellows Gear Shaper Co.)

Helical gears can be generated with a helical cutter (Fig. 9.34).   In addition to the motions for cutting straight spur gears there is super-

Fig. 9.34.   (Courtesy of The Fellows Gear Shaper Co.)

imposed an oscillatory rolling of the cutter and gear blank pitch circles to produce the necessary helical path of the cutter relative to the gear blank.

Hobbing is the most rapid method of producing gears.   The hobbing
process is shown in Figs. 9.35 and 9.36.   In Fig. 9.35 the third gear

Fig. 9.35.   (Courtesy of Barber-Colman Co.)

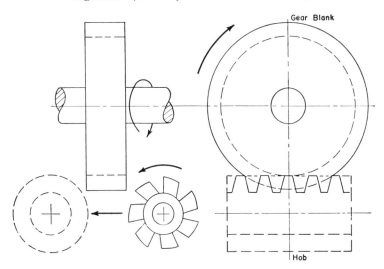

Fig. 9.36

from the left in the cluster is being generated.   The hob is similar to a
helical gear having a small number of teeth or threads, in some cases one.
Axial gashes are made to produce cutting edges.   The motions involved
in hobbing a gear are shown in Fig. 9.36.   The axes of the hob and the
gear blank are set to produce the desired helix angle.   The hob and the
gear blank are rotated with an angular velocity ratio that is inversely

as the numbers of teeth on the hob and gear.   The hob is then fed across the face of the gear.

Shaving.   Gears can be made to a high degree of accuracy by finishing them with the shaving process (Fig. 9.37).   A gear shaver is similar to

Fig. 9.37.   (Courtesy of National Broach & Machine Co.)

either a straight or helical spur gear with circumferential gashes in it to produce cutting edges.   The gear and shaver are forced together while rotating, and the gear is reciprocated along its axis.   Surface smoothness is improved, and errors of index, helix angle, tooth profile, and eccentricity are reduced by the small amount of metal that is removed in the form of needle-like chips.

Grinding is an accurate method for finishing gears.   Gears that are heat treated after rough machining can be finished by this process.   The process is shown in Fig. 9.38.   The flat side of a grinding wheel is used

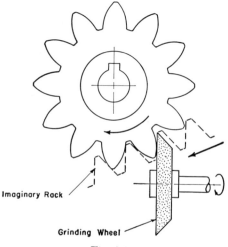

Imaginary Rack

Grinding Wheel

Fig. 9.38

to simulate a rack tooth profile.   The gear and grinding wheel are moved in a manner that is equivalent to rolling of the gear pitch circle on the rack pitch line.

9.22. Unequal-addendum gears.   The undercutting that results from the use of a small pinion and a large gear can often be eliminated by using unequal-addendum gears.   This can be understood most easily by considering a rack and pinion.   A 12-tooth pinion and rack of the full-depth 20° system is shown in Fig. 9.39(a).   If the pinion is generated

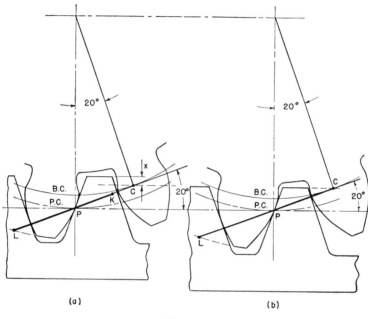

Fig. 9.39

with a rack cutter, it will be undercut as shown.   The pinion teeth are weakened.   The path of contact LK corresponds to a contact ratio of 1.049.   It can be seen that the rack tooth is too long by an amount x.   In (b) the rack has been withdrawn an amount x and the pinion addendum increased by the same amount.   The resulting conjugate pinion tooth is shown.   It is stronger, and the contact ratio has been increased to approximately 1.44.   The base circle, pitch circle, and pressure angle remain the same.

The method of cutting unequal-addendum gears with standard generating cutters is to decrease the radius of the gear blank so that interference is eliminated.   The gear teeth are cut to the standard whole depth.   The radius of the pinion blank is increased by the amount that the gear was decreased, and the teeth are cut to the standard whole depth.

9.23. Worm gears are similar to crossed helical gears. The drive shown in Fig. 9.40 is of crossed helical gears. The pinion, or worm, shown at the right has one tooth. Because the appearance of a worm is

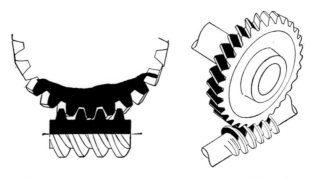

Fig. 9.40.   (Courtesy of Socony-Vacuum Oil Co.)

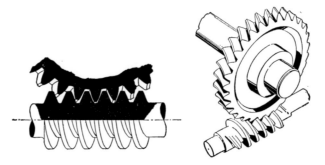

Fig. 9.41.   (Courtesy of Socony-Vacuum Oil Co.)

Fig. 9.42.   (Courtesy of Socony-Vacuum Oil Co.)

similar to that of a screw, the teeth are usually called threads. Three worms are shown in Fig. 9.43; (a) has one thread and is called a single worm, (b) has two threads and is called a double worm, (c) is a triple worm. The capacity of a worm drive can be increased by introducing line contact instead of point contact that is present in crossed helical

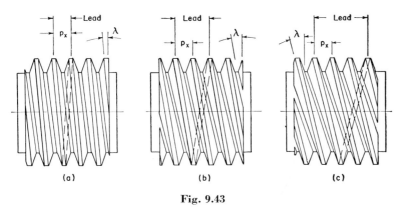

Fig. 9.43

gears. This is done by making the gear, or worm wheel, envelop the worm (Fig. 9.41). The method by which this is accomplished can be understood if the cutting process is considered (Fig. 9.44). Instead of

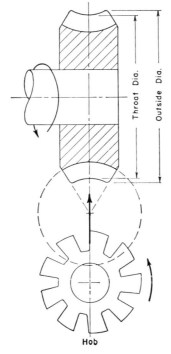

Hob

Fig. 9.44

passing the hob across the face of the gear as is done in cutting helical gears, it is fed into the face along the central plane of the gear. When a worm that is substantially the same size as the hob is meshed with the worm wheel, conjugate tooth action with line contact results.

In Fig. 9.42 both the worm and worm wheel are throated, each envelops the other. This is called a Hindley worm. The Hindley worm has the advantage that more teeth are in contact, but has the disadvantage that the axial location of the worm relative to the worm wheel must be accurately maintained or binding will result. The type shown in Figs. 9.41 and 9.45 is most widely used.

As with all gear drives the angular velocity ratio is inversely as the numbers of teeth. The lead (Fig. 9.43) is always equal to or a multiple

Fig. 9.45.   (Courtesy of The Cleveland Worm & Gear Co.)

of the pitch. The axes of most worm drives are at right angles. When this is the case the axial pitch of the worm is equal to the circular pitch of the worm wheel. The relationships of Fig. 9.26(b) and (c) apply to the worms of Fig. 9.43.

Worm drives form compact units, especially for large gear ratios. They are quiet and highly efficient when the lead angle of the worm is between 30° and 60°. Excessive sliding reduces the efficiency when the lead angle is small.

9.24. Bevel gears are used to connect shafts that have intersecting axes. External bevel gears and their rolling pitch cones are shown in Fig. 9.3. Rolling cones have spherical motion. Each point in a bevel gear remains a constant distance from the common apex of the cones; hence there is no sliding along the tooth elements. A pinion and a crown gear are shown in Fig. 9.46. The pitch surface of a crown gear is a plane and corresponds to a rack in spur gearing. An internal bevel gear is shown in Fig. 9.47. Due to limitations in the machining of this type of bevel gear the pitch angle cannot greatly exceed 90°.

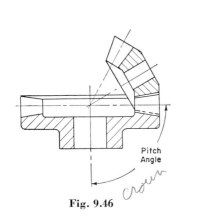

Pitch
Angle

Fig. 9.46

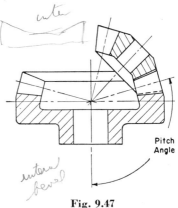

Pitch
Angle

Fig. 9.47

Bevel gear terminology is shown in Fig. 9.48. All tooth elements converge at the apex of the cone. The teeth, if extended to this point, would be difficult to cut, the small portions would not carry a large load, a more accurate alignment of the axes would be required, and the shaft could not extend through the gear. For these reasons the face width is usually limited to one-third of the cone distance.

A pair of bevel gears with equal numbers of teeth and with axes at right angles are called *miter gears*.

Involute Bevel Gears. It was shown that one of the principal advantages of involute spur gears was that an involute rack tooth has a straight profile. This does not hold for bevel gearing. An involute crown gear tooth is shown in Fig. 9.49. The base cone angle must be less than the 90° pitch angle. When the generating plane is rolled on the base cone

line of sight

a line drawn of virtual tooth business

drawn ⊥ to the pitch cone element.

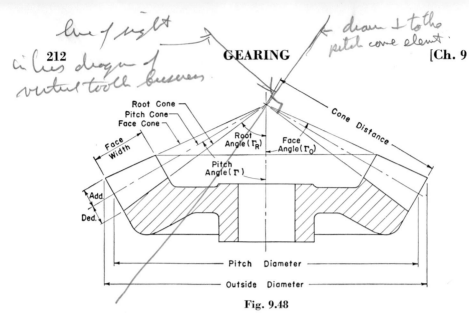

Root Cone —
Pitch Cone—
Face Cone ⌐

Face Width

Add.
Ded.

Root Angle (Γ_R)
Face Angle(Γ_O)
Pitch Angle(Γ)

Cone Distance

Pitch   Diameter
Outside   Diameter

Fig. 9.48

the generating line WV sweeps out the spherical involute tooth shown.

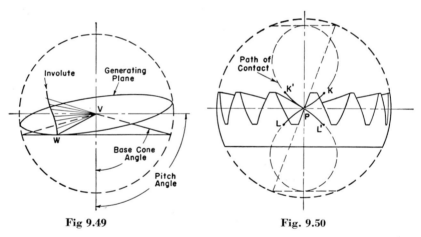

Involute   Generating Plane

V

W

Base Cone Angle

Pitch Angle

Fig 9.49

Path of Contact

K'   K

L   P   L'

Fig. 9.50

Octoid Bevel Gears are gears that are conjugate to a crown gear having teeth made with straight sides. An octoid crown gear is shown in Fig. 9.50. The sides of the teeth lie in planes that pass through the center of the sphere. When meshed with a conjugate gear the complete path of contact on the surface of a sphere is in the form of a figure 8; hence the name octoid. Only a portion of the path is used, KLP or $K'PL'$. These portions are nearly straight. Because of the symmetry of the tooth the path of contact will also be symmetrical and gears conjugate to this basic crown gear will be conjugate to each other.

Bevel Gear Tooth Action should be considered on the basis of spherical motion. Because of the difficulty of working with a spherical surface

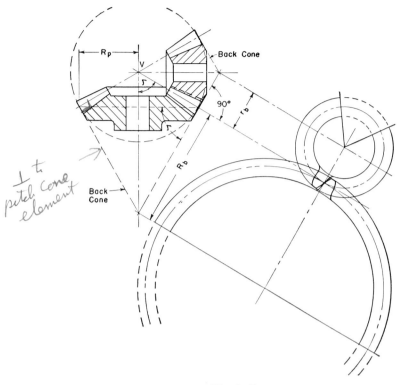

Fig. 9.51

an approximation in a plane is used. The back of the gear is usually made conical instead of spherical, Fig. 9.51. The back cones very nearly approximate the sphere in the region of tooth contact. The slight variation in distances from the center V to points on the outer ends of the meshing teeth means that they are not quite flush. This does not affect the theoretical tooth action in the least. In order to study the bevel gear tooth action the back cones are laid out flat. Each cone forms a portion of a spur gear. The pitch radii are equal to the back cone distances R_b and r_b. The flat surface is a close approximation of the spherical surface in the region of tooth contact. This is called Tredgold's approximation. The tooth action of the bevel gears is the same as the tooth action for the larger spur gears. The number of teeth N_b on the spur gear in terms of N_G, the number on the bevel gear, is

$$N_b = N_G \frac{R_b}{R_p} = \frac{N_G}{\cos \Gamma} \qquad (9.9)$$

Spiral Bevel Gears. The tooth action of spiral bevel gears, Fig. 9.52, compared with that of straight bevel gears is similar to a comparison of tooth action of helical and straight spur gears. Tooth contact begins gradually, more teeth are in contact, and there is a variety of contact.

Fig. 9.52.   (Courtesy of Socony-Vacuum Oil Co.)

A diagram for obtaining the face contact ratio is shown in Fig. 9.53(b). To gain the full advantage of the spiral tooth, the face advance should be at least 1.25 times the circular pitch.   The tooth curve is not a true spiral but a circular arc.

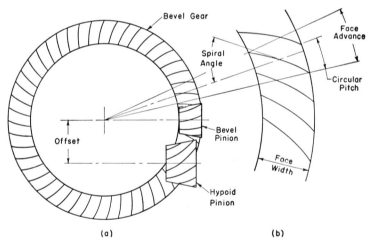

Fig. 9.53

Crown Gear Generation.   The principle of generating a straight bevel gear that is conjugate to a crown gear is illustrated in Fig. 9.54(a).   A reciprocating tool simulates one side of a crown gear tooth.   When the pitch cone of the pinion blank is rolled on the pitch surface of the crown gear, the reciprocating tool generates one side of a pinion tooth.   The motion required to roll the pitch surfaces is produced by the machine.

Spiral gear generation is shown in Fig. 9.54(b).   In this case the cutter simulates one side of a curved tooth.

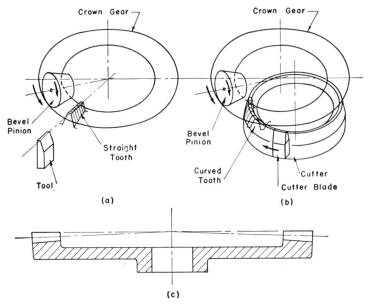

Fig. 9.54

In practice the cutters do not simulate a true crown gear tooth but an approximate crown tooth [Fig. 9.54(c)]. The tips of the cutters move in a plane. The pitch angle is slightly less than 90°. The error in tooth form that results from this approximation is negligible.

Fellows "On Center" Face Gear. Another type of bevel gear drive (Fig. 9.55) consists of an involute spur pinion and a conjugate face gear.

Fig. 9.55.   (Courtesy of The Fellows Gear Shaper Co.)

The method of generation is shown in Fig. 9.56. This is similar to spur gear generation; the cutter reciprocates, and the rotations of cutter and face gear are inversely as their numbers of teeth. When a pinion of

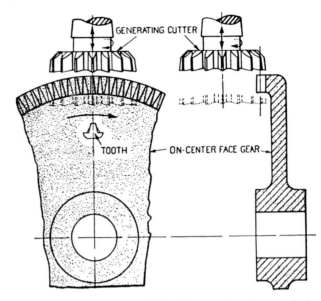

GENERATING CUTTER

TOOTH

ON-CENTER FACE GEAR

Fig. 9.56.   (Courtesy of The Fellows Gear Shaper Co.)

substantially the same size as the cutter is meshed with the face gear, conjugate tooth action results.

The pitch surfaces are rolling cones, Fig. 9.57.   The portion of the line of contact of the pitch cones between P and P' is the locus of the pitch points.   The common normal at any point of contact of meshing teeth passes through this line of contact.   This results from a variable pressure angle across the face of the gear.   It is a maximum at r_0, as is shown at (b).   The common normal is tangent to the pinion base circle of radius r_b and passes through pitch point P.   The pressure angle is a minimum at r_i as shown at (c).   The common normal is tangent to the pinion base circle and passes through pitch point P'.

It was shown in Art. 9.16 that an involute spur gear does not have a pitch circle until it is meshed with another gear.   The following general statement is also true: *no single gear has a pitch surface.   The pitch surfaces do not exist until two gears are meshed together.*

If, in Fig. 9.56, a helical cutter is used, a helical pinion of substantially the same size as the cutter will mesh with the face gear and conjugate tooth action will result.   The pitch surfaces will be cones as before.

The Fellows face gear drive can be made for axes that intersect at any angle.

9.25. Hypoid gears.   Hypoid gears are used to connect nonparallel, nonintersecting axes.   The pitch surfaces are hyperboloids of revolution as described in Art. 8.6.   The line of contact of the two hyperboloidal pitch surfaces is the locus of the pitch points.   There is sliding along the

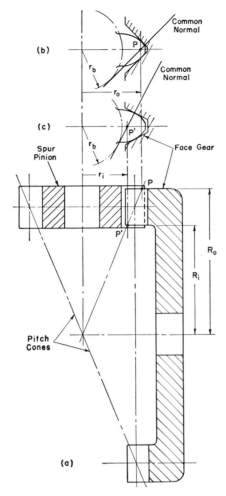

Fig. 9.57

line of contact of rolling hyperboloids; hence there is sliding along the tooth elements of hypoid gears.

Theoretically it is possible to develop an interchangeable tooth system for hypoid gears. In practice only those gears that can be conveniently cut are produced. At the present time all hypoid gear sets consist of a pair, one of which, within reasonable limits, is arbitrarily chosen and the other is made conjugate to the chosen one.

The Fellows "Off Center" Face Gear, Fig. 9.58, is one of the simplest hypoid gear sets to produce. The axis of the cutter is offset as shown; with the exception of this offset, the generation is the same as in Fig. 9.56. When a pinion of substantially the same size as the cutter is meshed

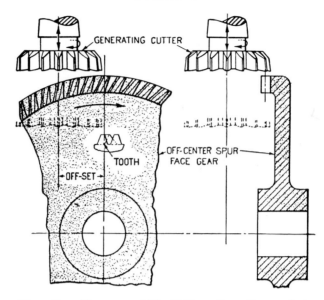

Fig. 9.58. (Courtesy of The Fellows Gear Shaper Co.)

with the off-center face gear, a hypoid pair having hyperboloidal pitch surfaces is formed.

Bevel Type Hypoid Gears Are the Most Widely Used. A pair consists of a bevel gear and a conjugate pinion. When these two are meshed, hyperboloidal pitch surfaces are formed. The generation of a hypoid pinion is similar to the generation of a bevel pinion. Some additional adjustments are required on the gear-cutting machine.

A bevel gear and conjugate bevel pinion are shown in Fig. 9.53(a). A conjugate hypoid pinion having the same number of teeth as the bevel pinion, when offset in the direction that increases the spiral angle, has a larger diameter. A hypoid set of this type is shown in an automobile drive, Fig. 11.12.

9.26. Noncircular gears are used to produce a variable angular velocity ratio. Noncircular rolling curves were discussed in Chapter 8. If rolling curves are used for pitch curves, toothed gears can be made to produce motion that is equivalent to that of the rolling curves. The fundamental law for noncircular gears is: *the common normal of teeth in contact must pass through the point on the line of centers where the pitch curves are tangent.* The law for circular gearing is a special case of this general law, for circular gears the point is fixed. Noncircular gears would be more widely used if they could be produced more economically.

The gears in Fig. 9.59 were generated with a Fellows cutter. A cam was used to produce rolling of the pitch circle of the cutter on the pitch

Fig. 9.59.   (Courtesy of Miehle Printing Press & Mfg. Co.)

curve of the noncircular gear.   The design and production of this type
of gear has been described in a paper by Golber.*

PROBLEMS

9.1. A pair of meshing spur gears have 17 and 32 teeth, respectively.   The
diametral pitch is 8 and the pinion speed is 1160 rpm.   Determine the following:
(a) pitch diameters, (b) center distance, (c) circular pitch, (d) pitch line velocity
in fps, (e) rpm of gear.

9.2. Same as Prob. 9.1 except 15 and 40 teeth, 10 diametral pitch, pinion speed
1800 rpm.

9.3. A pair of spur gears have a diametral pitch of 10, a velocity ratio of 2.5,
and a center distance of 3.5 in.   Determine the number of teeth on each gear.

9.4. A pair of spur gears have 16 and 22 teeth, 2 diametral pitch, $\frac{1}{2}$ in. addendum, $\frac{9}{16}$ in. dedendum, and 20° pressure angle.   The pinion drives in a CCW direc-

* Golber, H. E., "Rollcurve Gears," *Trans. ASME*, 1939, 61:223.

tion. Determine the following: (a) pitch circle radii, (b) base circle radii, (c) circular pitch, (d) base pitch, (e) length of path of contact, (f) contact ratio, (g) angles of approach and recess for driver and follower. Indicate the pitch point and the first and last points of contact.

9.5. Same as Prob. 9.4, except 13 and 17 teeth, $1\frac{1}{2}$ diametral pitch, $\frac{9}{16}$ in. addendum, $\frac{5}{8}$ in. dedendum, and $22\frac{1}{2}°$ pressure angle. The pinion is the driver in a CW direction.

9.6. Same as Prob. 9.4, except the pinion is replaced with a rack. The gear drives in a CCW direction.

9.7. Same as Prob. 9.5, except the pinion is replaced with a rack. The gear drives in a CW direction.

9.8. The diametral pitch of a rack is 2 and the addendum is $\frac{1}{2}$ in. Determine the smallest pinion that will mesh with a rack without interference when the pressure angle is (a) $14\frac{1}{2}°$, (b) $20°$, (c) $22\frac{1}{2}°$.

9.9. A pair of gears have 14 and 16 teeth, the diametral pitch is 2, the addendum is $\frac{1}{2}$ in., and the pressure angle is $14\frac{1}{2}°$. Show that the gears have interference. Determine graphically the amounts of the addendums of the gears that must be removed if interference is to be eliminated. Determine the contact ratio for this new condition.

9.10. Same as Prob. 9.9, except that the gears have 12 and 18 teeth.

9.11. A gear has 30 teeth, 3 diametral pitch, $\frac{3}{8}$ in. addendum, and $20°$ pressure angle. Determine (a) the smallest pinion that will mesh with the gear without interference, (b) the contact ratio.

9.12. A gear has 26 teeth, 2 diametral pitch, $\frac{7}{16}$ in. addendum, and $22\frac{1}{2}°$ pressure angle. Determine (a) the smallest pinion that will mesh with the gear without interference, (b) the contact ratio.

9.13. A pair of gears have 24 and 36 teeth, 6 diametral pitch, and $20°$ pressure angle. Determine the center distance of the axes. The center distance is increased 0.12 in. Determine the pressure angle that corresponds to the new center distance.

9.14. Same as Prob. 9.13 except 30 and 40 teeth, 8 diametral pitch, and $14\frac{1}{2}°$ pressure angle.

9.15. For a gear having a 6 diametral pitch, determine the addendum, dedendum, and clearance for the following systems: $14\frac{1}{2}°$ composite, $14\frac{1}{2}°$ full depth, $20°$ full depth, $20°$ stub, Fellows stub.

9.16. Same as Prob. 9.15, except the diametral pitch is 4.

9.17. A 24-tooth helical spur gear has a diametral pitch in the plane of rotation of 8, and a face width of 1.25 in. The tooth advance is 1.15 times the circular pitch. Determine: (a) pitch helix angle, (b) lead, (c) axial pitch, (d) normal pitch, (e) pitch diameter.

9.18. An 18-tooth helical spur gear has a diametral pitch in the plane of rotation of 6, a face width of 1.5 in. and a helix angle of $23°$. Determine the (a) tooth advance in terms of the circular pitch, (b) axial pitch, (c) normal pitch, (d) lead, (e) pitch diameter.

9.19. A pair of helical gears have 20 and 30 teeth. The pinion speed is 900 rpm and the normal diametral pitch is 8. The pinion is left-hand and the helix angle is 30°. The gear is left-hand and the helix is 40°. Determine: (a) angular relationship of the axes, (b) circular pitches in the planes of rotation, (c) pitch diameters, (d) velocity of sliding in the tangent plane when the gears are in contact at the pitch point. (*Note:* The relationship between the diametral pitch and the normal pitch is the same as for the diametral pitch and circular pitch in the plane of rotation, i.e., the product of the normal pitch and normal diametral pitch is π.)

9.20. A pair of gears are to have 9 and 36 teeth. They are to be cut with a 20° full depth cutter of 3 diametral pitch.

(a) Determine the amount that the addendum of the gear must be decreased in order to eliminate interference.

(b) The addendum of the pinion is to be increased the same amount. Determine the contact ratio.

9.21. A double-thread worm drives a gear having 58 teeth. The axes are at 90°. The axial pitch of the worm is $1\frac{1}{4}$ in. and the pitch diameter is 3 in. Determine the helix angle of the worm, the lead, and the center distance of the gears.

9.22. The relationship of the axes of a worm and gear are shown in Fig. P 9.22. The right-hand triple worm has an axial pitch of $\frac{1}{2}$ in. and a pitch diameter of 3 in. The gear has 40 teeth. Determine the circular pitch, helix angle, and pitch diameter of the gear.

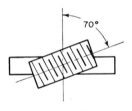

70°

Fig. P 9.22

9.23. A pair of bevel gears have 20 and 40 teeth. The diametral pitch is 5 and the axes are 90°. The addendum and dedendum are the same as for 20° involute stub teeth. Determine the following for the gear: (a) pitch angle, (b) face angle, (c) root angle, (d) pitch diameter, (e) outside diameter, (f) cone distance, (g) formative radius, (h) formative number of teeth.

9.24. Same as Prob. 9.23, except gears have 20 and 60 teeth and the diametral pitch is 4.

CHAPTER 10

Flexible Connectors

10.1. Introductory. Belts, chains, and ropes are common members of this class of links. Some of these can be used in three-dimensional drives. They are usually used in tension, although there is one notable exception, the use of flexible cables in torsion.

There are two types of flexible connectors:

1. Connectors that obtain their flexibility from distortion of the material; for example, belts, ropes, and thin steel bands. Motion is usually transmitted by means of friction.

2. Connectors made from small rigid parts that are joined in such a manner as to permit relative motion of the parts; for example, chains. Motion is usually transmitted by positive means.

They can also be classified according to use in three major groups:

1. Hoisting
2. Conveyors
3. Power transmission

10.2. Flat belts. The replacement of central power sources in shops with individual motor drives has reduced the use of flat belts. These belts still have a place in power transmission, especially for large center distances.

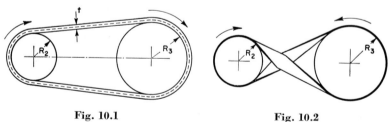

Fig. 10.1   Fig. 10.2

Belt drives can be either of the open or crossed type, Figs. 10.1 and 10.2. The pulleys of an open belt drive rotate in the same direction, and pulleys of the crossed belt drive rotate in opposite directions. When a belt is bent around a pulley the outer fibers are in tension and the inner

fibers in compression. The neutral axis is approximately at the center.
The angular velocity ratio of the pulleys is (Art. 2.12)

$$\frac{\omega_2}{\omega_3} = \frac{R_3 + t/2}{R_2 + t/2} \cong \frac{R_3}{R_2} \tag{10.1}$$

Since the belt thickness is small in comparison with the pulley radius it
is usually neglected.

In order to design and specify a belt drive it is necessary to determine
the angles of contact and the belt length.   These can be found as follows:

Open belt (Fig. 10.3)

$$\phi = \frac{1}{57.2}\sin^{-1}\frac{R_3 - R_2}{C}, \quad K = C\cos\phi, \quad \begin{array}{l} \theta_2 = \pi - 2\phi \\ \theta_3 = \pi + 2\phi \end{array}$$

where ϕ and θ are in radians.

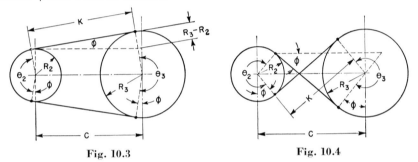

Fig. 10.3   Fig. 10.4

The length of the belt is the sum of the two arcs of contact and $2K$.

$$\text{length} = \theta_2 R_2 + \theta_3 R_3 + 2C\cos\phi \tag{10.2}$$

Crossed belt (Fig. 10.4)

$$\phi = \frac{1}{57.2}\sin^{-1}\frac{R_3 + R_2}{C}, \quad K = C\cos\phi, \quad \theta_2 = \theta_3 = \pi + 2\phi$$

$$\text{length} = \theta_2(R_2 + R_3) + 2C\cos\phi \tag{10.3}$$

Like all friction drives the transmission of motion is not positive.
In addition to slipping as it is usually thought of there is another type
called creep.   The belt on the tight side stretches more than on the loose
side.   An element of belt becomes shorter as it passes around the driver
from the tight to the loose side and becomes longer when it passes around
the follower from the loose to the tight side.   This is always present and
causes the follower to turn at a lower speed.   In an average drive the
combined slip and creep is 2 to 4 per cent of the ideal speed.

A flat belt will work off a pulley during operation unless means are
taken to keep it centered.   The most common method is to crown one
or both pulleys.   The surface of a crowned pulley (Fig. 10.5) consists
of the frustra of two cones with their common base at the center.   A belt
when placed on one side of a crowned pulley and subjected to tension will
take the form shown.   When the pulley is rotated one-quarter turn the

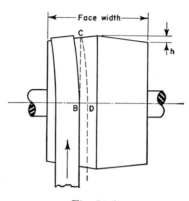

Fig. 10.5

friction between the belt and pulley will move point B on the belt to C. The edge of the belt will lie along line CD. Further rotation will carry the belt to the center of the pulley. If the belt on a moving pulley is forced to one side and then released, it will very quickly climb to the center. The crowning, indicated as h, is usually $\frac{1}{8}$ to $\frac{1}{4}$ in. per foot of width of the pulley face.

10.3. Flat belts connecting nonparallel shafts. The law of belting requires that the center line of the belt on the side approaching the pulley must lie in the plane of the pulley. A quarter-turn belt is shown in Fig. 10.6. For the directions of rotation shown, the law of belting is fulfilled. If the directions are reversed, the belt will not stay on the pulleys. If a quarter turn belt is to operate in either direction

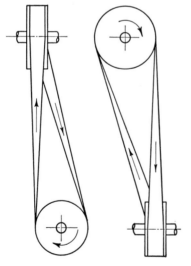

Fig. 10.6

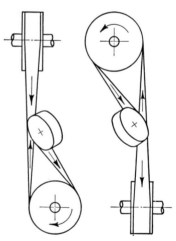

Fig. 10.7

(Fig. 10.7), a guide pulley must be used.   This pulley must be properly placed so that the law will be fulfilled for either direction of rotation.

Any two pulleys in space can be connected with a flat belt if a sufficient number of properly spaced guide pulleys are used.

10.4. V-Belts.   The cross section of a V-belt is trapezoidal.   A typical section is shown in Fig. 10.8(a).   In order to utilize the advantages of a V-belt the groove should be deep enough so that the belt does not bottom in the groove.   This produces a wedging action and the belt will transmit power with very little initial tension.   This permits the use of short center distances, and frequent adjustments are not required.

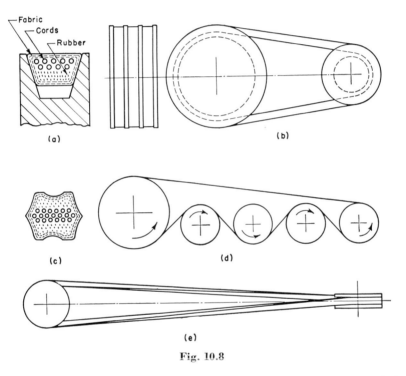

Fig. 10.8

V-belts are usually made endless, the several components being vulcanized in a mold.   If one belt will not transmit the power, two or more can be used in parallel.   When it is necessary to replace one belt the entire set should be replaced.   A new belt when used with worn belts will carry more than its share of the load.

If both sides of a belt are to be used for driving, the type shown at (c) should be used.

A V-belt can be used on a quarter-turn drive [Fig. 10.8(e)] if the speed ratio is not greater than 2.4:1 and the center distance is 6 to $6\frac{1}{2}$ times the diameter of the larger pulley.

10.5. Roller chains are used principally for power transmission. A section of chain is shown in Fig. 10.9. The pin is fastened to the outer set of links so that it does not rotate relative to them. The bushing is fastened to the inner links. This insures that the only sliding in the joint will be that due to the pin turning in the bushing. The area of contact is large and the wear is slight. The hardened steel roller is free to turn on the bushing.

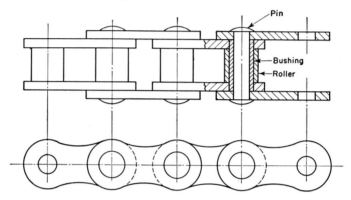

Fig. 10.9

If a single-strand chain does not have the required capacity, a multiple-strand chain can be used. These are equivalent to two or more single strands placed side by side, with long pins passing through the entire width of the chain.

The seating of a roller chain on a sprocket is shown in Fig. 10.10. When the chain is new the rollers seat at the bottom of the tooth spaces. As the chain wears the pitch becomes longer. The tooth profiles are made so that the force of the sprocket on the roller has a component

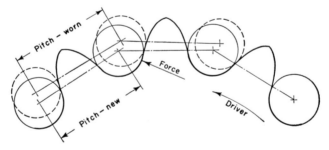

Fig. 10.10

radially outward. This force causes a worn chain to take a position on the sprocket teeth that corresponds to the worn pitch. This distributes the load among all the teeth that are in contact with the chain.

Roller chains can be used for drives similar to that in Fig. 10.8(d).

10.6. Impact loading. It was shown in the chapter on gearing that theoretically correct gear teeth come into contact without impact.

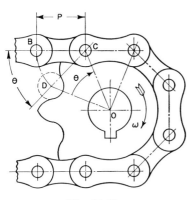

Fig. 10.11

Because of inaccuracies in machining and deflections there is always some impact. This can be reduced by using gears made with a high degree of accuracy. In roller chains, impact loading is inherent in the design. The impact velocity between a chain roller and a sprocket can be determined using Fig. 10.11. When the sprocket turns with uniform angular velocity through angle θ, link BC rotates relative to the sprocket through angle θ with velocity ω and strikes the sprocket. This can be seen if inversion is considered. The sprocket is fixed and the chain is wrapped around it with angular velocity ω. The impact velocity is the velocity of B along the arc BD. It is

$$V = R\omega = \frac{P}{12}\,\omega = \frac{\pi P N}{6} \text{ fps}$$

where P is the pitch in inches and N is the speed of the sprocket in revolutions per second. The presence of impact loading is one reason why chains with large pitches cannot be operated at high speeds.

10.7. Chordal action. In general the sprockets of a chain drive do not have a constant angular velocity ratio, and the linear velocity of the chain is not constant. This is because the chain does not wrap around the sprocket in the form of a pitch circle, but in the form of a pitch polygon. It was shown in the previous article that this also produced impact loading.

Two 6-tooth sprockets and a chain are shown in Fig. 10.12. For a constant ω the linear velocity of the chain for the phase shown with solid lines is $V = R\omega$ and for the phase shown with broken lines is $V = R\omega \cos 30°$. The centerline of the chain on the driving side remains

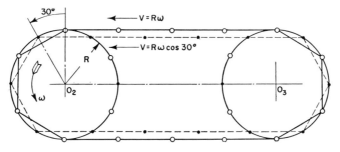

Fig. 10.12

parallel to the line of the centers for all phases, and the angular velocity ratio of the two sprockets is constant.

Chordal action is more pronounced with sprockets having a small number of teeth. The per cent variation in chain velocity, (100 C/R), for sprockets having different numbers of teeth is shown in Fig. 10.13.

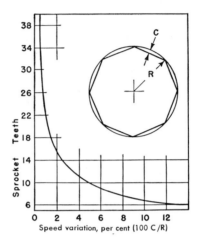

Fig. 10.13

When it is necessary to use small sprockets those with an odd number of teeth are usually selected. When the chain velocity is increasing on one side it is decreasing on the other. The inertia forces on the two sides tend to balance each other.

Unequal sprockets are shown in Fig. 10.14. In addition to a variable chain velocity the angular velocity ratio of the sprockets is not constant.

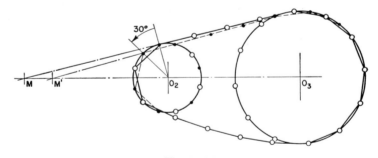

Fig. 10.14

The line of transmission cuts the line of center at different points. Two locations, M and M', are shown.

10.8. Silent or inverted tooth chains are used for power transmission. A Morse Hy-Vo silent chain drive is shown in Fig. 10.15 and

Fig. 10.15. (Courtesy of Morse Chain Co.)

a conventional Morse silent chain and sprocket is shown in Fig. 10.16. A rocker joint consisting of two parts A and B is used. Each part is

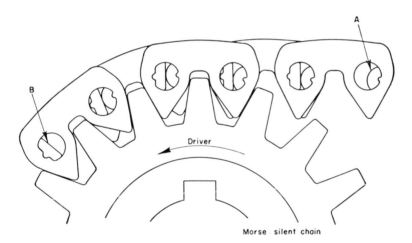

Driver

Morse silent chain

Fig. 10.16

fixed relative to one set of links. When a joint is flexed there is approximate rolling of A on B. The joint of a Link Belt chain is shown in Fig. 10.17. Two partial bushings and a cylindrical pin are used. One bushing is fixed relative to one set of links and the other bushing is fixed relative to the other set of links. When a joint is flexed the only sliding that occurs is between the bushings and the pin. Compared with a pin only, this arrangement nearly doubles the area of contact and provides a single area that facilitates lubrication.

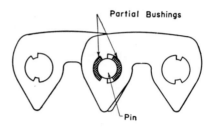

Partial Bushings

Pin

Fig. 10.17

In many silent chain drives chordal action is present. In some designs it has been practically eliminated. One such chain is made by the Link Belt Company, Fig. 10.18. The chain profiles are curved to produce

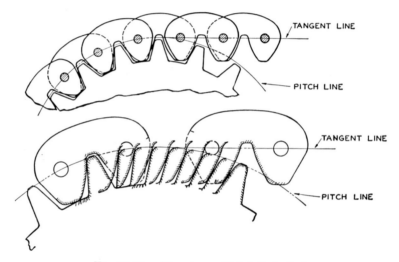

TANGENT LINE

PITCH LINE

TANGENT LINE

PITCH LINE

Fig. 10.18.   (Courtesy of Link-Belt Co.)

gradual seating and to hold the tangent line in a fixed position. A series of positions are shown to illustrate the seating of a link. The determination of these contours is somewhat analogous to designing a conjugate rack and pinion. Another type that has very little chordal action is the Morse Hy-Vo. In this drive the chain profiles are straight and the sprocket teeth are involute. A comparison of a roller chain (top) and a Hy-Vo chain (bottom) is shown in Fig. 10.19. Both chains are 2 in. pitch and are operating at a speed of 3600 fpm.

10.9. Bead chains. A three-dimensional bead chain drive is shown in Fig. 10.20. The beads in these chains range in size from $\frac{3}{32}$ to $\frac{3}{8}$ in. in diameter. The range of tensile strength is from 18 to 185 pounds. They are used in applications where a positive drive is desired and the load is small, as for example, in business machines. These drives are inexpensive.

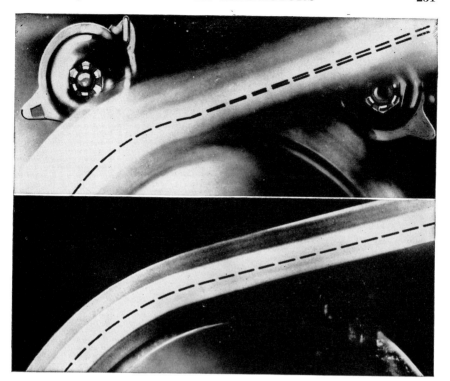

Fig. 10.19.   (Courtesy of Morse Chain Co.)

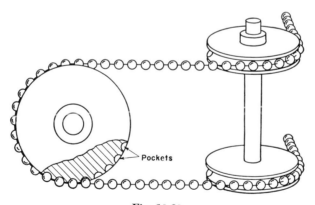

Pockets

Fig. 10.20

10.10. Conveyor chains. There are many types of conveyor chains, two of which are shown in Fig. 10.21.   The Ewart detachable link chain is shown at (b); one link is shown in a partially assembled position.   These links are malleable castings.   The Ewart link at (a) is made from strip steel.   It is one of the many types of attachment links. A pintle chain is shown at (c).

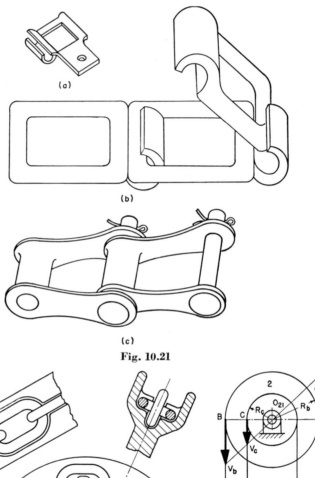

(a)

(b)

(c)

Fig. 10.21

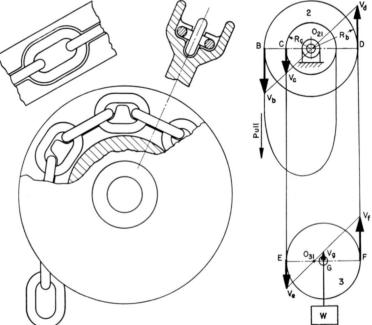

Fig. 10.22

10.11. Differential chain hoist. A differential hoist using coil chain is shown in Fig. 10.22. The manner in which the links engage the sprocket is shown at the left. A load W is raised by pulling on the chain indicated. The two sprockets at the top are fastened together and form a compound sprocket. The circumference of the pitch polygon of the larger sprocket is $N_B P$, where N_B is the number of the pitches and P is the pitch. The circumference of the smaller sprocket is $N_C P$. When the compound sprocket is turned once, the chain that supports the lower pulley is shortened the amount $(N_B - N_C)P$. The movable pulley is supported by two chains; hence the lift is $\frac{1}{2}(N_B - N_C)P$. The mechanical advantage is

$$\text{M. A.} = \frac{N_B P}{\frac{1}{2}(N_B - N_C)P} = \frac{2}{(1 - N_C/N_B)}$$

The mechanical advantage can also be determined by the use of velocity vectors (Art. 4.4), where V_b is the assumed input velocity. Velocities V_c and V_d are determined and then transferred to E and F. Velocity V_g is the upward velocity of the weight. The mechanical advantage is V_b/V_g.

10.12. Variable-speed drives. One of the simplest types of variable speed drives is shown in Fig. 10.23. The sides of each pulley can be moved axially relative to each other. This produces variable-pitch

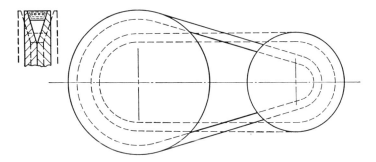

Fig. 10.23

pulleys. Two positions for the belt are shown. V-belts that are standard except for their extra width are made for use in this type of drive. The extra width makes a wider speed range possible.

The Link Belt Company's P.I.V. (Positive Infinitely Variable) drive is shown in Fig. 10.24. The conical surfaces of the sprockets are fluted, the ridges on one side being opposite grooves on the other. Each link in the chain contains a stack of thin flat steel strips that are free to move perpendicularly to the length of the chain. As the chain engages the sprockets, the ridges on one side push strips into the grooves on the opposite side, making a positive drive. The hand wheel at the left

Fig. 10.24.   (Courtesy of Link-Belt Co.)

controls the speed ratio.   The sprocket halves are mounted in such a way that when one pair is moved closer together the other pair moves farther apart.

PROBLEMS

10.1. The diameter of the small pulley of an open belt drive is 10 in., the rpm is 900, and that of the large pulley is 300.   The center distance is 8 ft.   Neglect slip and creep.   Determine: (a) diameter of the large pulley, (b) belt speed, (c) angles of belt contact on the two pulleys, (d) length of belt.

10.2. Same as Prob. 10.1, except rpm of large pulley is 250 and center distance is 6.5 ft.

10.3. Same as Prob. 10.1, except belt is crossed.

10.4. Same as Prob. 10.2, except belt is crossed.

10.5. Same as Prob. 10.1, except the combined slip and creep is assumed to be 3%.

10.6. Step pulleys, Fig. P 10.6, are used to obtain different angular velocity ratios by shifting the belt. Show that a single crossed belt that fits on one pair will fit on any pair if $D_1 + d_1 = D_2 + d_2 = D_3 + d_3 =$ constant. (This is not true for an open belt. A graphical solution for this type of drive is given in the Marks *Handbook*.)

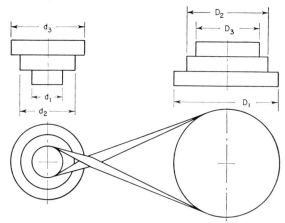

Fig. P 10.6

10.7. A 0.75-in. pitch roller chain engages two sprockets, each having 10 teeth. The driver turns with a constant speed of 1200 rpm.

(a) Determine the maximum, minimum, and average linear speed of the chain. This is the horizontal speed in Fig. P 10.7 (a). Use the circumference of the pitch polygon to determine the average linear speed.

(b) Determine the impact velocity between sprocket and chain.

(c) Show that the linear velocity-time curve consists of portions of sine curves as shown at (b). Determine the maximum horizontal acceleration of the chain. Determine a time interval t_1. Note that the chain also has vertical velocity and acceleration. Values can be determined in the same manner as above. If whip of the chain is neglected, the analysis can be made using the equivalent 4-bar linkage shown at (c).

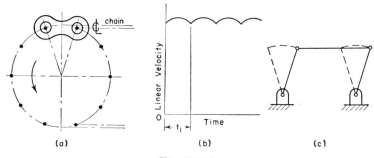

Fig. P 10.7

10.8. Same as Prob. 10.7, except pitch is 0.625 in., number of sprocket teeth is 9, rpm is 1400.

10.9. The compound sprocket of a differential chain hoist has 20 and 22 teeth. Assuming a pull on the hand chain of 150 lb and 100% efficiency, determine the weight that can be lifted.

10.10. The compound sprocket of a differential chain hoist has 15 and 16 teeth. The load to be lifted is 1800 lb and the efficiency is 100%. Determine the required pull on the hand chain.

10.11. All of the tape of a tape recorder is on the left spool as shown in Fig. P 10.11. The right spool will turn faster than the left spool until half of the tape is on each spool. Determine the number of turns that the right spool will make in attaining this condition, and the difference in the number of turns of the right and left spools.

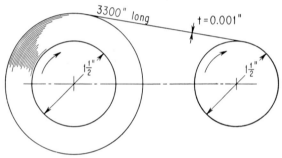

Fig. P 10.11

CHAPTER 11

Gear Trains, Translation Screws

11.1. Definitions. Two or more gears form a gear train when they are used to transmit motion from one shaft to another. Belts, chains, and screws are often used in conjunction with gear trains and are considered a part of the train. There are two types of gear trains, ordinary and epicyclic. The axes of all gears of an ordinary gear train are fixed relative to the frame. In the epicyclic train the axis of at least one gear moves in the path of a circle.

The angular velocity ratio of any pair of meshing gears is always inversely as the numbers of teeth. In general, when there is sliding along the tooth elements as in worm, helical, and hypoid gears, the angular velocities are not inversely as the diameters. If gears having parallel axes rotate in the same direction, the ratio is positive, if in opposite directions, it is negative.

11.2. Ordinary gear trains are of two types, simple and compound. In a simple train, Fig. 11.1, there is only one gear on each axis. Gear *A*

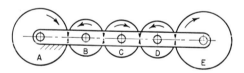

Fig. 11.1

drives *B*, *B* drives *C*, *C* drives *D*, and *D* drives *E*. The pitch line velocities of all gears are the same. The angular velocity ratio of *A* to *E* is inversely as the numbers of teeth on *A* and *E*. Gears *B*, *C*, and *D* are called idler gears. They are used for two purposes: to control the directional relationship of *A* and *E* and to make possible a large center distance without the use of large gears. A train similar to Fig. 11.1 has been used in opposed-piston Diesels for connecting the two crankshafts. The easiest way to keep track of directions is to draw directional arrows on the gears.

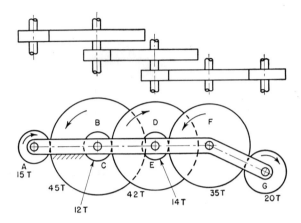

Fig. 11.2

A compound train has one or more shafts with two gears (Fig. 11.2). If the speed of A is 1200 rpm CW, the speeds of the other shafts will be

$$\omega_B = 1200 \times \tfrac{15}{45} = 400 \text{ rpm CCW}$$

$$\omega_D = 400 \times \tfrac{12}{42} = 114 \text{ rpm CW}$$

$$\omega_F = 114 \times \tfrac{14}{35} = 45.6 \text{ rpm CCW}$$

$$\omega_G = 45.6 \times \tfrac{35}{20} = 80 \text{ rpm CW}$$

The train value is the ratio of the speeds of the first and last shafts. In this case it is

$$e = \frac{-1200}{-80} = +15$$

The train value can be found from the products of the ratios of all pairs of gears. It is

$$e = \frac{\text{product of numbers of teeth on driven gears}}{\text{product of numbers of teeth on driving gears}}$$

$$= \left(\tfrac{45}{15}\right)\left(\tfrac{42}{12}\right)\left(\tfrac{35}{14}\right)\left(\tfrac{20}{35}\right) = +15$$

The idler F serves as both a driver and driven gear. Its only effect on the train value is on the sign.

11.3. Automobile transmission. A typical three-speed transmission is shown in Fig. 11.3. When the input and output shafts are coaxial, as is the case here, the train is called a reverted train. Gear A turns with the engine shaft. Gears B, C, E, and G are made in one unit or are rigidly fastened to the countershaft. Gear H is an idler that meshes with G. These gears are always in motion when the shaft to engine is in motion. Gears D and F can slide axially on the spline shaft to rear wheels. The transmission is shown in neutral, so that there is no connection between the shaft to engine and shaft to rear wheels.

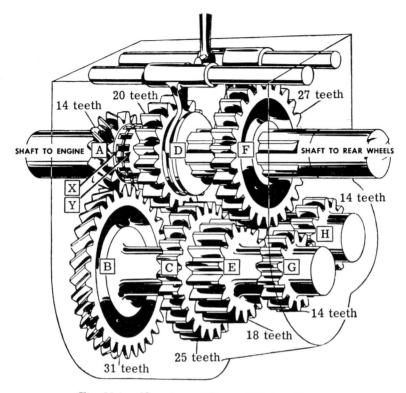

14 teeth 20 teeth 27 teeth

SHAFT TO ENGINE A D F SHAFT TO REAR WHEELS

X
Y

14 teeth

H

B C E G

14 teeth

18 teeth

25 teeth

31 teeth

Fig. 11.3. (Courtesy of General Motors Corp.)

For low or first speed, F is shifted to the left and meshes with E. The train value of $ABEF$ is

$$e = \tfrac{31}{14} \times \tfrac{27}{18} = 3.32$$

For second or intermediate speed, D is shifted to the right and meshes with C. The train value of $ABCD$ is

$$e = \tfrac{31}{14} \times \tfrac{20}{25} = 1.77$$

Gear A is made with a jaw clutch face X and D with clutch face Y. For high or third speed D is shifted to the left, engaging X and Y. This gives a direct drive with velocity ratio of 1.

For reverse F is shifted to the right and engages with idler H. The ratio of the drive through $ABGHF$ is

$$\tfrac{31}{14} \times \tfrac{14}{14} \times \tfrac{27}{14} = -4.27$$

11.4. Epicyclic gear trains are also called planetary gear trains. The gear at the center is called the sun, and the gears that have moving axes are called planets. A few words about the movement of the earth will help in understanding epicyclic gear trains. The earth turns on its axis $366\tfrac{1}{4}$ times in one year. A sidereal day has 23 hours, 56 minutes,

4.09 seconds of mean solar time.   An astronomer when tracking a star in space must set his telescope to rotate at the rate of one revolution per sidereal day.   When tracking the sun he sets it to rotate at one revolution in a solar day or 24 hours.

If the earth had no rotation about its own axis relative to the universe but still moved around the sun in the manner of a ferris wheel car, there would be one day in a year.   This is shown in Fig. 11.4.   Here O is an

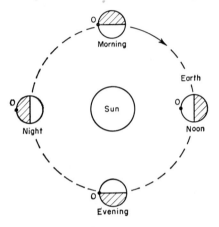

Fig. 11.4

observer on the earth.   If the earth turned on its axis in the opposite direction or went around the sun in the opposite direction there would be $367\frac{1}{4}$ days in a year instead of $365\frac{1}{4}$.   The absolute rotation would still be $366\frac{1}{4}$ turns a year.   The principle of relative motion that is involved here appears in the calculations of every epicyclic gear train.

In Fig. 11.5(a) gear C is attached to an arm.   If the gear does not turn relative to the arm and the arm is turned one revolution, the gear will also turn once in the same direction, $i.e.$, the gear makes one absolute

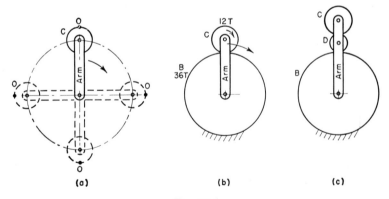

Fig. 11.5

turn.   At (b) gear C of 12 teeth meshes with the fixed gear B of 36 teeth.
Gear C is free to turn relative to the arm.   If the arm is rotated once in
a negative (CW) direction, C will roll on the outside of B and make
$\frac{36}{12} = 3$ turns relative to the arm in a CW direction.   But the arm has
also made one CW turn.   Hence the absolute turns of C is $-3 - 1 = -4$.
At (c) an idler gear D is placed between B and C.   When the arm is
rotated once CW, gear C makes 3 CCW turns relative to the arm.   The
absolute turns of C is then

$$+3 - 1 = +2$$

It is possible to solve epicyclic gear train problems step by step using
this type of reasoning.   Most problems become so involved that it is
almost impossible to prevent errors.   It is desirable to develop a simple
general method that can be applied in all cases.   Equation (11.1)
expresses a relationship that is easy to apply.

$$e = \frac{n_f - a}{n_l - a} \tag{11.1}$$

where n_f = number of absolute turns of the first gear in the train
$\quad\quad n_l$ = number of absolute turns of the last gear in the train
$\quad\quad a$ = number of absolute turns of the arm
$\quad\quad e$ = train value relative to the arm
It was shown in Art. 2.7 that the motion of one body relative to
a second body is the vector difference of their absolute motions.   In
this case the turns of the first gear in the train relative to the arm is the
absolute turns of the gear minus the absolute turns of the arm, $n_f - a$.
Likewise the turns of the last gear in the train relative to the arm is
$n_l - a$.   The ratio of the turns of the first and last gears in the train
relative to the arm is the train value e relative to the arm.   The motions
of all parts of the train are correctly related in this equation.   Any one
of the terms can be the unknown.   The use of this equation will be
illustrated with several examples.

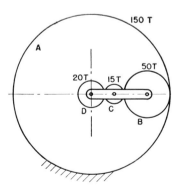

Fig. 11.6

Example 1.   The arm of the train shown in Fig. 11.6 turns once in a positive direction.   It is desired to find the number of turns made by gear D.   Using Eq. (11.1),

$$e = \left(\frac{N_l \ldots \ldots \ldots}{\ldots \ldots \ldots N_f} \right) = \frac{n_f - a}{n_l - a}$$

the train value is determined from the numbers of teeth on the gears, N_l, N_f, ...   The gear on either end can be considered the first.   In this example let D be the first and the fixed internal gear A the last; then

$$e = \frac{150}{50} \times \frac{50}{15} \times \frac{15}{20} = +7\tfrac{1}{2} = \frac{n_f - (+1)}{0 - (+1)}$$

$$n_f = -6\tfrac{1}{2}$$

The arm and gear D turn in opposite directions.

Example 2.   A reverted train is shown in Fig. 11.7.   It is desired to find the number of turns that the arm makes when A turns once.   Let the fixed gear D be the first, and A be the last gear.   Then from Eq. (11.1),

$$\frac{101}{100} \times \frac{101}{100} = +1.021 = \frac{0 - a}{1 - a}$$

$$a = +50.7$$

The arm and gear A turn in the same direction.

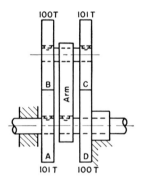

Fig. 11.7

11.5. Tabular method.   Another method of solving epicyclic gear trains is to break the motions of all elements into a sequence of two absolute motions.   In Example 1 (Fig. 11.6) the arm was rotated once in a positive direction.   This produced definite angular displacements of B, C, and D.   These same displacements can be made as follows.   Lock the train so that the parts can have no relative motion and rotate it one positive turn.   The arm has now been displaced its proper amount but the gears have not.   Gear A should have remained fixed.   This is taken care of by holding the arm fixed and rotating A one negative turn.   This brings it back to its original fixed position.   The rotation of A rotates B, C, and D so that they arrive at their proper displacements.

Example 3.   Example 1 will be worked by this method.   It is convenient to use a table similar to the one shown below.

MEMBER	Arm	A	B	C	D
Train locked and given one positive turn	+1	+1	+1	+1	+1
Arm fixed, A given one negative turn	0	−1	$-\frac{150}{50}$	$+\frac{150}{50} \times \frac{50}{15}$	$-\frac{150}{50} \times \frac{50}{15} \times \frac{15}{20}$
Resultant turns	+1	0	−2	+11	$-6\frac{1}{2}$

Example 4.   Example 2, Fig. 11.7, will be worked by this method.

MEMBER	Arm	A	B	C	D
Train locked and given one positive turn	+1	+1	+1	+1	+1
Arm fixed, D given one negative turn	0	$-\frac{100}{101} \times \frac{100}{101}$	$+\frac{100}{101}$	$+\frac{100}{101}$	−1
Resultant turns	+1	+0.0197	1.99	1.99	0

The ratio of the turns of the arm to gear A is

$$\frac{1}{0.0197} = 50.7$$

11.6. Epicyclic trains having no fixed gear

Example 5.   An example of this type of train is shown in Fig. 11.8.   The speed of the shaft carrying A and B is +300 rpm.   The speed of gear J is wanted.

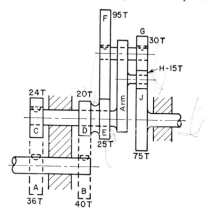

Fig. 11.8

The speed of gear C and the arm is

$$+300 \times (-\tfrac{36}{24}) = -450 \quad \text{rpm}$$

The speed of gears D and E is

$$+300 \times (-\tfrac{40}{20}) = -600 \quad \text{rpm}$$

Gears A and B are drawn with broken lines since they are not part of the epicyclic train. The basic train consists of $EFGHJ$ and the arm. Let E be the first gear and J the last. Then

$$\frac{75}{15} \times \frac{15}{30} \times \frac{95}{25} = -9.5 = \frac{-600 - (-450)}{n_J - (-450)}$$

$$n_J = -434.3 \quad \text{rpm}$$

11.7. Epicyclic drive for controllable-pitch propeller. This is shown in Figs. 11.9 and 11.10. Two trains are used, $ABCDE$ and

Fig. 11.9.   (Courtesy of Curtiss Wright Corp.)

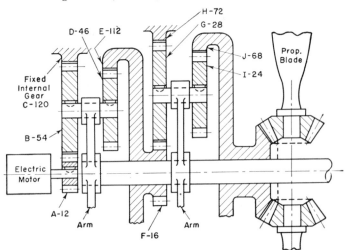

Fig. 11.10

FGHIJ. The total reduction ratio is the product of the reduction ratios of the individual trains. This will be worked as an example.

Example 6. Train *ABCDE* will be considered first. Neither the relationship between *A* and the arm nor between *E* and the arm is known. There are too many unknowns to work this in one step. Here *ABC* and the arm will be considered first to obtain a relationship between *A* and the arm. Let *A* be the first gear, *C* the last, and let the arm have one positive turn. Then

$$\frac{120}{54} \times \frac{54}{12} = -10 = \frac{n_a - 1}{0 - 1}$$

$$n_a = 11$$

Gear *C* can now be disregarded if this relationship between *A* and the arm is maintained. This is the type of problem treated in the previous example. Consider the train *ABDE* and the arm. Let *A* be the first and *E* the last. Then

$$\frac{112}{46} \times \frac{54}{12} = -10.956 = \frac{11 - 1}{n_e - 1}$$

$$n_e = 0.08725$$

When *A* turns 11 times *E* turns 0.08725 times in the same direction. The ratio of *A* to *E* is

$$\frac{11}{0.08725} = 126$$

In like manner the reduction ratio of train *FGHIJ* is found to be 59.5. The over-all reduction is then

$$\text{over-all reduction} = 126 \times 59.5 = 7497$$

By changing the numbers of teeth it is possible to design a similar reducer to fit in the same housing having a ratio of 188,400:1. This is equivalent to the reduction of a single pair of gears, the pinion being 1 in. in diameter and the gear diameter approximately 3 miles.

11.8. Epicyclic bevel-gear trains. A compound train is shown in Fig. 11.11. This train can be analyzed in the manner of the previous example. Here *A* turns +1200 rpm. The speed of *E* is desired. The

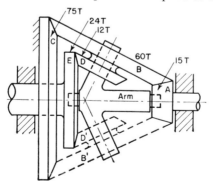

Fig. 11.11

train ABC and the arm are considered first to obtain a relationship between A and the arm. Let A be the first gear and C the last. Then

$$\frac{75}{60} \times \frac{60}{15} = -5 = \frac{1200 - a}{0 - a}$$

$$a = +200 \quad \text{rpm}$$

Next consider the train $ABDE$ and the arm. Let A be the first gear and E the last. Then

$$\frac{24}{12} \times \frac{60}{15} = -8 = \frac{1200 - 200}{n_E - 200}$$

$$n_E = +75 \quad \text{rpm}$$

Gears B' and D' are shown with broken lines. Kinematically they are not necessary but are usually included to maintain balance. Their use also distributes the tooth load among more gears, and the gears can be made smaller.

11.9. The automobile differential or epicyclic equalizing gear (Figs. 11.12 and 11.13) is used to prevent slipping of the wheels when

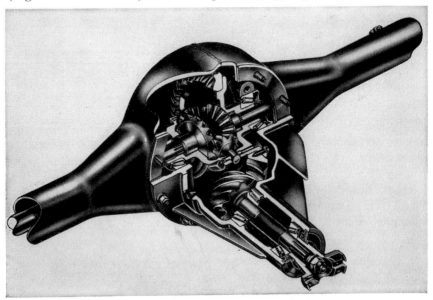

Fig. 11.12.   (Courtesy of Ford Motor Co.)

the automobile moves in a curved path. It is necessary to permit the outside wheel to rotate faster than the inside wheel. In Fig. 11.13 the arm is attached to the ring gear. Gears A and C are the same size. Let the angular velocity of the ring gear and arm be k. Let A be the first gear, C the last, and N the number of teeth. Then

$$e = \frac{N_c}{N_b} \times \frac{N_b}{N_a} = -1 = \frac{n_A - k}{n_C - k}$$

w of ring gear = w arm = k

giving $n_A + n_C = 2k$.   When the automobile is traveling in a straight path, $n_A = n_C = k$.   Here A, B, and C have no rotation relative to each other.   If the left wheel is on dry pavement and the right wheel is on ice with insufficient friction to cause motion of the automobile, the left wheel will remain stationary and the right wheel will rotate at twice

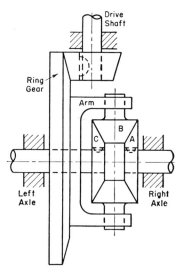

Fig. 11.13

the ring gear speed.   This is a disadvantage of this mechanism.   When the automobile moves in a curved path, A and C adjust their speeds so that there is no sliding.   Their sum is always $2k$.

11.10. Translation screws.   Screw fastenings such as bolts, cap-screws, and setscrews are used for holding.   When they are put in place they are not disturbed unless it is necessary to disassemble the machine. Translation screws are used to produce motion.   The shapes of the threads often differ from the threads of screw fasteners in order to produce better wearing qualities and reduce friction losses.   Four thread forms are shown in Fig. 11.14.   The American standard thread is used for screw fasteners.

The lead and pitch of a screw have the same meaning as for worms (Fig. 9.43).   Unless otherwise stated it is assumed that a screw is right-hand and single.   A jack having a single right-hand thread with $\frac{1}{4}$ in. pitch is shown in Fig. 11.15.   One clockwise turn of the handle when viewed from below will raise the load $\frac{1}{4}$ in.   If the thread is triple, one turn of the handle will raise the load $\frac{3}{4}$ in.   The base of the jack serves as a stationary nut.

A compound screw consists of two screws in series arranged so that the resultant motion produced is the sum of the individual motions.

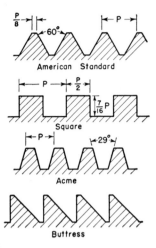

Fig. 11.14

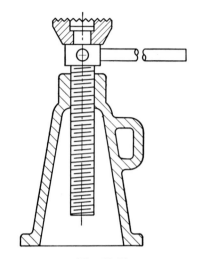

Fig. 11.15

In Fig. 11.16 the large screw has 6 threads per inch and the small screw 7 threads per inch. If the handle is turned once clockwise when viewed from the right, the screw moves $\frac{1}{6}$ inch to the left relative to the frame and block 3 moves $\frac{1}{7}$ inch to the left relative to the screw. The total movement of the block relative to the frame is $\frac{1}{7} + \frac{1}{6} = 0.31$ inch to the left.

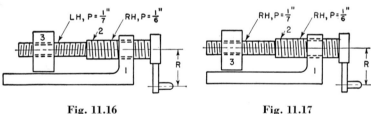

Fig. 11.16   Fig. 11.17

A differential screw consists of two screws in series arranged so that the resultant motion produced is the difference of the individual motions. In Fig. 11.17 the handle is turned once clockwise when viewed from the right. The screw moves $\frac{1}{6}$ inch to the left relative to the frame. The block moves $\frac{1}{7}$ inch to the right relative to the screw. The resultant motion of the block relative to the frame is $\frac{1}{6} - \frac{1}{7} = 0.0238$ inch to the left.

PROBLEMS

11.1. Determine the speed and direction of rotation of gear G in the gear train shown in Fig. P 11.1.

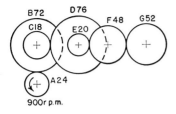

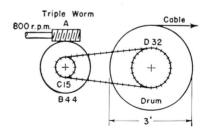

Fig. P 11.1

Fig. P 11.2

11.2. Determine the speed and direction of rotation of shaft F in the gear train shown in Fig. P 11.2.

11.3. Gear H in the train shown in Fig. P 11.3 is to rotate at approximately 14.3 rpm. Determine the number of teeth on gear H. Do H and A rotate in the same or opposite directions?

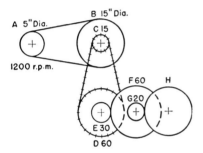

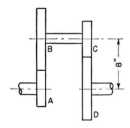

Fig. P 11.3

Fig. P 11.4

11.4. A conveyor belt, Fig. P 11.4, is to move with the velocity shown. Determine the number of teeth on gear B and the direction of rotation of gear A.

11.5. The train value of the reverted train shown in Fig. P 11.5 is to be 12. The diametral pitches of gears A and B is 8, and of gears C and D is 10. Determine suitable numbers of teeth for the gears. No gear is to have less than 24 teeth.

Fig. P 11.5

Fig. P 11.6

11.6. Determine the speed of the cable shown in Fig. P 11.6.

11.7. Determine the mechanical advantage of the cable-winding mechanism shown in Fig. P 11.7.

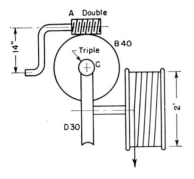

Fig. P 11.7

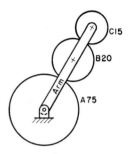

Fig. P 11.8

11.8. In Fig. P 11.8, gear A is fixed and the arm is turned 3 revolutions in a clockwise direction. Determine the number and direction of absolute turns of gear C.

11.9. In Fig. P 11.8, gear A turns 2 revolutions in a counterclockwise direction while the arm turns 4 revolutions in a clockwise direction. Determine the directions and absolute turns of gears B and C.

11.10. In Fig. P 11.10, gear A is fixed. The arm is turned once in a clockwise direction. Determine the number of absolute turns and directions of gears B, C, D, and E.

11.11. In Fig. P 11.10, gear B is fixed. The arm is turned once in a clockwise direction. Determine the number of absolute turns and directions of gears A, C, D, and E.

11.12. Determine the speed and direction of rotation of gear F in Fig. P 11.12.

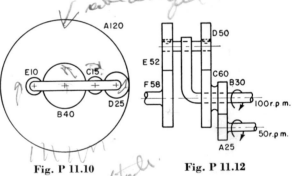

Fig. P 11.10

Fig. P 11.12

11.13. A ball bearing is shown in Fig. P 11.13. The inner race rotates with the shaft at 1000 rpm. Assume pure rolling between the rollers and races. Determine the speed of the roller cage.

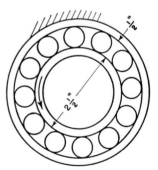

Fig. P 11.13

epicyclic

11.14. In Fig. P 11.14, the diameter of the hand-chain sprocket A is 14 in. and the diameter of the hoisting chain sprocket F is 5 in. Determine the mechanical advantage of the hoist.

11.15. Determine the speed and direction of rotation of gear E in Fig. P 11.15.

Dotted shaft are free to rotate.

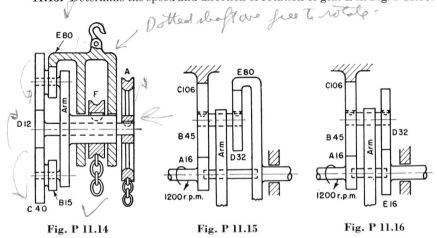

Fig. P 11.14	**Fig. P 11.15**	**Fig. P 11.16**

11.16. Determine the speed and direction of rotation of gear E in Fig. P 11.16.

11.17. Determine the speed and direction of rotation of gear A in Fig. P 11.17. Gears B and C are fastened to E to form a rigid unit.

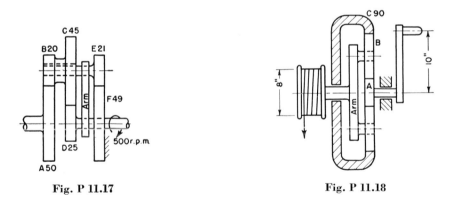

Fig. P 11.17	**Fig. P 11.18**

11.18. The mechanical advantage of the hoist shown in Fig. P 11.18 is to be approximately 25. Determine the numbers of teeth on gears A and B.

11.19. The mechanism shown in Fig. P 11.19 is similar to that of Fig. 8.9. Cone B turns 10 times and cone D turns 4 times. Determine the number and directions of the turns of E.

11.20. In Fig. P 11.20, gears A and C turn once. Determine the number and directions of the turns of gear L.

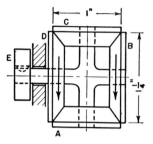

Fig. P 11.19

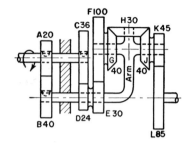

Fig. P 11.20

11.21. In Fig. P 11.21, gears A and H turn once.   Determine the number and direction of the turns of the arm.

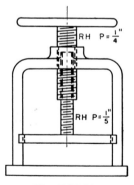

Fig. P 11.21

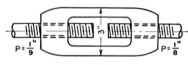

Fig. P 11.23

11.22. The pitch of the screwjack thread (Fig. 11.15) is $\frac{3}{8}$ in. and the radius of the handle is 12 in.   Determine the mechanical advantage.

11.23. The turnbuckle (Fig. P 11.23) is to be turned without the use of a lever or wrench.   Determine the mechanical advantage when: (a) the threads are the same hand, (b) the threads are of opposite hand.

11.24. A differential screw press is shown in Fig. P 11.24.   How many times must the handwheel be turned to lower the plate $\frac{1}{16}$ in.

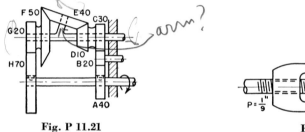

Fig. P 11.24

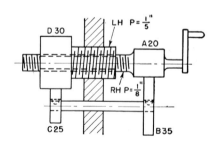

Fig. P 11.25

11.25. The crank in Fig. P 11.25 is turned once in a clockwise direction when viewed from the right.   Determine the direction and distance that the small screw moves relative to the frame.

CHAPTER 12

Dimensional Synthesis

12.1. Introduction. The concept of the word synthesis implies the combination of parts to produce a complex whole; it is the opposite of analysis. Kinematic synthesis can be divided into three classes.*

1. Type synthesis consists in determining the best type of mechanism to solve a particular motion problem. It would be desirable to have a scheme whereby a mechanism would be uniquely specified on naming a desired motion transformation. This, however, is impossible. The designer must use his judgment in selecting the kind of constructional units, as linkwork, gears, cams, screws, belts, and so forth. In many cases he will make alternate designs before selecting the best one.

2. Number synthesis has to do with the relations of the number of links and pairs or joints necessary to produce constrained motion. The theory of number synthesis is included in Chapter 14.

3. Dimensional synthesis is also called size or geometric synthesis. It is concerned with the determination of the basic geometry of the links—the spacing of the elements—necessary to give a specific motion transformation. This is the subject of the present chapter. In many cases, especially if simple linkages are to be used, only approximate solutions can be found. Some graphical methods for synthesis have been available for many years, but not until recently have analytical methods been developed. One of the major reasons for the revival of interest in synthesis is the development and wide use of computers.

Many dimensional synthesis problems are included in one of the three following categories:

(a) The movement of a link through two or more specified positions

(b) The movement of a point on a link through a specified path (coupler curve)

(c) The generation of a function by means of the relative positions of two links when moved over a finite range

In this chapter the three categories listed above will be considered;

---

* R. S. Hartenberg and J. Denavit, "Kinematic Synthesis," *Transactions of the Third Conference on Mechanisms*, The Penton Publishing Co., Cleveland, 1956.

and a number of methods for synthesizing a linkage, both graphical and analytical, will be developed and illustrated with examples.

12.2. Position of a link. In Fig. 12.1(a) link 3 which is shown in one position by two points, B_1C_1, is moved to a second position, B_2C_2.

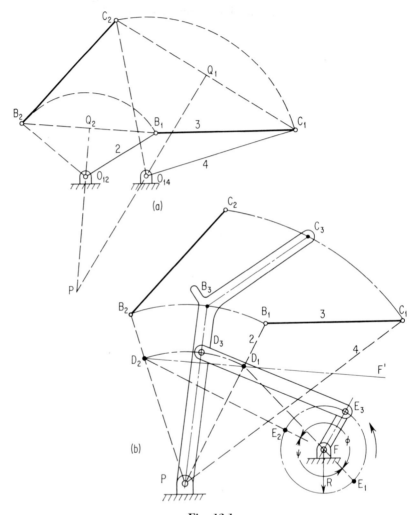

Fig. 12.1

A four-bar linkage can easily be designed to produce the required displacement by arbitrarily selecting centers O_{12} and O_{14} on the perpendicular bisectors of B_2B_1 and C_2C_1, respectively.

If it is required that the velocity of the link in the two specified positions be zero, the design can be altered as shown at Fig. 12.1 (b). Since O_{12} and O_{14} can be arbitrarily chosen on the perpendicular bisectors, they can both be chosen at P, the intersection of the bisectors. Links 2, 3, and 4 of Fig. 12.1 (b) now become a structure, and can be replaced by a single rigid body which has unconstrained rotation about point P. The intermediate third position, PB_3C_3, is added for clarity and is not a specified position. Two additional links, FE_3 and E_3D_3, are added to produce constrained motion and zero velocity at positions B_1C_1 and B_2C_2. The length PD_2 and the position of F can be arbitrarily chosen.

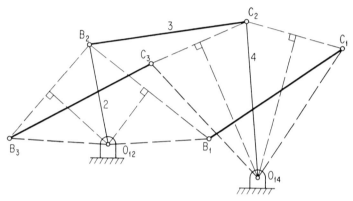

Fig. 12.2

This fixes the distances D_2F and D_1F which can be measured from the drawing. From the relations (to simplify the notation, let $D_1E_1 = D_2E_2 = DE$)

$$DE + R = D_2F \qquad \text{and} \qquad DE - R = D_1F$$

The length of the coupler can be determined by adding the above equations, and the crank can be determined by subtracting the second from the first

$$DE = \frac{D_2F + D_1F}{2} \qquad \text{and} \qquad R = \frac{D_2F - D_1F}{2}$$

In this example the times for the forward and return motions of link PBC are not equal; their ratio is ϕ/ψ. If it is desired that the times for the two strokes be equal, the center F must be located at some point F' arbitrarily chosen on a line through D_1D_2. For this case, $\phi = \psi = 180°$.

An extensive catalog of four-bar linkages, systematically arranged for the selection of a linkage which has certain desired characteristics, is available.*

A method for designing a four-bar linkage to carry a link through three assumed positions, B_1C_1, B_2C_2, and B_3C_3, is shown in Fig. 12.2. Center O_{12} is located at the intersection of the perpendicular bisectors

* A. S. Hall, A. R. Holowenko, and H. G. Laughlin, "Four-bar Lever Crank Mechanism," *Design News.*

B_3B_2 and B_2B_1, and center O_{14} is located at the intersection of the perpendicular bisectors C_3C_2 and C_2C_1. Methods have been developed for the design of a four-bar linkage to carry a link through four specified positions.*

12.3. Coupler-point curves. The use of the coupler-point curve has numerous applications in machine design. The linkage shown in Fig. 12.4 (c) is used to move the film in a motion picture projector. Point E on the coupler link traces the path shown. Rotation of crank BA causes the catcher E to move into a film slot, pull the film down one

Fig. 12.3. (Courtesy of *Machine Design*.)

frame, then out of the slot and up so as then to be in position to engage another slot. Other examples can be found in automatic machines such as those for wrapping, packaging, printing, weaving, vending, and so forth.

Methods have been developed for synthesizing a four-bar linkage to trace a coupler-point curve through several prescribed points.† By spacing these points along a portion of the curve it is possible to obtain a linkage that traces this portion of the curve very accurately. In many applications, e.g., the film-transporting mechanism shown in Fig. 12.4 (c), it is more important to obtain a fair degree of accuracy over the entire curve. For this type of problem a mechanism for rapid drawing of coupler curves can be made, or a catalog of coupler curves can be used. One such mechanism is shown in Fig. 12.3 and 12.4 (a).‡ The lengths of the four links, AB, BC (coupler), CD, and DA can be controlled by

---

* N. Rosenauer and A. H. Willis, KINEMATICS OF MACHINES, Associated General Publications, Sydney, Australia, 1953.

† F. Freudenstein, and G. N. Sandor, "Synthesis of Path-Generating Mechanisms by Means of a Programed Digital Computer," ASME Paper No. 58–a–85.

‡ Josef Boehm, "Four-bar Linkages," *Machine Design*, August, 1952.

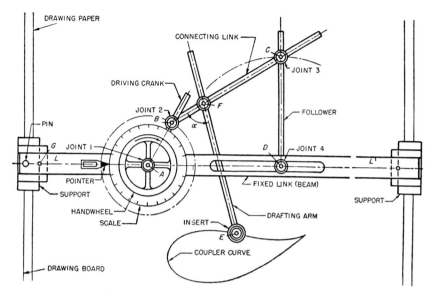

Fig. 12.4a. (Courtesy of *Machine Design.*)

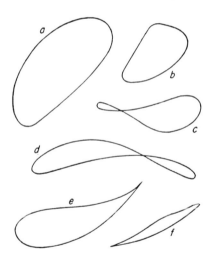

Fig. 12.4b. (Courtesy of
Machine Design.)

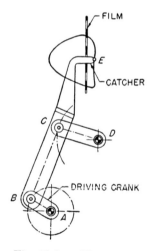

Fig. 12.4c. (Courtesy of
Machine Design.)

adjustments at joints 2, 3, and 4. The position of point E relative to B and C is controlled by the adjustment at F. When the handwheel is turned, the pencil, which is carried at point E, traces the coupler curve. Some typical curves are shown in Fig. 12.4 (b). The proportions of the mechanism can be changed repeatedly until a satisfactory curve is obtained. The approximate velocity of point E can be obtained by using a sharp point instead of a pencil at E. The coupler curve is plotted as a series of points pricked in the paper which correspond to a series of equal angular settings of the handwheel. The distance between the points can be used to estimate the velocity of the point on the coupler. After a satisfactory curve is obtained, an accurate velocity and acceleration analysis can be made. In the following examples use will be made of a coupler curve catalog.

   Example 1. Design a six-link mechanism with rotating input crank and intermittently oscillating output link.* The mechanism is to be of the type shown in Fig. 12.5 where link 2 is the driving crank and link 6 is the oscillating

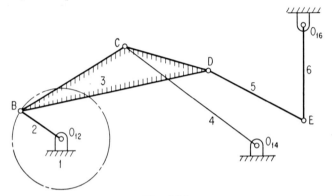

Fig. 12.5

output link. The output link is to oscillate through 50°, dwelling in one extreme position while the crank rotates through 105°. The motion of the output link from dwell to the opposite extreme position is to take place during 105° of crank rotation, then return during the remaining 150° of crank rotation. The coupler catalog is examined and a suitable curve with a general elliptical shape is chosen.† The linkage O_{12}, B, D, C, O_{14} is taken from the coupler-curve catalog and laid out on the drawing, Fig. 12.6. The distances between the dots on the coupler curve correspond to 15° of crank displacement. In the coupler catalog, where the drawings are large, the coupler curve is drawn with a dashed line, each dash representing 5° of crank rotation; thus the velocity of a point can be estimated. A tracing paper overlay with center E and a group of concentric circles can be useful in the selection of a suitable coupler curve and in locating the center E on the mechanism. If the dwell is to be 105°, 21 dashes of the coupler curve should coincide with a circular arc on the overlay.

   In this example, 21 dashes of the coupler curve, (point D_1 to D_2) form a circular arc with center at E. It can be seen that if link 5 is taken as DE with center at E, D can move from D_1 to D_2 with point E stationary. This corresponds to dwell of link 6. Point D' is located by going clockwise around the

---

   * A. S. Hall, Jr., "Advanced Kinematics, Synthesis," prepared for ASEE Machine Design Summer Session, June, 1954.
   † J. A. Hrones and G. L. Nelson, *Analysis of the Four Bar Linkage*, The Massachusetts Institute of Technology Press and John Wiley & Sons, Inc., New York, 1951.

coupler curve 105° (21 dashes). E' is located by drawing a line through D' perpendicular to the coupler curve, and making $D'E' = DE$. E' is the extreme right position of link 6. This can be seen by drawing an arc, ff, with E' as center. Any movement of D' along the coupler path will pull joint E' to the left. The entire coupler curve lies between the arc gg, which has E for its center, and arc ff, except for the portion D_1D_2 which coincides with arc gg. Thus, it can be seen that E and E' are the extreme positions of link 6. Center O_{16} is located on the perpendicular bisector of EE' such that the angle of oscillation is 50°.

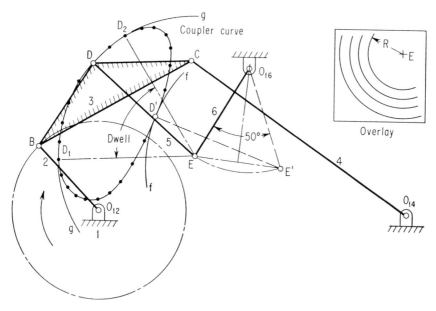

Fig. 12.6

It should be understood that, in general, a finite portion of a coupler curve (in this case D_1D_2) is not an exact circular arc, but usually a very close approximation can be obtained.

Example 2. Design a six-link mechanism with rotating input crank and intermittently oscillating output link. The mechanism is to be of the type shown in Fig. 12.5 where link 2 is the driving crank and link 6 is the oscillating output link. The output link is to oscillate through 30 degrees and is to dwell in the two extreme positions.* There are fewer solutions to this type of problem than the type of the previous example. It is necessary to find a linkage with a kidney shaped coupler curve having circular arcs of equal radii on both the concave and convex sides. Two portions of the coupler curve, DD_1 and D_2D_3 are circular arcs of equal radii, $DE = D_2E'$. Except for the two circular arc portions, the coupler curve lies between the arcs gg and ff the centers of which are E and E'; hence, E and E' are the extreme positions of link 6. Center O_{16} is

---

* T. P. Goodman, "Linkages *vs* Cams," *Transactions of the Fourth Conference on Mechanisms*," The Penton Publishing Co., 1958.

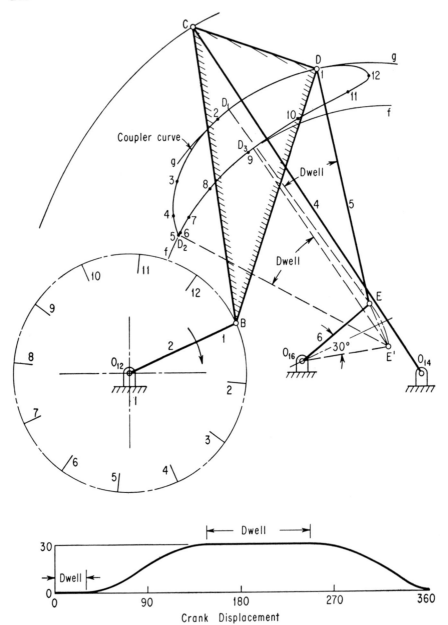

Fig. 12.7

chosen on the perpendicular bisector of EE' such that the angle of oscillation is 30°.

The displacement graph of crank 2 vs link 6 is plotted at the bottom of Fig. 12.7. The starting point on the graph corresponds to crank 2 in position 1.

12.4. Roberts' law.* Sometimes, when a four-bar linkage has been designed or selected from a catalog, it is found that one of the pivot points is not conveniently located or that the transmission angles are

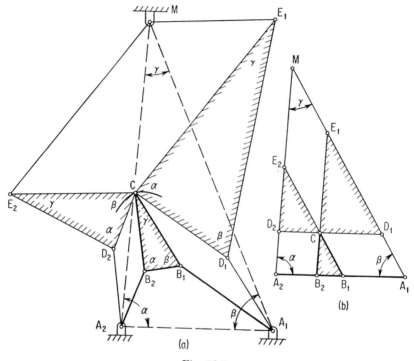

Fig. 12.8

not suitable. According to Roberts' law, there are two other four-bar linkages, related to the first by similar triangles, that will generate the same coupler curve. One of these additional linkages may be more suitable than the original one.

Because the law is "almost obvious," it will be discussed before giving a formal proof. In Fig. 12.8(a), point C of the original linkage (drawn with heavy lines) will trace the coupler curve shown. Point C on the two alternate linkages will trace the same coupler curve provided the linkages are properly related to the original linkage by similar triangles and parallelograms. A simple way of determining the dimensions

* S. Roberts, "On Three-bar Motion," *Proceedings* of the London Mathematical Society, 1876, Vol. 7, p. 14. Rudolf Beyer, *Technische Kinematic*, Verlag von Johann Ambrosius Barth, Leipzig, 1931.

of the alternate linkages is shown at (b) where the original linkage is stretched out so that $A_2B_2B_1A_1$ lie on a straight line. The remainder of the diagram is obtained by drawing lines parallel to the sides of the original coupler link. It will be shown in the proof that triangle A_1A_2M, Fig. 12.8(a), is similar to the coupler link triangle. Thus, the position of M in relation to A_1 and A_2 can be easily calculated.

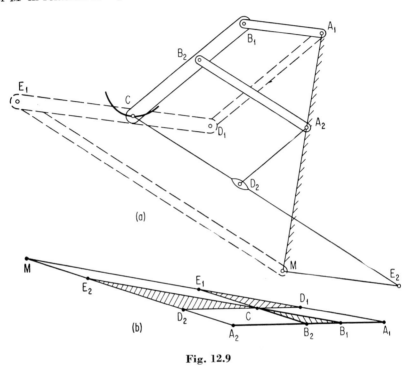

Fig. 12.9

It is not uncommon for the coupler point C to lie on a line through B_1B_2 as shown in Fig. 12.9. This is only a special case of Fig. 12.8 and the same theory holds. If, in Fig. 12.8(a), a line is parallel to B_2C or B_1C, it will be parallel to B_2B_1 in Fig. 12.9(a), etc. The following relations can be written from similar triangles, Fig. 12.8(a).

$$CD_1:CE_1 = B_1B_2:B_2C$$
$$CD_2:D_2E_2 = B_1B_2:B_2C$$
$$A_1A_2:A_2M = B_1B_2:B_2C$$

These relations must also hold for Fig. 12.9(a).

It may be helpful to make a drawing similar to Fig. 12.9(b). After stretching out the original linkage, $A_2B_2B_1A_1$, the coupler point C is moved off of the line so that a triangular diagram can be completed. Now it can be seen that in the first alternate linkage, point C lies between

E_1D_1, and closer to D_1 than to E_1. In the second alternate linkage, C lies outside of E_2D_2 in the direction E_2 to D_2.

Roberts' law applies to the slider crank mechanism when that is considered to be a special case of a four-bar linkage. In Fig. 12.10(a), the original slider crank mechanism is $A_2B_2B_1$. This linkage is stretched out at (b) and the diagram is completed in the usual manner. Here it can be seen that the first alternate linkage is of no value because all of the links are infinite, but the second alternate linkage is satisfactory.

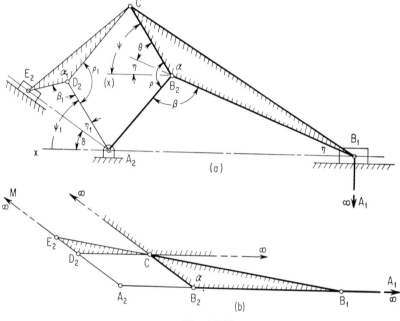

Fig. 12.10

The fact that M lies at infinity means that E_2 must have straight line motion just as B_1 has straight line motion because A_1 lies at infinity. For this alternate linkage, Fig. 12.10(a), it is only necessary to establish the direction of motion of E_2. Assume a link A_2E_2 that is free to rotate about A_2 and allow E_2 as a point in the coupler link to slide along it. From (b) it can be seen that $E_2D_2:D_2A_2 = A_2B_2:B_2B_1$. In (a), $\beta = \beta_1$ since $\rho = \rho_1$ and $\alpha = \alpha_1$. Triangles $E_2D_2A_2$ and $A_2B_2B_1$ are therefore similar which establishes the equality, $\eta = \eta_1$. D_2A_2 and CB_2 being parallel, $\psi = \psi_1$. The last two equalities prove that $\delta = \theta$. Since θ does not vary, δ is a fixed angle. Link E_2A_2 is therefore fixed in the plane, and the path of E_2 is along this link.

Roberts' law can be proved as follows.* In Fig. 12.11 the original

* R. S. Hartenberg and J. Denavit, "The Fecund Four-Bar," *Transactions of the Fifth Conference on Mechanisms*, Penton Publishing Co., Cleveland, 1958.

linkage is shown with solid lines and the alternate linkages with broken lines. It is only necessary to show that M is a fixed point. In complex notation, this requirement is expressed as

$$z = A_2M(\cos \delta + i \sin \delta) = A_2Me^{i\delta} = \text{constant} \qquad (12.1)$$

This means that A_2M and the angle δ must be expressed in terms of the

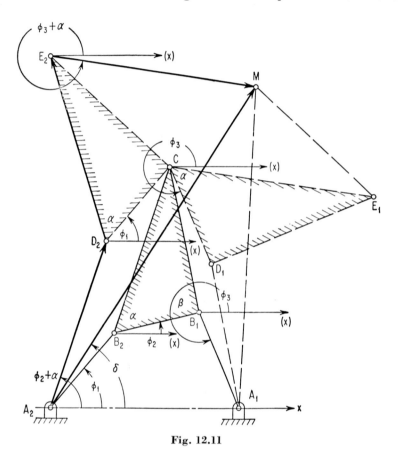

Fig. 12.11

invariant dimensions of the original linkage $A_2B_2B_1A_1$, and be independent of the angular displacements ϕ_1, ϕ_2, and ϕ_3 of this linkage. These angles are measured counterclockwise from the x axis, which, for convenience, is laid through centers A_2 and A_1. With the aid of parallelograms, the angles of the three vectors A_2D_2, D_2E_2 and E_2M are written in terms of the original linkage. The sum of these vectors is

$$z = A_2D_2e^{i(\phi_2+\alpha)} + D_2E_2e^{i(\phi_1+\alpha)} + E_2Me^{i(\phi_3+\alpha)} \qquad (12.2)$$

From parallelograms and similar triangles, the first factors of the above equation may be written in terms of the link lengths of the original linkage

$$A_2D_2 = B_2C \tag{a}$$

$$\frac{D_2E_2}{D_2C} = \frac{B_2C}{B_2B_1} \qquad \text{or (since } D_2C = A_2B_2) \qquad D_2E_2 = \frac{B_2C}{B_2B_1} A_2B_2 \tag{b}$$

$$\frac{CE_1}{CD_1} = \frac{B_2C}{B_2B_1} \qquad \text{or (since } CE_1 = E_2M \text{ and } CD_1 = B_1A_1)$$

$$E_2M = \frac{B_2C}{B_2B_1} B_1A_1 \tag{c}$$

Equation (a) can be written in the following form

$$A_2D_2 = \frac{B_2C}{B_2B_1} B_2B_1 \tag{a'}$$

Substituting Eqs. (a'), (b) and (c) in Eq. (12.2), ordering the terms and factoring, gives,

$$z = \frac{B_2C}{B_2B_1} e^{i\alpha} [A_2B_2e^{i\phi_1} + B_2B_1e^{i\phi_2} + B_1A_1e^{i\phi_3}] \tag{12.3}$$

The terms in the bracket are recognized as the vector path A_2B_2, B_2B_1, B_1A_1 which is equivalent to A_2A_1, or

$$z = \frac{B_2C}{B_2B_1} A_2A_1e^{i\alpha} \tag{12.4}$$

Each of the terms in the above equation is a constant. On comparing Eq. (12.1) with Eq. (12.4), we see that

$$A_2M = \frac{B_2C}{B_2B_1} A_2A_1 = \text{constant} \tag{d}$$

and $$\qquad\qquad \delta = \alpha = \text{constant} \tag{e}$$

Relationship (d) shows that M is a fixed point, while (d) and (e) show that triangle A_2MA_1 is similar to the coupler triangle B_2CB_1.

12.5. Function generator—Overlay method. The nature of a function generator can best be understood by examining Fig. 12.17. The angular positions of links b and d correspond to some function $y = f(x)$; e.g., $y = x^2$ where the value of x varies between 1 and 6. If the pointer is set at 3 on the x scale, the y pointer should indicate 9. It will be shown later that most functions cannot be generated exactly over a finite range by a four-bar linkage but can be made exact at several points and to closely approximate the function in the regions between these points. The overlay method for designing a four-bar linkage as a function generator will be illustrated with an example.

Example 3. A four-bar linkage is to be designed so that the angular displacement of the two cranks will be related according to the following table

Position number	Displacement from Starting Position, Degrees	
	Driving crank	Follower crank
0	0	0
1	25	10
2	50	24
3	75	44
4	100	70

The length of the driving crank and its starting position are arbitrarily chosen and drawn as $O_{12} B$, Fig. 12.12(a). The other positions, 1, 2, 3, and 4, are laid off from this position. The length of the coupler link BC is assumed, and a family of arcs is drawn from the five positions of B. A second layout, Fig. 12.12(b), showing successive positions of the second crank and a series of possible lengths for this crank, is made on a separate piece of tracing paper.

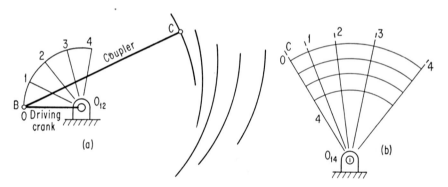

(a)   (b)

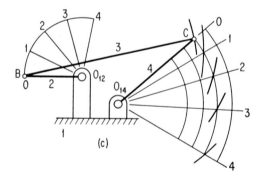

(c)

Fig. 12.12

This second layout is placed over the first, as shown in Fig. 12.12(c), and moved about with the object of making the circle arcs of the first pass in correct order through one of the series of possible crank pin positions of the second layout. When this is accomplished, the location of center O_{14} and the length $O_{14}C$ are determined. It may be necessary to try other coupler lengths, redrawing the first layout, before a satisfactory fit is obtained.

The overlay method, which can be applied to a wide variety of problems, has been treated extensively by Nickson.* This method can become tedious, and it does not guarantee that its application will result in a satisfactory solution, but these same things can be said of most other methods.

12.6. Function generator—Direct graphical method. A method of designing a four-bar linkage to satisfy three pairs of positions will be considered first. The problem to be solved is shown in Fig. 12.13(a) as pairs of angular displacements. When link b moves through angle ψ_{12}, link d is to move through angle ϕ_{12}, and the additional movement of link b through angle ψ_{23} is to move link d through angle ϕ_{23}. The three pairs of positions for links b and d are called precision points.

To obtain a solution by the method that follows, a number of assumptions must be made. These are: the length of a, the initial or starting angle Γ_1 for link d, and the length of link d. The desired linkage is constructed with the aid of inversion: link b is fixed in any one of its three precision points (or positions). The construction is shown in Fig. 12.13(b) where link b is considered to be fixed in position BD_2 even though we do not know this position since Δ is not yet known. The length of link d is arbitrarily chosen and laid off as E_2C_2 at angle Γ_2 with link a. The position of link d for the inversion corresponding to the first precision position is obtained by drawing BIE_1 at angle ψ_{12} [in Fig. 12.13(a) ψ_{12} is measured ccw from position 2, but in Fig. 12.13(b), because of inversion, it is measured cw from position 2] and drawing IE_1IC_1 (equal to E_2C_2) at angle Γ_1. Similarly, IE_3IC_3 is constructed for the third precision point. The three points, IC_1, C_2, IC_3, determine a circle with center at D_2 which is located at the intersection of the perpendicular bisectors of IC_1C_2 and C_2IC_3. This determines $BE_2C_2D_2$, the desired linkage. An examination of Fig. 12.13(b) will show that all angles are correct and that corresponding links are equal in the three positions.

Example 4. Design a four-bar linkage to approximately generate the function $y = x^{2.1}$ where x, the input, is to have a range from 1 to 5, corresponding to 100° of crank rotation, with precision points at 1, 3, and 5. The output link b is to move through 50°. The graph of this function is shown in Fig. 12.14. The linkage is to generate this function in terms of the chosen angle ranges; i.e., x which varies from 1 to 5 is to be represented by an angle ϕ which varies

* P. T. Nickson, "A Simplified Approach to Linkage Designs," *Machine Design*, December, 1953.

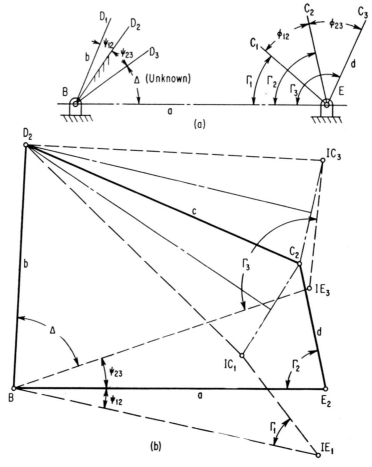

Fig. 12.13

from 0° to 100°, and y, which varies from 1 to 29.366, is to be represented by an angle ψ which varies from 0° to 50°. The equation in terms of these angular ranges is determined as follows:

$$x = \left(\frac{x_{max} - x_{min}}{\phi_{max}}\right)\phi + x_{min} = \left(\frac{5 - 1}{100}\right)\phi + 1 \tag{12.5}$$

$$y = \left(\frac{y_{max} - y_{min}}{\psi_{max}}\right)\psi + y_{min} = \left(\frac{29.366 - 1}{50}\right)\psi + 1 \tag{12.6}$$

Substitution of these values for x and y in the original equation gives:

$$\psi = 1.7627\left[\left(\frac{\phi}{25} + 1\right)^{2.1} - 1\right] \tag{12.7}$$

The graph of Eq. (12.7) is plotted in Fig. 12.14. The ϕ angles on this graph corresponding to precision points $x = 1$, 3, and 5, are $\phi_1 = 0$, $\phi_2 = 50$, and

$\phi_3 = 100$. These values, when substituted in Eq. (12.7), give, $\psi_1 = 0, \psi_2 = 15.85$, and $\psi_3 = 50$. The angles between the precision points are then, $\phi_{12} = 50$, $\phi_{23} = 50$, $\psi_{12} = 15.85$, and $\psi_{23} = 34.15$. These values are shown in Fig. 12.15(a) where it is assumed that the function increases as d moves in a ccw direction. The assumed orientation of the precision positions for link d is

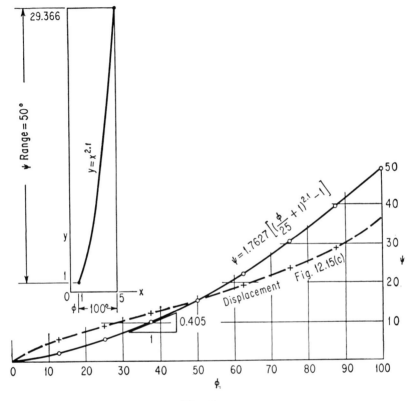

Fig. 12.14

indicated by the 85° angle. The construction of the linkage is shown in Fig. 12.15(b) where inversion about link b was again arbitrarily chosen in the second position. Links a and d were arbitrarily chosen as BE_2 and E_2C_2. Point IC_3 was located by rotating link a 34.15 cw while maintaining the 85° relative position of a and d as shown in Fig. 12.15(a). The arbitrarily chosen length of d is maintained; i.e., $E_2C_2 = IE_3IC_3 = IE_1IC_1$. Point IC_1 is located in a similar manner. The perpendicular bisectors of IC_1C_2 and IC_3C_2 intersect at D_2 giving the desired linkage, $E_2BD_2C_2$.

The linkage is drawn again in Fig. 12.15(c). Here, link a is fixed and link d is moved through its 100° range. The values of ψ for each 12.5°-increment of ϕ are plotted in Fig. 12.14. From this it can be seen that the linkage obtained in Fig. 12.15 is not satisfactory; in fact, the third precision point is not even reached.

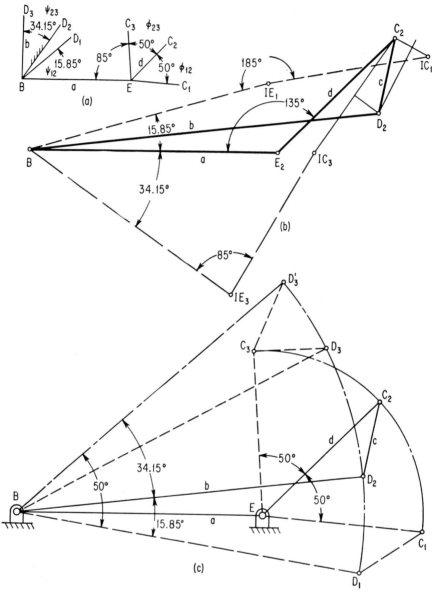

Fig. 12.15

The reason for this can be seen in (c). If the joint at D_3 is disconnected it can be reconnected at D_3' giving the correct precision point.

This example was included to show that the various methods of designing a four-bar linkage as a function generator are usually only approximate. Very few functions can be generated exactly. Shaffer and Cochin have derived a differential equation which they call the compatibility equation for the four-bar linkage.* With this equation it is possible to determine whether a given function can be generated exactly over a finite range. Further, if the function is compatible, they give equations for designing the linkage. Most functions are not compatible over a finite range but are compatible at a few points. If a solution based on precision points is not satisfactory, additional solutions can be made by varying the length of link d and its starting angle.

Example 5. The problem in Example 4 will be solved again, but with an additional refinement. The precision points are now assumed to be, $\phi_1 = 0$, $\phi_2 = 37.5$, and $\phi_3 = 100$, which produces the following link angles: $\phi_{12} = 37.5$, $\phi_{23} = 67.5$, $\psi_{12} = 10.3$, and $\psi_{23} = 39.7$. Since it is desired to obtain a linkage that will closely approximate the desired function over the entire range, there is usually considerable freedom in selecting precision points. The reason for changing the intermediate precision point will soon be apparent.

The orientation of the precision points for link d, Fig. 12.16(a), is so chosen that the extension of link a bisects the angle between the positions of one pair of points. In this example the angle between C_1 and C_3 was arbitrarily chosen. The solution is shown in Fig. 12.16(b). Inversion is again made about the second position. The length of link d is not chosen until the inversions are made for the precision points whose angle was bisected. From symmetry, which resulted from bisecting the angle, it can be seen that $IE_3IC_3 = IE_1IC_1$. If IE_3IC_3 is chosen for the length of link d, the ends of d in the two positions, IC_3 and IC_1 will coincide. This is called point-position-reduction (*Punktlagenreduktion*).† C_2 is located by making $EC_2 = IE_3IC_3$. Point D_2 can now be arbitrarily chosen on the perpendicular bisector of C_2IC_3. A closer approximation to the ideal function can be obtained by choosing a fourth precision point which will give a second perpendicular bisector that will intersect the first giving a definite location of D_2. Another method that will often produce a good approximation is to specify the slope of the ideal curve at one of the precision points. This method will be illustrated by specifying the slope at the second precision point. The derivative of Eq. (12.7) is

$$\frac{d\psi}{d\phi} = \frac{(1.7627)(2.1)}{25}\left(\frac{\phi}{25} + 1\right)^{1.1} \tag{12.8}$$

At the second precision point $\phi = 37.5°$. The slope at this point, which is shown in Fig. 12.14, is

$$\frac{d\psi}{d\phi} = 0.405$$

From the angular velocity ratio theorem it is known that the angular velocity ratio of driver and follower is inversely proportional to the segments which the line of transmission (the coupler link or the link extended) cuts on the line of centers. This point of intersection M is also O_{bd}, the instant center of links

---

* B. W. Shaffer and I. Cochin, "Synthesis of the Quatric Chain When the Position of Two Members is Prescribed," ASME *Transactions*, October, 1954.

† Kurt Hain, *Angewandte Getriebelehre*, Herman Schroedel Verlag, Berlin, 1952.

b and d. Then

$$\frac{d\psi}{d\phi} = \frac{\omega_b}{\omega_d} = \frac{EM}{BE + EM} = 0.405 \qquad (12.9)$$

In the original drawing $BE = 6$ in. Substituting this value in the above equation gives $EM = 4.09$ in. After plotting M in Fig. 12.16, a line is drawn

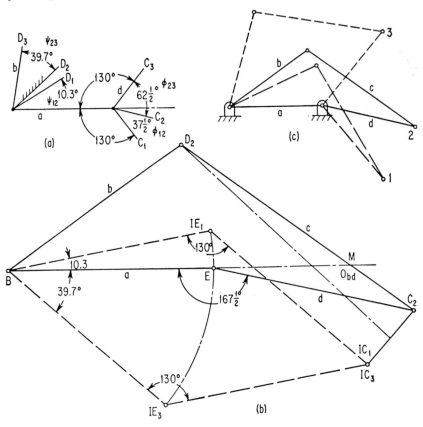

Fig. 12.16

through C_2M, intersecting the perpendicular bisector of C_2IC_1 at D_2 which completes the desired linkage BEC_2D_2. The coupler link in position D_2C_2 then satisfies the coordinates and slope of the ideal curve at this position. A graphical plot of the displacement of this linkage does not deviate more than $0.5°$ from the ideal, Fig. 12.14. The linkage in the three precision position is shown in Fig. 12.16(c).

The reason why the second precision point was changed from that of the previous example is now apparent. If link d and the extension of link a coincide, all four links are collinear, making the solution indeterminate.

12.7. Freudenstein's method.* This is an analytical method for designing a four-bar linkage to generate a function. It is first necessary to derive an expression relating the four sides, a, b, c, d, the input angle, ϕ,

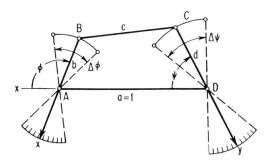

Fig. 12.17

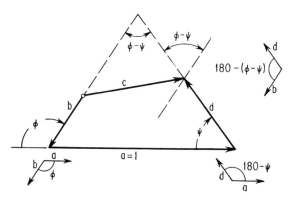

Fig. 12.18

measured cw from A x, and the output angle ψ, measured cw from DA, see Fig. 12.17. This can be done most easily by using vectors. In the work that follows boldface letters represent vectors. From Fig. 12.18

$$\boldsymbol{c} = \boldsymbol{b} + \boldsymbol{a} + \boldsymbol{d} \tag{12.10}$$

The scalar or dot product of two vectors is the product of the lengths of the two vectors and the cosine of the angle between them; i.e.

$$\boldsymbol{a} \cdot \boldsymbol{b} = |\boldsymbol{a}|\,|\boldsymbol{b}|\,\cos \phi = ab \cos \phi$$
$$\boldsymbol{c} \cdot \boldsymbol{c} = |\boldsymbol{c}|\,|\boldsymbol{c}|\,\cos 0 = c^2$$

If each side of Eq. (12.10) is dotted with itself, (this is often called

* F. Freudenstein, "Approximate Synthesis of Four-Bar Linkages," *ASME Transactions,* 1955, Vol. 77, p. 853.

self-product) ϕ and ψ will be introduced and all quantities will become scalars giving the required expression for the four-bar linkage.

$$c \cdot c = (b + a + d) \cdot (b + a + d)$$

or $c^2 = b^2 + a^2 + d^2 + 2a \cdot b + 2a \cdot d + 2d \cdot b$

or $c^2 = b^2 + a^2 + d^2 + 2ab \cos \phi + 2ad \cos (180 - \psi)$
$$+ 2db \cos [180 - (\phi - \psi)]$$

Let $a = 1$; then

$$\frac{1 + b^2 - c^2 + d^2}{2db} + \frac{2ab \cos \phi}{2db} - \frac{2ad \cos \psi}{2db} = \cos (\phi - \psi)$$

or

$$R_1 \cos \phi - R_2 \cos \psi + R_3 = \cos (\phi - \psi) \qquad (12.11)$$

where $\qquad R_1 = \dfrac{1}{d}, R_2 = \dfrac{1}{b}, R_3 = \dfrac{1 + b^2 - c^2 + d^2}{2bd} \qquad (12.12)$

It can now be seen why a four-bar linkage will not generate most functions exactly over a finite range.

A function $\psi = f(\phi)$ that a four-bar linkage will generate, must be compatible with Eq. (12.11). An algebraic equation, e.g., Eq. (12.7), is not compatible with Eq. (12.11). Using Freudenstein's method, a function can be made compatible with Eq. (12.11) at three, four, or five points. Only three points will be considered in this Article.

The three precision points are specified as pairs of positions, ϕ_i and ψ_i, where $i = 1, 2, 3$. For these three positions, Eq. (12.11) is

$$\left.\begin{array}{l} R_1 \cos \phi_1 - R_2 \cos \psi_1 + R_3 = \cos (\phi_1 - \psi_1) \\ R_1 \cos \phi_2 - R_2 \cos \psi_2 + R_3 = \cos (\phi_2 - \psi_2) \\ R_1 \cos \phi_3 - R_2 \cos \psi_3 + R_3 = \cos (\phi_3 - \psi_3) \end{array}\right\} \qquad (12.13)$$

These can be solved most easily using determinants.

$$R_1 = \frac{\begin{vmatrix} \cos (\phi_1 - \psi_1) & \cos \psi_1 & 1 \\ \cos (\phi_2 - \psi_2) & \cos \psi_2 & 1 \\ \cos (\phi_3 - \psi_3) & \cos \psi_3 & 1 \end{vmatrix}}{\begin{vmatrix} \cos \phi_1 & \cos \psi_1 & 1 \\ \cos \phi_2 & \cos \psi_2 & 1 \\ \cos \phi_3 & \cos \psi_3 & 1 \end{vmatrix}}$$

The negative signs in the second columns were eliminated by multiplying numerator and denominator by -1. In both numerator and denominator, subtract the first row from the second and third rows, giving

$$R_1 = \frac{\begin{vmatrix} \cos (\phi_1 - \psi_1) & \cos \psi_1 & 1 \\ \cos (\phi_2 - \psi_2) - \cos (\phi_1 - \psi_1) & \cos \psi_2 - \cos \psi_1 & 0 \\ \cos (\phi_3 - \psi_3) - \cos (\phi_1 - \psi_1) & \cos \psi_3 - \cos \psi_1 & 0 \end{vmatrix}}{\begin{vmatrix} \cos \phi_1 & \cos \psi_1 & 1 \\ \cos \phi_2 - \cos \phi_1 & \cos \psi_2 - \cos \psi_1 & 0 \\ \cos \phi_3 - \cos \phi_1 & \cos \psi_3 - \cos \psi_1 & 0 \end{vmatrix}}$$

or

$$R_1 = \begin{vmatrix} \cos(\phi_2 - \psi_2) - \cos(\phi_1 - \psi_1) & \cos\psi_2 - \cos\psi_1 \\ \cos(\phi_3 - \psi_3) - \cos(\phi_1 - \psi_1) & \cos\psi_3 - \cos\psi_1 \\ \cos\phi_2 - \cos\phi_1 & \cos\psi_2 - \cos\psi_1 \\ \cos\phi_3 - \cos\phi_1 & \cos\psi_3 - \cos\psi_1 \end{vmatrix}$$

or

$$R_1 = \frac{\omega_3\omega_6 - \omega_4\omega_5}{\omega_2\omega_3 - \omega_1\omega_4} \tag{12.14}$$

where

$$\left. \begin{aligned} \omega_1 &= \cos\phi_1 - \cos\phi_2 \\ \omega_2 &= \cos\phi_1 - \cos\phi_3 \\ \omega_3 &= \cos\psi_1 - \cos\psi_2 \\ \omega_4 &= \cos\psi_1 - \cos\psi_3 \\ \omega_5 &= \cos(\phi_1 - \psi_1) - \cos(\phi_2 - \psi_2) \\ \omega_6 &= \cos(\phi_1 - \psi_1) - \cos(\phi_3 - \psi_3) \end{aligned} \right\} \tag{12.15}$$

Similarly

$$R_2 = \frac{\omega_1\omega_6 - \omega_2\omega_5}{\omega_2\omega_3 - \omega_1\omega_4} \tag{12.16}$$

With R_1 and R_2 known, R_3 can be determined from any one of the equations, Eq. (12.13), or Eq. (12.17)

$$R_3 = \cos(\phi_i - \psi_i) + R_2 \cos\psi_i - R_1 \cos\phi_i \tag{12.17}$$

where $i = 1, 2,$ or 3.

From the above development it can be seen that any three pairs of precision points can be arbitrarily chosen. The fact that ϕ and ψ are measured from link a as shown in Fig. 12.17 means that the initial positions of links b and d must also be arbitrarily chosen. This method will be illustrated with an example.

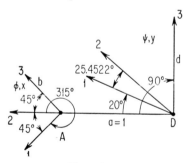

Fig. 12.19

Example 6. Design a four-bar linkage to generate the function $y = x^{1.8}$. The range of x is from 1 through 5 with precision points at 1, 3, and 5. The corresponding values of y are 1, 7.2247, and 18.1195. The x link is to have a range of $\Delta\phi = 90°$, and the y link range is $\Delta\psi = 70°$. All data are shown in Fig. 12.19 where the initial positions of the links have been arbitrarily chosen as 315° and 20°.

$$\phi_1 = 315° \qquad \psi_1 = 20°$$
$$\phi_2 = \quad 0° \qquad \psi_2 = 45.4522°$$
$$\phi_3 = \quad 45° \qquad \psi_3 = 90°$$

$$\cos \phi_1 = 0.70711 \qquad \cos \psi_1 = 0.93969$$
$$\cos \phi_2 = 1 \qquad\qquad \cos \psi_2 = 0.70150$$
$$\cos \phi_3 = 0.70711 \qquad \cos \psi_3 = 0$$
$$\cos (\phi_1 - \psi_1) = \cos (315 - 20) = \cos 295 = 0.42262$$
$$\cos (\phi_2 - \psi_2) = \cos (0 - 45.4522) = \cos 45.4522 = 0.70150$$
$$\cos (\phi_3 - \psi_3) = \cos (45 - 90) = \cos 45 = 0.70711$$

$$\omega_1 = \cos \phi_1 - \cos \phi_2 = 0.70711 - 1 = -0.29289$$
$$\omega_2 = \cos \phi_1 - \cos \phi_3 = 0.70711 - 0.70711 = 0$$
$$\omega_3 = \cos \psi_1 - \cos \psi_2 = 0.93969 - 0.70150 = 0.23819$$
$$\omega_4 = \cos \psi_1 - \cos \psi_3 = 0.93969 - 0 = 0.93969$$
$$\omega_5 = \cos (\phi_1 - \psi_1) - \cos (\phi_2 - \psi_2) = 0.42262 - 0.70150 = -0.27888$$
$$\omega_6 = \cos (\phi_1 - \psi_1) - \cos (\phi_3 - \psi_3) = 0.42262 - 0.70711 = -0.28449$$

$$d = \frac{1}{R_1} = \frac{\omega_2\omega_3 - \omega_1\omega_4}{\omega_3\omega_6 - \omega_4\omega_5} = \frac{(0)(0.23819) - (-0.29289)(0.93969)}{(0.23819)(-0.28449) - (0.93969)(-0.27888)}$$
$$= 1.41652$$

$$b = \frac{1}{R_2} = \frac{\omega_2\omega_3 - \omega_1\omega_4}{\omega_1\omega_6 - \omega_2\omega_5} = \frac{(0)(0.23819) - (-0.29289)(0.93969)}{(-0.29289)(-0.28499) - (0)(-0.27953)} = 3.30306$$

$$R_3 = \cos (\phi_1 - \psi_1) + R_2 \cos \psi_1 - R_1 \cos \phi_1$$
$$= (0.42262) + (0.30274)(0.93969) - (0.70595)(0.70711) = 0.20792$$
$$c^2 = 1 + b^2 + d^2 - 2bd\, R_3$$
$$= 1 + (0.30306)^2 + (1.41652)^2 - (2)(3.30306)(1.41652)(0.20792) = 11.97108$$
$$c = 3.4599$$

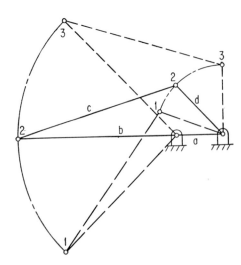

Fig. 12.20

This linkage in its three precision positions is shown in Fig. 12.20. The linkage can be made larger or smaller by multiplying all of the links by the same factor.

12.8. Worthley's method.* This is an analytical method that is based on Hain's graphical method (Art. 12.6). The equations are derived from the graphical solution shown in Fig. 12.21. After the

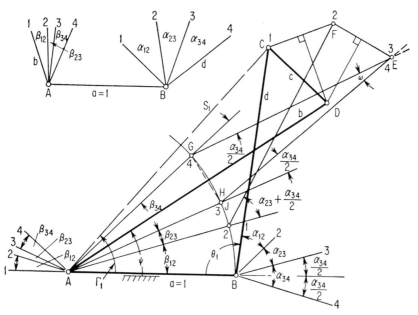

Fig. 12.21

angles between the precision points are determined, one set is placed at A and given β symbols, and the other set is placed at B with α symbols. The ideal function is used only to determine these sets of angles; thereafter we are concerned only with a geometrical problem involving these angles. For convenience, inversion is made about link b in position 1 which is shown horizontal. The α-range is oriented so that α_{34} is bisected by the extension of link a. Inversions of link d for positions 3 and 4 intersect at E giving the length of d. C is located by making $CB = HE$, and F is located in a similar manner from the inversion of position 2. The linkage, $ABCD$, is completed by locating D at the intersection of the perpendicular bisectors of CF and FE. The following nomenclature will be used.

* W. W. Worthley and R. T. Hinkle, "Four-Bar Linkages, Approximate Synthesis," *ASME* Paper No. 58–A–130.

$i = 1, 2, 3, 4 =$ subscripts which refer to precision points (or positions)

$\Gamma_i =$ angle BAC, measured positive counterclockwise from AB to AC

$\psi =$ angle BAD, measured positive counterclockwise from AB to AD (this angle gives the position of link b at the first precision point)

$\theta_i =$ angle ABC, measured positive clockwise from AB to BC

The remaining nomenclature is shown in Fig. 12.21.

The values of θ are

$$\left. \begin{aligned} \theta_1 &= 180 - \left(\alpha_{12} + \alpha_{23} + \frac{\alpha_{34}}{2} \right) \\ \theta_2 &= 180 - \left(\alpha_{23} + \frac{\alpha_{34}}{2} \right) \\ \theta_3 &= \theta_4 = 180 - \left(\frac{\alpha_{34}}{2} \right) \end{aligned} \right\} \qquad (12.18)$$

The value of θ_4 is not required since points 3 and 4 were used for point reduction; the necessary information can be obtained from θ_3. Applying the law of cosines to triangles GAH and GEH, and equating sides GH, gives

$$d^2 + d^2 - 2d^2 \cos \omega = a^2 + a^2 - 2a^2 \cos \beta_{34} \qquad (12.19)$$

where ω is obtained from the expression for the interior angles of quadrilateral $AGEH$

$$\beta_{34} + \left(180 - \frac{\alpha_{34}}{2} \right) + \left(180 - \frac{\alpha_{34}}{2} \right) + \omega = 360$$

or
$$\omega = \alpha_{34} - \beta_{34}$$

Replacing ω in Eq. (12.19) by the foregoing value and letting $a = 1$, d is found to be

$$d = \left[\frac{1 - \cos \beta_{34}}{1 - \cos (\alpha_{34} - \beta_{34})} \right]^{1/2} \qquad (12.20)$$

With links a and d and the angles $\theta_{1,2,3}$ known, there are three remaining unknowns; namely, links b and c, and angle ψ. By noting the trigonometric relationships of these unknowns in positions 1, 2 and 3, three equations can be written and solved simultaneously

Position 1, triangle CAD

$$c^2 = b^2 + S_1^2 - 2bS_1 \cos (\psi - \Gamma_1) \qquad (12.21)$$

where $(\psi - \Gamma_1) =$ angle CAD

Position 2, triangle FAD

$$c^2 = b^2 + S_2^2 - 2bS_2 \cos [\psi - (\beta_{12} + \Gamma_2)] \qquad (12.22)$$

where $[\psi - (\beta_{12} + \Gamma_2)]$ is angle FAD, and Γ_2 is the angle JAF

Position 3, triangle EAD

$$c^2 = b^2 + S_3^2 - 2bS_3 \cos [\psi - (\beta_{12} + \beta_{23} + \Gamma_3)] \qquad (12.23)$$

where $[\psi - (\beta_{12} + \beta_{23} + \Gamma_3)]$ is angle EAD, and Γ_3 is the angle EAH.

Eliminating c^2 and b^2 by subtracting Eq. (12.22) from Eq. (12.21) gives
$$0 = 0 + S_1^2 - S_2^2 - 2b\{S_1 \cos(\psi - \Gamma_1)$$
$$- S_2 \cos[\psi - (\beta_{12} + \Gamma_2)]\} \qquad (12.24)$$
Letting $(\beta_{12} + \Gamma_2) = \alpha$ and solving for b gives
$$b = \frac{S_1^2 - S_2^2}{2[S_1 \cos(\psi - \Gamma_1) - S_2 \cos(\psi - \alpha)]} \qquad (12.25)$$
Subtracting Eq. (12.23) from Eq. (12.21) gives
$$0 = 0 + S_1^2 - S_3^2 - 2b\{S_1 \cos(\psi - \Gamma_1)$$
$$- S_3 \cos[\psi - (\beta_{12} + \beta_{23} - \Gamma_3)]\} \qquad (12.26)$$
Letting $[\beta_{12} + \beta_{23} + \Gamma_3] = \mathcal{B}$ and solving for b gives
$$b = \frac{S_1^2 - S_3^2}{2[S_1 \cos(\psi - \Gamma_1) - S_3 \cos(\psi - \mathcal{B})]} \qquad (12.27)$$
Equations (12.25) and (12.27) are equated giving
$$\frac{S_1^2 - S_2^2}{2[S_1 \cos(\psi - \Gamma_1) - S_2 \cos(\psi - \alpha)]}$$
$$= \frac{S_1^2 - S_3^2}{2[S_1 \cos(\psi - \Gamma_1) - S_3 \cos(\psi - \mathcal{B})]} \qquad (12.28)$$
This can be written in the form
$$r \cos(\psi - \Gamma_1) + s \cos(\psi - \mathcal{B}) = t \cos(\psi - \alpha) \qquad (12.29)$$
where
$$\left.\begin{array}{l} r = S_1(S_3^2 - S_2^2) \\ s = S_3(S_2^2 - S_1^2) \\ t = S_2(S_3^2 - S_1^2) \end{array}\right\} \qquad (12.30)$$
When expanded, Eq. (12.29) is
$$r[\cos\psi \cos\Gamma_1 + \sin\psi \sin\Gamma_1] + s[\cos\psi \cos\mathcal{B} + \sin\psi \sin\mathcal{B}]$$
$$= t[\cos\psi \cos\alpha + \sin\psi \sin\alpha]$$
Collecting terms and solving for ψ gives
$$\psi = \tan^{-1}\left[\frac{r \cos\Gamma_1 + s \cos\mathcal{B} - t \cos\alpha}{t \sin\alpha - r \sin\Gamma_1 - S \sin\mathcal{B}}\right] \qquad (12.31)$$
Triangle CAB for position 1 is used for reference to write the general equations
$$\Gamma_i = \sin^{-1}\left[\frac{d \sin\theta_i}{S_i}\right] \qquad (12.32)$$
and
$$S_i^2 = a^2 + d^2 - 2ad \cos\theta_i \quad \text{where} \quad i = 1, 2, 3 \qquad (12.33)$$
It is now possible to solve for b in Eq. (12.27). With b known, c can be determined from Eq. (12.21).

Example 7. Design a four-bar linkage to generate the function $y = x^{2.1}$, where x is to range from 1 to 5 with precision points at 1, 2.5, 3.5, and 5. From the equation, the y-range corresponding to the x-range is from 1 to 29.366. The α-range corresponding to the x-range, is to be from 0° to 100°, and the β-range is to be from 0° to 50°. The function and ranges for this example are the same as those for Example 4. The function to be approximately generated, in the symbols of this method, is

$$\beta = 1.7627 \left[\left(\frac{\alpha}{25} + 1 \right)^{2.1} - 1 \right]$$ (12.34)

For the precision points, the corresponding angles are

$$\alpha_{12} = 37°30.00' \qquad \beta_{12} = 10°18.68'$$
$$\alpha_{23} = 25°0.00' \qquad \beta_{23} = 12°24.07'$$
$$\alpha_{34} = 37°30.00' \qquad \beta_{34} = 27°17.26'$$

From Eq. (12.18)

$$\theta_1 = 180° - 81°15' = 98°45'$$
$$\theta_2 = 180° - 43°45' = 136°15'$$
$$\theta_3 = 180° - 18°45' = 161°15'$$

From Eq. (12.20)

$$d = \left[\frac{1 - \cos 27°17.26'}{1 - \cos 10°12.74'} \right]^{1/2} = 2.6505$$

From Eq. (12.33)

$$S_1^2 = 1 + 7.0252 - 2(2.6505)\cos 98°45' = 8.8316$$
$$S_2^2 = 1 + 7.0252 - 2(2.6505)\cos 136°15' = 11.8544$$
$$S_3^2 = 1 + 7.0252 - 2(2.6505)\cos 161°15' = 13.0449$$
$$S_1 = 2.9718, \; S_2 = 3.4430, \; S_3 = 3.6118$$

From Eq. (12.3)

$$r = 2.9718(13.0449 - 11.8544) = 3.5379$$
$$s = 3.6118(11.8544 - 8.8316) = 10.9177$$
$$t = 3.4430(13.0449 - 8.8316) = 14.5064$$

From Eq. (12.32)

$$\Gamma_1 = \sin^{-1} \left[\frac{2.6505 \sin 98°45'}{2.9718} \right] = 61°49.43'$$

$$\Gamma_2 = \sin^{-1} \left[\frac{2.6505 \sin 136°15'}{3.4430} \right] = 32°9.83'$$

$$\Gamma_3 = \sin^{-1} \left[\frac{2.6505 \sin 161°15'}{3.6118} \right] = 13°38.64'$$

$$\alpha = (\beta_{12} + \Gamma_2) = 42°28.51'$$
$$\beta = (\beta_{12} + \beta_{23} + \Gamma_3) = 36°21.39'$$

From Eq. (12.31)

$$\psi = \tan^{-1} \left[\frac{(3.5379) \cos 61°49.43' + (10.9177) \cos 36°21.39' - (14.5064) \cos 42°28.51'}{(14.5064) \sin 42°28.51' - (3.5379) \sin 61°49.43' - 10.9177 \sin 36°21.39'} \right]$$

$$\psi = -49°5.13'$$

From Eq. (12.27)

$$b = \frac{8.8316 - 13.0449}{2[2.9718 \cos (-110°54.56') - 3.6118 \cos (-85°26.52')]} = 1.5629$$

From Eq. (12.23)

$$c^2 = 2.4426 + 8.8316 - 2(1.5629)(2.9718) \cos(-110°54.56') = 14.5894$$
$$c = 3.8196$$

This linkage, in its starting position, is shown at the lower right of Fig. 12.22.

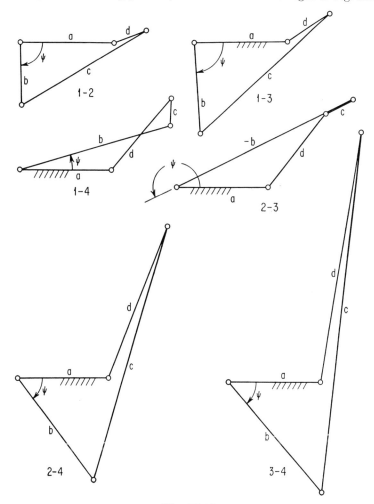

Fig. 12.22

The solution given here is one of six that can be obtained from the given data; any two of the precision points can be used for point reduction. The derivations for the other five combinations are similar to the one given here. The equations for the six solutions are given in Table 12.1, and the six solutions for the above example are given in Table 12.2. An examination of these six linkages, Fig. 12.22, will show that all but 1–4 and 2–3 are reasonably good approximations. Now, if

TABLE 12.1

	1–2	1–3	1–4
α	$\beta_1 + \beta_2 + \Gamma_3$	$\beta_1 + \Gamma_2$	$\beta_1 + \Gamma_2$
β	$\beta_1 + \beta_2 + \beta_3 + \Gamma_4$	$\beta_1 + \beta_2 + \beta_3 + \Gamma_4$	$\beta_1 + \beta_2 + \Gamma_3$
r	$S_1(S_4^2 - S_3^2)$	$S_1(S_4^2 - S_2^2)$	$S_1(S_3^2 - S_2^2)$
s	$S_4(S_3^2 - S_1^2)$	$S_4(S_2^2 - S_1^2)$	$S_3(S_2^2 - S_1^2)$
t	$S_3(S_4^2 - S_1^2)$	$S_2(S_4^2 - S_1^2)$	$S_2(S_3^2 - S_1^2)$
θ_1	$180 - \dfrac{\alpha_{12}}{2}$	$180 - \left(\dfrac{\alpha_{12} + \alpha_{23}}{2}\right)$	$180 - \left(\dfrac{\alpha_{12} + \alpha_{23} + \alpha_{34}}{2}\right)$
θ_2	——	$180 + \left(\dfrac{\alpha_{12} - \alpha_{23}}{2}\right)$	$180 - \left(\dfrac{-\alpha_{12} + \alpha_{23} + \alpha_{34}}{2}\right)$
θ_3	$180 + \left(\alpha_{23} + \dfrac{\alpha_{12}}{2}\right)$	——	$180 - \left(\dfrac{-\alpha_{12} - \alpha_{23} + \alpha_{34}}{2}\right)$
θ_4	$180 + \left(\alpha_{34} + \alpha_{23} + \dfrac{\alpha_{12}}{2}\right)$	$180 + \left(\alpha_{34} + \dfrac{\alpha_{12} + \alpha_{23}}{2}\right)$	——
Γ_i, S_i^2	$i = 1, 3, 4$	$i = 1, 2, 4$	$i = 1, 2, 3$

$$d = \left[\frac{1 - \cos \beta_{12}}{1 - \cos(\alpha_{12} - \beta_{12})} \cdot (S_1^2 - S_4^2)\right]^{1/2}$$
$$b = 2[S_1 \cos(\psi - \Gamma_1) - S_4 \cos(\psi - \beta)]$$

$$d = \left[\frac{1 - \cos(\beta_{12} + \beta_{23})}{1 - \cos(\alpha_{12} + \alpha_{23} - \beta_{12} - \beta_{23})} \cdot (S_1^2 - S_2^2)\right]^{1/2}$$
$$b = 2[S_1 \cos(\psi - \Gamma_1) - S_2 \cos(\psi - \alpha)]$$

$$d = \left[\frac{1 - \cos(\beta_{12} + \beta_{23} + \beta_{34})}{1 - \cos(\alpha_{12} + \alpha_{23} + \alpha_{34} - \beta_{12} - \beta_{23} - \beta_{34})} \cdot (S_1^2 - S_3^2)\right]^{1/2}$$
$$b = 2[S_1 \cos(\psi - \Gamma_1) - S_3 \cos(\psi - \beta)]$$

the input and output ranges are interchanged, i.e., the β-range is put at B and assigned α symbols, and the α-range put at A with β symbols, there will be six additional solutions giving a total of twelve.

Two special cases must be considered. If the portion of the α-range that is used for point reduction is equal to the corresponding portion of the β-range, point E will lie at infinity, which will give an indeterminate

TABLE 12.1 (cont.)

	2–3	2–4	3–4
α	$\beta_1 + \Gamma_2$	$\beta_1 + \Gamma_2$	$\beta_1 + \Gamma_2$
β	$\beta_1 + \beta_2 + \beta_3 + \Gamma_4$	$\beta_1 + \beta_2 + \Gamma_3$	$\beta_1 + \beta_2 + \Gamma_3$
r	$S_1(S_4^2 - S_2^2)$	$S_1(S_3^2 - S_2^2)$	$S_1(S_3^2 - S_2^2)$
s	$S_4(S_2^2 - S_1^2)$	$S_3(S_2^2 - S_1^2)$	$S_3(S_2^2 - S_1^2)$
t	$S_2(S_4^2 - S_1^2)$	$S_2(S_3^2 - S_1^2)$	$S_2(S_3^2 - S_1^2)$
θ_1	$180 - \left(\alpha_{12} + \dfrac{\alpha_{23}}{2}\right)$	$180 - \left(\alpha_{12} + \dfrac{\alpha_{23} + \alpha_{34}}{2}\right)$	$180 - \left(\alpha_{12} + \alpha_{23} + \dfrac{\alpha_{34}}{2}\right)$
θ_2	$180 - \left(\dfrac{\alpha_{23}}{2}\right)$	$180 - \left(\dfrac{\alpha_{23} + \alpha_{34}}{2}\right)$	$180 - \left(\alpha_{23} + \dfrac{\alpha_{34}}{2}\right)$
θ_3	——	$180 - \left(\dfrac{-\alpha_{23} + \alpha_{34}}{2}\right)$	$180 - \dfrac{\alpha_{34}}{2}$
θ_4	$180 + \left(\alpha_{34} + \dfrac{\alpha_{23}}{2}\right)$	——	——
Γ_i, S_i^2	$i = 1, 2, 4$	$i = 1, 2, 3$	$i = 1, 2, 3$

$$d = \left[\frac{1 - \cos \beta_{23}}{1 - \cos(\alpha_{23} - \beta_{23})}\right]^{1/2}$$

$$b = \frac{S_1^2 - S_2^2}{2[S_1 \cos(\psi - \Gamma_1) - S_2 \cos(\psi - \alpha)]}$$

$$d = \left[\frac{1 - \cos(\beta_{23} + \beta_{34})}{1 - \cos(\alpha_{23} + \alpha_{34} - \beta_{23} - \beta_{34})}\right]^{1/2}$$

$$b = \frac{S_1^2 - S_3^2}{2[S_1 \cos(\psi - \Gamma_1) - S_3 \cos(\psi - \beta)]}$$

$$d = \left[\frac{1 - \cos \beta_{34}}{1 - \cos(\alpha_{34} - \beta_{34})}\right]^{1/2}$$

$$b = \frac{S_1^2 - S_3^2}{2[S_1 \cos(\psi - \Gamma_1) - S_3 \cos(\psi - \beta)]}$$

solution.   If the portion of the α-range that is used for point reduction is less than the corresponding β-range, point E will lie to the left of arc GH (Fig. 12.21) which will result in a negative d link.   For this case ψ and Γ must be measured positive counterclockwise from the extension of link a to the left of AB, but the positive value of d must be used in Eq. (12.32).

TABLE 12.2

	1–2	1–3	1–4	2–3	2–4	3–4
θ_1	161°15′	148°45′	130° 0′	130°00′	111°15′	98°45′
θ_2	—	186°15′	167°30′	167°30′	148°45′	136°15′
θ_3	233°45′	—	192°30′	—	173°45′	161°15′
θ_4	261°15′	248°45′	—	230°00′	—	—
d	0.3824	0.5786	1.0000	0.9843	1.7166	2.6505
S_1	1.3676	1.5245	1.8126	1.7984	2.2784	2.9718
S_2	—	1.5764	1.9881	1.9725	2.6233	3.4430
S_3	1.3033	—	1.9881	—	2.7129	3.6118
S_4	1.1236	1.3244	—	1.7984	—	—
r	−0.5965	−1.1142	0.0000	−1.1806	1.0884	3.5379
s	−0.1929	+0.2132	1.3261	1.1806	4.5870	10.9177
t	−0.7923	−0.8984	1.3261	0.0000	5.6886	14.5064
Γ_1	5° 9.41′	11°21.31′	25° 0.0′	24°47.31′	44°36.24′	61°49.43′
Γ_2	—	−2°17.41′	6°15.0′	6°12.04′	19°50.63′	32° 9.83′
Γ_3	−11°42.39′	—	−6°15.0′	—	3°57.00′	13°38.64′
Γ_4	−19°39.36′	−24° 1.63′	—	−24°47.31′	—	—
α	11° 0.36′	8° 1.27′	16°33.68′	16°30.72′	30° 9.31′	42°28.51′
β	30°20.64′	25°58.37′	16°27.75′	25°12.69′	26°39.75′	36°21.39′
ψ	−89°20′	−86.6637	16°13.22′	205°0.17′	−51°49.56′	−49°5.13′
b	0.6766	0.9592	1.6955	−2.1524	1.3611	1.5629
c	1.5726	1.9111	0.2900	0.3538	2.7818	3.8196

12.9. Structural error in linkages.* In Art. 12.7 it was shown that most functions cannot be generated precisely by a four-bar linkage. For any value ϕ of the input link, the structural error is the difference of the ψ values of the generated and the ideal function, Fig. 12.23(b). At most, seven precision points can be specified. In a four-bar function generator there are seven variables—three link ratios, two starting angles, and the two ranges of the input and output links. Usually the two ranges, $\Delta\phi$ and $\Delta\psi$, are specified which leaves five variables. A linkage that satisfies five precision points can then be designed by solving five equations written in terms of these five unknowns. The solution is so involved that the use of an electronic digital computer is the only practical way of solving the problem. Solutions for three and four point approximations can be worked on a desk calculator in a reasonable length of time.

If a fairly good solution is obtained, the structural error can usually be reduced by respacing the precision points. Perhaps the best first

* F. Freudenstein, "Structural Error Analysis in Plane Kinematic Synthesis," *Trans. ASME*, Series B, *Journal of Engineering for Industry*, Vol. 81, 1959, pp. 15–22.

assumption for the spacing of precision points is shown for three and four point approximations in Fig. 12.23(a).   A number of points (twice the number of precision points) are equally spaced on the circumference of a circle and then projected on a diameter to give the spacing in the

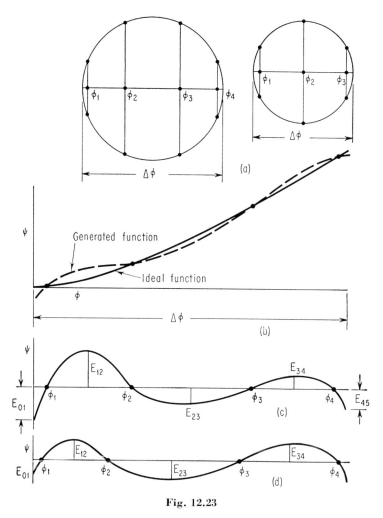

Fig. 12.23

$\Delta\phi$ range.   This is sometimes called Chebichev spacing.   A point and a slope, Fig. 12.16, is approximately equivalent to two points.

A typical example of this spacing is shown at (b) where the error is somewhat exaggerated.   In the greatly exaggerated error curve at (c), it can be seen that the maximum error is E_{12}.   Respacing of the precision points can be used to reduce the large errors by squeezing down the error curve at the proper places.   The maximum error is minimized at (d) by spacing the precision points so that the five errors are equal. This can be seen intuitively since changing any one of the points will increase at least one of the errors. Several trials may be required to minimize the maximum error.

In general, the errors E_{12}, E_{23}, and E_{34} will not be maximum at the midpoint of the corresponding precision points, but this can be taken

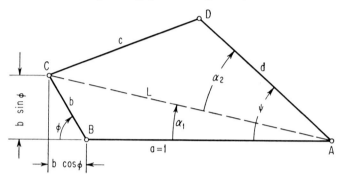

Fig. 12.24

as a close approximation; i.e., E_{12} is assumed to be maximum midway between ϕ_1 and ϕ_2, etc. The ψ values for the ideal function can be determined from the ideal function. The corresponding ψ values for the generated function can be determined from Eq. (12.35). This equation can be derived from Fig. 12.24 as follows. From triangle ABC

$$\alpha_1 = \tan^{-1} \frac{b \sin \phi}{1 + b \cos \phi}$$

$$L^2 = (b \sin \phi)^2 + (1 + b \cos \phi)^2 = (b \sin \phi)^2$$
$$+ 1 + 2b \cos \phi + (b \cos \phi)^2$$

or

$$L^2 = b^2 + 1 + 2b \cos \phi$$

From triangle ACD

$$\alpha_2 = \cos^{-1} \frac{L^2 + d^2 - c^2}{2Ld} = \cos^{-1} \frac{K^2 + 2b \cos \phi}{2Ld}$$

Where $K^2 = 1 + b^2 + d^2 - c^2$, a constant for a given linkage.

$$\psi = \alpha_1 + \alpha_2 = \tan^{-1} \frac{b \sin \phi}{1 + b \cos \phi} + \cos^{-1} \frac{K^2 + 2b \cos \phi}{2Ld} \quad (12.35)$$

12.10. Alternate solution. If a satisfactory solution cannot be obtained by one of the methods described in this chapter, it may be possible to obtain a better solution by reversing the direction of rotation of either the input or output link. Fig. 12.25 will serve to illustrate this. The problem shown is identical with that of Fig. 12.13 except the direction of rotation of link b has been reversed. The resulting linkage is shown at the bottom of Fig. 12.25. The function generated by the linkage of Fig. 12.25 is shown by the dotted curve which is plotted for the three precision points 1, 2, and 3, and two intermediate points, g and h. The reason why the curve is approximately straight from position 1 to position h can be seen when the linkage is examined: as

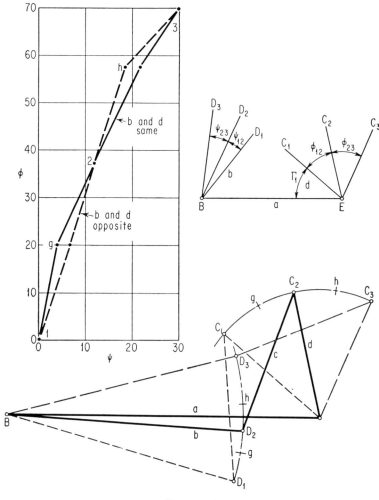

Fig. 12.25

link b moves from D_1 to h, the coupler intersects the line of centers at approximately the same point. When link b moves from h to D_3 the intersection of the coupler with the line of centers moves rapidly to the left giving a smaller slope in the curve from h to 3.

The function generated by the linkage shown in Fig. 12.13 is plotted with a solid line. In this case the intersection of the coupler curve with the line of centers moves more uniformly along the line of centers giving a more uniform change in slope of the curve.

The dotted curve should be plotted on the negative ψ axis, but, to make the comparison easier to see, it is plotted on the positive axis.

12.11. Function generator characteristics. The angular velocity ratio theorem can be useful in visualizing the linkage that will generate a required function. A linkage will be analyzed to make this clear. In Fig. 12.26 the function generated by the linkage for rotation of the input link b from positions D_1 to D_4 is shown. At position BD_1 the coupler

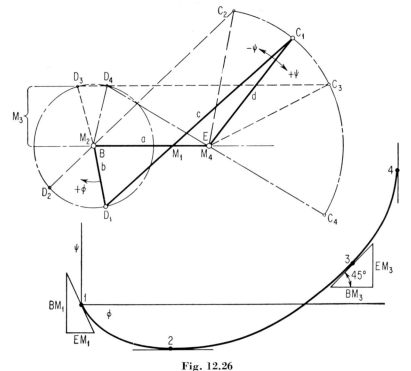

Fig. 12.26

link intersects the line of center at M_1 giving a negative slope (b and d rotate in opposite directions when M lies between the centers) of BM_1/EM_1. At BD_2 links b and c are collinear giving a zero slope; i.e., a small displacement of b will not cause an appreciable displacement of d. At D_3 the coupler is parallel to the line of centers, making $M_3B = M_3E$ which gives a slope of one. As b approaches D_4 a small displacement of b will cause a large displacement of d, and at the limit where c and d are collinear, the slope is infinite. Since link d is the follower, this is a theoretical limit and cannot be reached in practice.

The above discussion can be summarized as follows, if the term coupler be understood to mean the link itself or an extension of it.

1. A *positive slope* requires that the coupler intersect the line of center (BE) outside of the centers.

2. A *slope of 1* requires that the coupler be parallel to the line of centers.

3. A *negative slope* requires that the coupler intersect the line of center between the centers.

4. A *slope of −1* requires that the coupler intersect the line of centers midway between B and E.

5. A *zero slope* requires that the input link and coupler be collinear.

6. An *infinite slope* requires that the output link and coupler be collinear (the theoretical limit).

The graph of a function can then be examined to determine some of the characteristics of the linkage. The coordinates of a point on the graph give the relative angular displacements of links b and d, and the slope gives the point where the coupler intersects the line of centers. In some cases it will be obvious that a four-bar linkage cannot even approximately generate the function.

PROBLEMS

12.1. Design a four-bar linkage (Fig. P 12.1) to perform the following function. Two points B_1 and C_1 on a link are to be moved to position B_2C_2 in 0.35 seconds and are to be returned in 0.25 seconds. The two positions are the extreme positions of the link. The driving crank and coupler link must lie between line 1 and line 2. Determine the speed of the crank (rpm) and its direction of rotation. (The drawing can be made on an $8\frac{1}{2} \times 11$ sheet with point C_2 located $2\frac{1}{2}$ inches from the top and 1 inch from the left edge of the paper.)

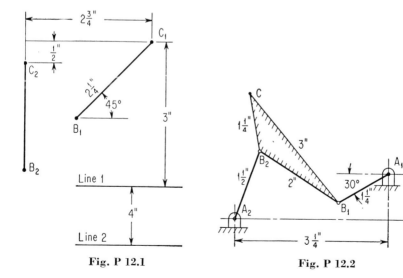

Fig. P 12.1   **Fig. P 12.2**

12.2. Use Roberts' law to construct the alternate linkages for Fig. P 12.2.

12.3. Use Roberts' law to construct the alternate linkages for Fig. P 12.3.

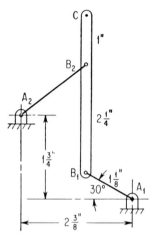

Fig. P 12.3

12.4. (a) Design a four-bar linkage to satisfy the angular displacements shown in Fig. P 12.4. Invert about position BD_1. (b) Same as (a), except invert about position BD_2. (c) Same as (a), except invert about position BD_3.

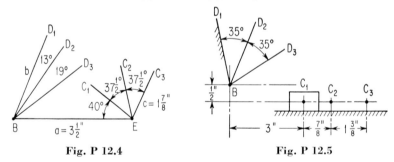

Fig. P 12.4   **Fig. P 12.5**

12.5. Design an offset slider-crank mechanism to satisfy the conditions shown in Fig. P 12.5. Invert about position BD_1.

12.6. Use point-position-reduction to design a four-bar linkage to satisfy the requirements shown in Fig. P 12.6. Invert about position BD_3.

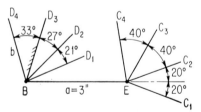

Fig. P 12.6

12.7. A four-bar linkage is to generate the function $y = x^{3.2}$. x varies from 2 to 4. The $\phi(x)$ range of the linkage is to be 0° to 80°, and the $\psi(y)$ range is to be 0° to 100°. Write the equation of the function in terms of ϕ and ψ for the ranges given.

12.8. A four-bar linkage is to generate the function $y = \log_{10} x$. x is to vary from 1 to 10. The $\phi(x)$ range of the linkage is to be 0° to 135°, and the $\psi(y)$ range is to be 0° to 80°. Write the equation in terms of ϕ and ψ for the ranges given.

12.9. Design a four-bar linkage to generate the function $y = \log_{10} x$. x is to vary from 1 to 5. Precision points are to be at 1, 2, and $4\frac{1}{2}$, and the slope at 2 is to be specified. The $\phi(x)$ range is to be 80° and the $\psi(y)$ range is to be 100°. Use point-position-reduction between 1 and 2, Fig. P 12.9.

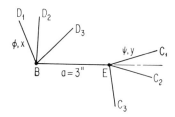

Fig. P 12.9

12.10. Design a four-bar linkage to generate the function $y = \log_{10} x$. x is to vary from 1 to 10. Precision points are to be at 1, 2, 4, and 9. The $\psi(y)$ range is to be 100°, and the $\phi(x)$ range is to be 90°. Use point-position-reduction between 3 and 4, Fig. P 12.10.

12.11. Design a four-bar linkage to generate the function $y = x^{1.4}$. x is to vary from 1 to 7. Precision points are to be at 1, 3, 5, and 7. The $\psi(y)$ range is to be 80°, and the $\phi(x)$ range is to be 120°. Use point-position-reduction between 1 and 2, Fig. 12.11. Invert about position BD_3.

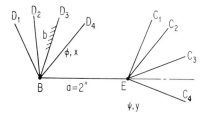   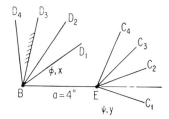

Fig. P 12.10   Fig. P 12.11

12.12. Use Freudenstein's method to design a four-bar linkage to generate the function $y = e^x$. x is to vary from 0 to 1 with precision points at 0, $\frac{1}{2}$, and 1. Assume 90° ranges for both ϕ and ψ. Assume starting angles $\phi_1 = 62°$ and $\psi_1 = 40°$.

12.13. Use Freudenstein's method to design a four-bar linkage to generate the function $y = \dfrac{1}{x}$· x is to vary from 1 to 2 with precision points at 1, $1\frac{1}{2}$ and 2. Assume 90° ranges for both ϕ and ψ.

12.14. Resolve problem 12.10 using Worthley's method. Put the x range at the right and the y range at the left.

CHAPTER 13

Mechanical Computing Mechanisms*

13.1. Introduction. Computers are of two fundamental types—digital and analog. A digital or arithmetical computing machine accepts inputs in numerical form and calculates in discrete steps a single result from a set of supplied quantities. The machine is essentially an assembly of counting devices. More complex digital computers may use special number systems adapted to this type of computation, such as the binary system. These more complex machines present their results as a series of numbers on counters, punched cards, or magnetic tape.

In operation there is an appreciable delay between the input and the result, but there is no theoretical limit on accuracy. Enough counting devices can be aggregated to handle any required number of digits. The adding machine, the electrical desk calculator, and the electronic digital computer are typical examples of digital computers.

An analog computer, which represents a variable by the magnitude of a physical quantity, accepts continuous-variable inputs and is theoretically capable of response to infinitesimally small variations in the inputs. Analog computers are further divided into three types according to the general nature of the analog quantity—electrical, pneumatic, and mechanical.

A mechanical system employs analogs in the forms of force, torque, velocity, and position. The answers are expressed as the magnitudes of such physical quantities, interpreted on appropriate scales.

Analog computers are particularly adaptable to continuous solutions and may be constructed for virtually instantaneous response. Limitations on accuracy are dependent, apart from fabrication errors, only on accuracy of measurement. With mechanical analog computers it is

---

* The author is indebted to "Mechanical Computing Mechanisms," by R. R. Reid and DuRay E. Stromback (*Product Engineering*, August, September, October, November, 1949) for the approach to the material in the first part of this chapter. Other references include M. Fry, "Designing Computing Mechanisms," *Machine Design*, August–December, 1945; G. W. Michalec, "Analog Computing Mechanisms, *Machine Design*, March, 1959; A. Svoboda, *Computing Mechanisms and Linkages*, McGraw-Hill Book Company, Inc., 1948; J. H. Billings, *Applied Kinematics*, 3rd ed., D. Van Nostrand Company, Inc.

possible to perform such operations as addition, subtraction, multiplication, division, generation of functions of one or two variables, resolution of vectors, integration, and differentiation. Because of growing emphasis on automatic control and instrumentation, mechanical analog computers are of increasing importance to design engineers.

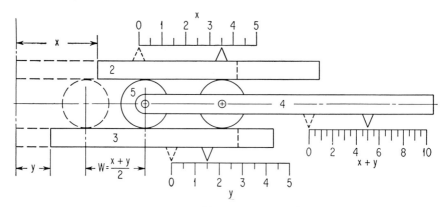

Fig. 13.1

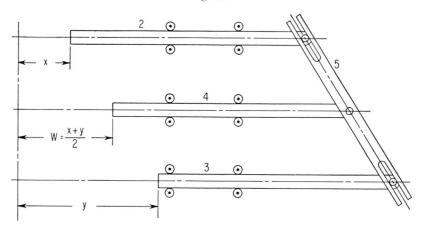

Fig. 13.2

Before we consider the design of a computer, individual mechanisms will be analyzed.

13.2. Addition and subtraction. Some form of differential mechanism is used universally for adding and subtracting two variables by mechanical means. Two basic types are the bevel or spur gear differential and the link and slide differential. These devices solve the general equation

$$w = \frac{x \pm y}{2} \tag{13.1}$$

where w is usually the output and x and y are the inputs. One of the simplest differential adders is shown in Fig. 13.1 where the displacements of bars 2 and 3 represent the inputs x and y, and the displacement of bar 4 represents the sum of $x + y$. The 2 in the denominator is eliminated by making the scale of the sum $x + y$ twice that of the inputs,

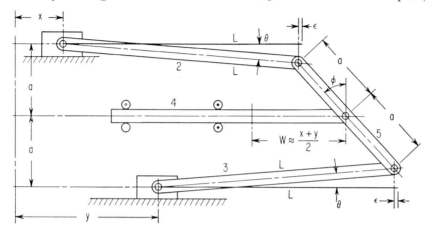

Fig. 13.3

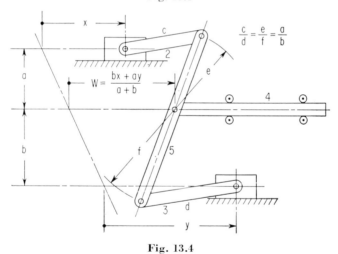

Fig. 13.4

x and y. To prevent slipping, racks and pinions are usually used in place of bars and rollers. Subtraction can be performed by extending the scales to the left.

Three types of linkage differentials are shown in Figs. 13.2, 13.3, and 13.4. The first linkage, Fig. 13.2, is exact but requires a slotted link 5 with sliders. If pin joints are substituted for the sliders, Fig. 13.3, the angularities of links 2 and 3 will introduce an error ϵ in the sum. In

Fig. 13.4, the input sliders are put on opposite sides of link 5. The errors due to the angularities of links 2 and 3 will compensate each other

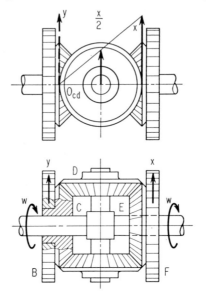

Fig. 13.5

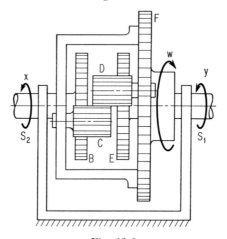

Fig. 13.6

providing $c/d = e/f = a/b$. The output

$$w = \frac{bx \pm ay}{a + b} \qquad (13.2)$$

will reduce to Eq. (13.1) if $a = b$.

Perhaps the most commonly used adder is the bevel gear differential, Figs. 13.5 and 13.7. The angular displacements of gears F and

B are the inputs x and y, and the output w is represented by the angular displacement of the spider, or arm. The operation of this mechanism can be understood most easily by considering instantaneous velocities.   Let x be the velocity of the point of contact of gears E and D, and assume that gear C is stationary.   Then, since O_{cd} is the instant center of gears C and D, the velocity of the center of gear D which carries the arm will be $x/2$.   If at all times the angular velocity of the arm is half that of gear E, the displacement of the arm will be half that of

Fig. 13.7.   Bevel gear differential.   (Courtesy of Librascope, Inc.)

gear E.   Similarly, if gear E is considered to be fixed and a velocity y is assumed, the velocity of the center of gear D will be $y/2$ which will add or subtract from $x/2$ depending on the directions of rotation of gears C and E.   Equation (13.1) therefore holds for this type of differential. The operation of the spur gear differential, Fig. 13.6, is similar to that of the bevel gear differential.   Gear differentials are compact and have unlimited angular displacement capacity.

In general, linkage differentials are used with linear displacements, and gear differentials are used with angular displacements; however, by including the required gears and racks, either type can be used with either linear or angular displacements.

13.3. Multiplication and division.   The simplest multiplication to mechanize is multiplication of a variable by a constant. That is, $y = cx$, which may be done by a gear ratio equal to the required c for rotary motion or by a simple lever system for straight line motion.

The problem of multiplying two variables is more complex.   The form of the equation is $xy = cw$.   The similar triangle method of performing this multiplication is shown in Fig. 13.8.   This mechanism

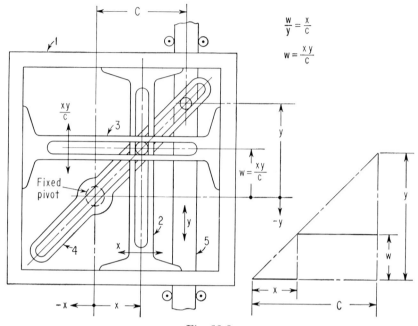

Fig. 13.8

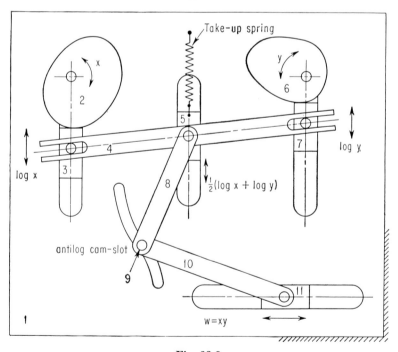

Fig. 13.9

provides a theoretically exact solution and, as shown in Fig. 13.8, may be constructed to permit both variables to change algebraic sign.

A second, theoretically exact method for multiplying is to add the logarithms of the input variables, Fig. 13.9.   Cams 2 and 6 are designed so that the rotational inputs, x and y, produce respectively the linear

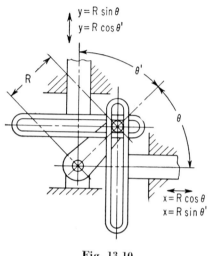

$$y = R \sin \theta$$
$$y = R \cos \theta'$$

$$R$$

$$\theta'$$

$$\theta$$

$$x = R \cos \theta$$
$$x = R \sin \theta'$$

Fig. 13.10

displacements $\log x$ and $\log y$.   A linkage differential adds these giving $\frac{1}{2}(\log x + \log y)$.   This is fed through an antilog cam slot giving the desired result, $w = xy$.

This method has several disadvantages.   Neither variable may be permitted to reach zero or negative values, or even approach zero, since the log of zero is indeterminate.   Trouble will ensue if the value of the variable becomes less than 1.0, since beyond this point the log becomes negative.   If such a condition is unavoidable, the method still may be used in the design if both sides of the equation can be multiplied by a factor so chosen as to make the minimum value of the variable always greater than 1.0.   For example, in the equation $w = (x)(y)$ where $1 \leq y \leq 5$ and $0.5 \leq x \leq 3$ we multiply both sides by 3 giving $3w = (3x)(y)$.   Then $\log 3 + \log w = \log 3x + \log y$, and the cam becomes actually a log $3x$ cam.   The answer taken from the antilog cam is clearly $3w$; but this may be accounted for in choosing the scale factor of w.

13.4. Trigonometric Functions.   The continuous trigonometric functions $y = \sin \theta$ and $y = \cos \theta$ may be generated over any portion of the entire range of θ from 0° to 360° with a Scotch yoke.   The radius R of the rotating arm determines the scale factor of the device.   Two Scotch yokes at right angles, Fig. 3.10, will produce simultaneously as two perpendicular motions the sine and cosine functions of the same angular input variable.

Another type of sine-cosine generator is based on a cyclic gear train, Fig. 13.13. A pinion of radius $r = R/2$ meshes with an internal gear of

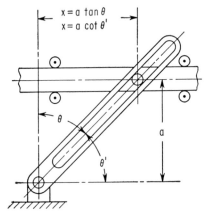

$$x = a \tan \theta$$
$$x = a \cot \theta'$$

Fig. 13.11

Fig. 13.12. Gear sine-cosine mechanism. (Courtesy of Librascope, Inc.)

radius R. When the pinion is rolled on the internal gear, a point C on the circumference of the pinion will trace a hypocycloid. The equations of a hypocycloid are

$$x = (R - r) \cos \theta + r \cos \frac{R - r}{r} \theta \qquad (13.3)$$

$$y = (R - r) \sin \theta - r \sin \frac{R - r}{r} \theta \qquad (13.4)$$

For the special case of $r = R/2$ the equations become $x = R \cos \theta$ and $y = 0$. These equations show that C moves horizontally with simple harmonic motion. A standard computer element based on this principle is shown in Fig. 13.12.

The trigonometric functions $y = \tan \theta$ and $y = \cot \theta$ are discontinuous at certain points in the range of θ between $0°$ and $360°$. There is, therefore, no geometric device or any cam mechanism which will

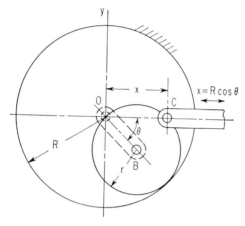

Fig. 13.13

mechanize the full range of these functions. A cam designed to mechanize a portion of the range of one of these functions must have a very steep slope as it approaches the point of discontinuity. Cams that cover a considerable range, say $0°$ to $80°$ for the tangent, must have a large average radius and a very small total throw to keep the pressure angle within practical limits. The result is a small scale factor output. A geometric device for tangent and cotangent mechanization is shown in Fig. 13.11.

13.5. Resolvers. The name of this mechanism, Fig. 13.14, is derived from its action as a resolver of a vector displacement into its rectangular components. The length R and orientation θ represent the vector, and x and y represent its components. The operation can be understood by considering each input separately. Assume that the magnitude of the vector R is to be held constant by holding shaft S_1, and that the orientation θ is to be changed by turning shaft S_2. In order that R remain constant it is necessary that gear A turn with the table (gear B) to prevent the rack from rolling on gear A and changing the value of R. This is accomplished by means of a bevel gear differential. For illustrative purposes, numbers of teeth have been assumed for the gears. When shaft S_2 is turned, gear B is driven by gear C with a reduction of 2 to 1. At the same time gear E, which is fastened to the spider

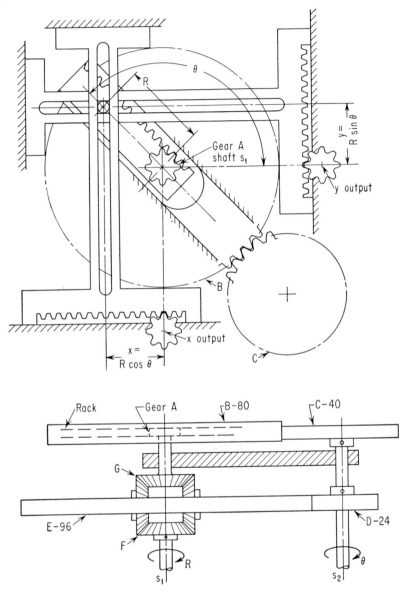

Fig. 13.14

or arm of the differential, is turned by gear D in the same direction as B but only half as far. With shaft S_1 fixed, gear G, which turns gear A, will turn twice as far as gear E. Thus, with shaft S_1 held stationary, any rotation of shaft S_2 will cause gear A to turn with gear B.

With shaft S_2 fixed, any turning of shaft S_1 will cause gear A to turn an equal amount in the opposite direction. This will drive the rack along the slot in gear B which changes the value of R.   The inputs to S_1 and S_2 can, of course, be applied simultaneously.

13.6. Inverter.   The linkage, Fig. 13.16, can be used for obtaining the reciprocal of a number.   From similar triangles

$$\frac{x}{e} = \frac{f}{y} \quad \text{or} \quad x = \frac{ef}{y} \quad\quad (13.5)$$

If desired, the scale factor ef can be made unity by a proper choice of

Fig. 13.15.   **Precision rack type component solver.**   (Courtesy of General Precision Lab., Inc.)

dimensions e and f.   This linkage, like the tangent linkage described earlier and the squaring linkage which follows, is limited to certain ranges of values because of unfavorable transmission angles of the links. It can be seen that link 2 approaches an infinite length as y approaches zero.

13.7. Squaring.   In Fig. 13.17, CDB is a right angle.   From similar triangles, the following relations can be written.

$$\frac{y}{x_1} = \frac{x_2}{y}, \quad y^2 = x_1x_2, \quad y = \sqrt{x_1x_2} \quad\quad (13.6)$$

The scales for the three variables are equal and start at point O.   The linkage can be used for several purposes.   If x_1 and x_2 are the inputs, the output y will be the square root of their product. If x_2 is made constant by fixing point C at $x_2 = 1$, the result is a square and square root relation. When C is not set at $x_2 = 1$, it is necessary to introduce a scale factor.

13.8. Integration. The classic two-disk integrator, Fig. 13.18, consists of a smooth disk, 2, rotated by an input variable, θ, and an output

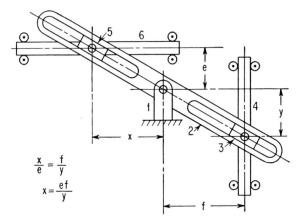

$$\frac{x}{e} = \frac{f}{y}$$

$$x = \frac{ef}{y}$$

Fig. 13.16

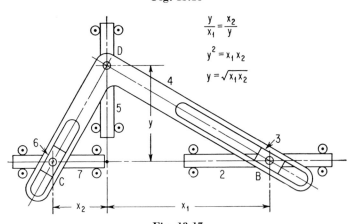

$$\frac{y}{x_1} = \frac{x_2}{y}$$

$$y^2 = x_1 x_2$$

$$y = \sqrt{x_1 x_2}$$

Fig. 13.17

disk, 3, perpendicular to and spring loaded against disk 2. The radial displacement of disk 3 from the center line of rotation of disk 2 is the input variable y. Assuming perfect rolling contact between the rotations of the disks, and perfect slipping as disk 3 moves radially along disk 2, the arc $y\, d\theta$ on disk 2 equals the arc $r\, dw$ on disk 3. Then

$$dw = \frac{1}{r} y\, d\theta \qquad \text{or} \qquad w = \frac{1}{r} \int y\, d\theta \qquad (13.7)$$

The value $\dfrac{1}{r}$ is known as the integrator constant.

The disadvantage of the two-disk integrator is that the output torque is limited by the frictional force developed between the two disks, but the force required to change the second variable, y, is directly proportional to the frictional force between the disks. The two requirements for good operation are opposed.

This objection is largely overcome in the design of the ball-disk integrator shown in Figs. 13.19 and 13.20. Disk 3 is replaced by a

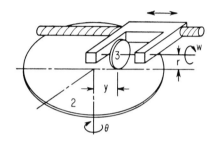

Fig. 13.18

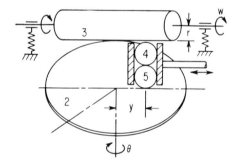

Fig. 13.19

roller which is driven by disk 2 through idler balls 4 and 5. There is then rolling action when the balls are shifted radially on disk 2. This permits a larger output torque which can be obtained by increasing the spring force between 2 and 3.

13.9. Differentiation. The general problem of differentiating one variable with respect to another is solved by reversing an integrator, but this does not yield a theoretically exact solution. The method requires an additional mechanical differential, Fig. 13.21. The required derivative is $w = dy/dx$; i.e., the derivative is the ratio of the instantaneous speeds of shafts S_1 and S_2, which is expressed by the position w of the ball carriage. The spider, or arm, of the differential is used to drive the ball carriage, either mechanically (in Fig. 13.21 the ball carriage is attached to rack 6, which is driven by a gear attached to the differential arm) or through a servo system. When Shafts S_1 and S_2 are turned, the rotations of gears A and B will cause the arm-gear to move the rack until a position is reached which produces equal speeds but opposite directions of rotation for gears A and B. At this time the position w of the carriage is a measure of the ratio of the speeds of shafts S_1 and S_2.

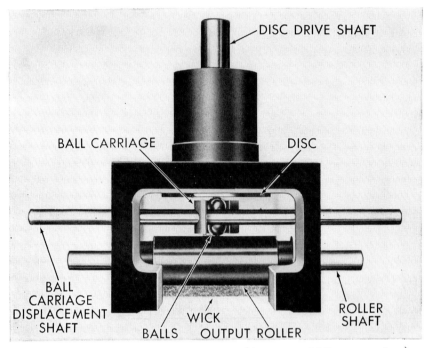

Fig. 13.20.   Ball and disc integrator.   (Courtesy of Librascope, Inc.)

The position w of the ball carriage in terms of the differential inputs is

$$y - \int w \, dx = \frac{w}{k} \qquad (13.8)$$

where k is a scale factor. When this equation is differentiated with respect to x we obtain

$$\frac{dy}{dx} = w + \frac{1}{k}\frac{dw}{dx} \qquad (13.9)$$

In order that $dy/dx = w$, dw/dx must be zero. This will occur only after an infinite time, but the last term can be made small by choosing a large value for k. Equation (13.9) can be written in the form

$$\frac{dw}{w - dy/dx} = -k \, dx \qquad (13.10)$$

For the case of $\frac{dy}{dx} = $ constant, we can integrate giving

$$ln\left(w - \frac{dy}{dx}\right) = -kx + C_1$$

or

$$w - \frac{dy}{dx} = e^{-kx+C_1} = e^{-kx}e^{C_1} = Ce^{-kx}$$

or

$$w = \frac{dy}{dx} + Ce^{-kx} \tag{13.11}$$

The following example will illustrate the above discussion.   In Fig. 13.21, assume that shaft S_1 is stationary and that the ball carriage is

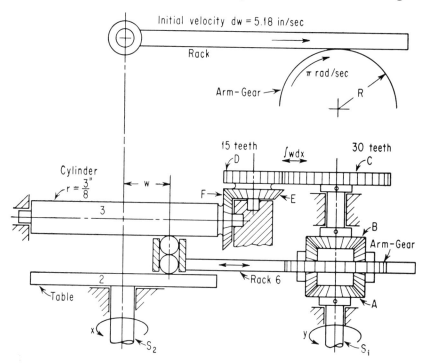

Fig. 13.21

on the centerline of shaft S_2.   This is the equilibrium position since there is no y input; $w = dy/dx = 0$.   Assume a unit step function; i.e., let dy/dx suddenly change from 0 to 1 and remain at 1.   If all measurements are started at this instant the initial conditions are $x = 0$ and $w = 0$.   Shaft S_1 begins to turn at a constant rate y which turns the arm-gear and moves the carriage off the centerline of shaft S_2.   This causes the cylinder to turn which drives gear B.   The turning of B subtracts from y in the differential and reduces the rate at which the carriage moves outward.   The ball carriage moves more and more slowly as it progresses and the speed of gear B approaches that of A.   At the end of an infinite time the ball carriage comes to rest.   This can be seen from Eq. (13.11); the Ce^{-kx} term is zero when x is infinite. For this condition gears A and B have equal speeds in opposite directions. The position of the carriage, w, will then represent $dy/dx = 1$.

We will now determine the size of the arm-gear needed to produce the required response in order that the error in w is 0.1 per cent after shaft S_2 has turned once. Substitution of the initial values, $w = 0$, $dy/dx = 1$, $x = 0$, into Eq. (13.11) gives the value of the constant, $C = -1$. It is not necessary, but convenient, to introduce time and work with velocities; assume $dy = dx = 2\pi$ radians per sec. Substitution of the value for the constant, and the final values, $w = 0.999$, $dy/dx = 1$, $x = 2\pi$, into Eq. (13.11) gives

$$0.999 = 1 - e^{-k2\pi}$$

$$e^{k2\pi} = 1000, \quad \text{or} \quad 2\pi k = 6.91, \quad k = 1.1$$

When this value of k and the initial values are substituted into Eq. (13.10), we obtain

$$\frac{dw}{0 - 1} = -1.1 \times 2\pi \quad \text{or} \quad dw = 6.91$$

This states that the initial velocity of the ball carriage is 6.91 units on the w scale per second. The length of one w unit in inches can be determined from the data given in Fig. 13.21.

$$\frac{dy}{dx} = 1 = \frac{w}{\text{cylinder radius, in.}} \times \frac{\text{teeth on } D}{\text{teeth on } C}$$

$$1 = \frac{w}{\frac{3}{8}} \frac{15}{30}, \quad \text{or} \quad w = 0.75 \text{ in.}$$

The initial velocity, dw, in inches is then

$$dw = 0.75 \times 6.91 = 5.18 \text{ in. per sec.}$$

The radius of the arm-gear (shown at the top of Fig. 13.21) can be determined if it is remembered that, initially, the speed of the arm-gear is half that of shaft S_1

$$R = \frac{V}{\omega} = \frac{5.18}{\pi} = 1.65 \text{ in.}$$

This example applies only to the data given for the example, but it does give some idea of the nature of the response.

In many cases it is necessary to obtain the derivative of a variable with respect to time. This can be done easily since any good tachometer will be satisfactory; i.e., the speed indicated by the tachometer will be dy/dt.

13.10. Four-bar linkages. These linkages have been widely used for a long time, and, as improved methods for designing them continue to be developed, they will be used more extensively in the future. Linkages are relatively inexpensive to construct, are positive in action, and have essentially no backlash if preloaded ball bearings are used.

Fourteen linkages, each with five precision points, are included in Table 13.1.* The sign conventions and nomenclature follow that of the linkage shown at the upper left of Fig. 13.22. To further illustrate the table, three of the linkages at the start and in the final positions are also shown in Fig. 13.22. Linkage number 10 differs from the others in

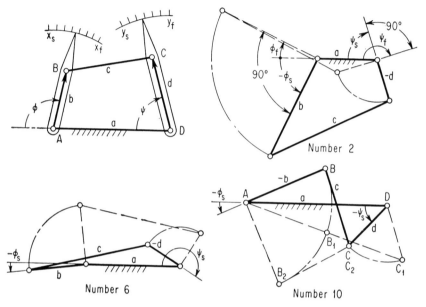

Fig. 13.22

that both the negative and positive branches of the function are generated. It is usually difficult to generate a function of this type with a small error, the error in this case being 2.34°. When link b is turned clockwise from the starting position B through half of its range, link d moves in a counter-clockwise direction through 60° to position C_1. This is the final position for the negative branch. Since the slope of the graph of the function is zero at this point, links b and c are collinear. As link b moves on into position B_2, link d turns in a clockwise direction to C_2.

The first precision point x_1 and the corresponding link angles ϕ_1 and ψ_1 are given in Table 13.1. The starting angles ϕ_s and ψ_s, calculated for the ideal function, are also given. Because of structural error (see Chapter 12) the starting angle ψ_s on the linkage may differ from the ideal given in the table, but the error will not exceed the maximum error listed

* F. Freudenstein, "Four-Bar Function Generators," *Machine Design*, November 27, 1958.

TABLE 13.1. Five Precision Point Linkages

Linkage number	Function $y = f(x)$	Range $x_s \leq x \leq x_f$	$\phi_f-\phi_s$	$\psi_f-\psi_s$	x_1	ϕ_1	ψ_1	ϕ_s	ψ_s	b/a	c/a	d/a	Maximum error degrees
							Link angles				Link proportions		
1	$\log_{10} x$	$1 \leq x \leq 2$	60	60	1.01446	52.628	259.077	51.760	257.840	-3.3523	0.8456	3.4855	0.0037
2	$\sin x$	$0 \leq x \leq 90°$	90	90	2.76337	-62.263	75.606	-65.027	71.268	1.8344	2.2385	-0.6936	0.1900
3	$\tan x$	$0 \leq x \leq 45°$	90	90	1.62460	269.709	124.190	266.460	121.638	-2.6603	7.4304	8.6856	0.038
4	e^x	$0 \leq x \leq 1$	90	90	0.02781	241.644	40.423	239.141	38.945	-3.4995	0.8785	3.3993	0.0258
5	$1/x$	$1 \leq x \leq 2$	90	-90	1.01303	33.804	120.213	32.631	122.530	-0.3848	1.0305	0.3845	0.0161
6	$x^{1.5}$	$0 \leq x \leq 1$	90	90	0.01183	-5.171	211.689	-6.236	211.573	0.6248	1.3089	-0.4006	0.146
7	x^2	$0 \leq x \leq 1$	90	90	0.03369	-29.321	233.836	-32.353	233.734	2.5233	3.3296	-0.5559	0.0673
8	$x^{2.5}$	$0 \leq x \leq 1$	90	90	0.02253	-88.315	44.492	-90.342	44.486	-1.8009	0.9083	1.2737	0.412
9	x^3	$0 \leq x \leq 1$	90	90	0.02932	-85.921	37.637	-88.561	37.634	-1.6056	0.9254	1.1074	0.5095
10	x^2	$-1 \leq x \leq 1$	90	60†	-0.9452	-21.18	-53.67	-23.646	-47.274	-0.6102	0.5656	0.3804	2.34
11	$-\log_{10} x$	$1 \leq x \leq 2$	60	-60	1.01665	60.042	100.012	59.043	101.442	-0.2872	1.0344	0.2614	0.00121*
12	$-\log_{10} x$	$1 \leq x \leq 2$	90	-90	1.01314	46.226	121.845	45.043	123.541	-0.1976	1.0109	0.1908	0.006*
13	$\log_{10} x$	$1 \leq x \leq 10$	60	90	1.000	19.372	-85.965	19.372	-85.965	-1.2163	2.8051	3.1917	0.382*
14	$x^{1.5}$	$0 \leq x \leq 1$	90	90	0.01179	-57.297	97.203	-58.358	97.088	-5.7825	3.2790	2.1766	**0.030***

* *Maximum error not minimized.*

† *This value refers to maximum output travel.*

310

in the last column of the table.   If the link proportions are correct and ϕ_s is taken as the starting angle for link b, the function will be generated with minimum error, i.e., least maximum error.   The linkage can be checked by setting link b at angle ϕ_1 and then comparing the angle of link d with ψ_1 in the table.   Since this is a precision point, the angles ϕ_1 and ψ_1 in the table are correct for both the ideal function and the function generated by the linkage.   For linkage number 13 note that the lower end of the range was taken as the first precision point; hence, $\phi_1 = \phi_s$ and $\psi_1 = \psi_s$.

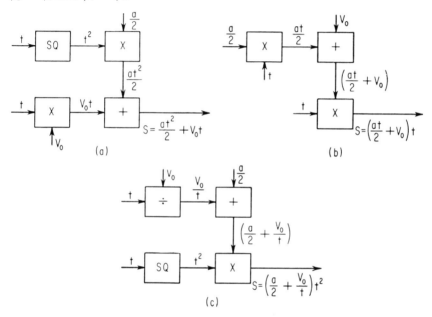

Fig. 13.23

13.11. Schematic design.   The design of a computer is usually started as a simple block diagram which shows the order in which the mathematical operations are to be performed.   The given equation should be studied, and, if possible, rewritten in several forms to provide a variety of additional possibilities.   For example, consider an equation of motion

$$s = \frac{1}{2} at^2 + v_0 t \tag{13.12}$$

By factoring, two other forms of this expression can be obtained

$$s = \left(\frac{at}{2} + v_0\right) t \tag{13.13}$$

$$s = \left(\frac{a}{2} + \frac{v_0}{t}\right) t^2 \tag{13.14}$$

The block diagrams for these three equations are shown in Fig. 13.23. Arrangement (c) requires a divider, a multiplier, a squaring device, and an adding mechanism. Arrangement (a) requires the same number of components, but the divider is replaced by a multiplier. This is an advantage if the range of t begins at zero, since division by a number close to zero results in a large value of the answer and creates serious mechanical difficulties; no such problem arises with multiplication by zero, where the answer itself approaches zero. Arrangement (b) uses three of the same components as (a), but eliminates the squaring device. Therefore (b) appears to be the most favorable approach, on the basis of block diagram analysis, and should be chosen for the first preliminary design.

Example. Design a computer to solve the equation

$$w = \sqrt{t^2 - v^2} \tag{13.15}$$

where t and v are the inputs. The range of v is from 0 to 5, and the range of t is from 5 to 15. This relation can be written in the following forms

$$w = v\sqrt{\frac{t^2}{v^2} - 1} \tag{13.16}$$

and

$$w = \sqrt{(t - v)(t + v)} \tag{13.17}$$

The block diagrams for these three expressions are shown in Fig. 13.24. The expression, Eq. (13.16), shown at (b), must be discarded because of division by zero. The arrangement at (c) can be mechanized, but multiplication is rela-

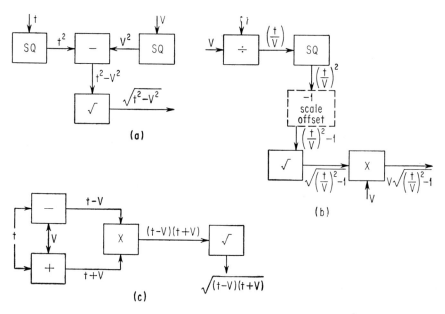

Fig. 13.24

tively complex and should be avoided if possible.   The first arrangement shown
at (a) is the simplest to mechanize and will be chosen for this example.

One solution using cams is shown in Fig. 13.25.   While cams are easy to
design, they are usually not as satisfactory as linkages.   If satisfactory linkages
are available, or if the production is to be large enough to warrant the engineering
cost of designing the linkages, they should be considered.

To illustrate the use of four-bar linkages, a detailed solution is shown in
Fig. 13.26.   A single basic linkage, number 7 in Table 13.1, serves for two squaring linkages (A) and (B), and the square root linkage (C).   Before we consider

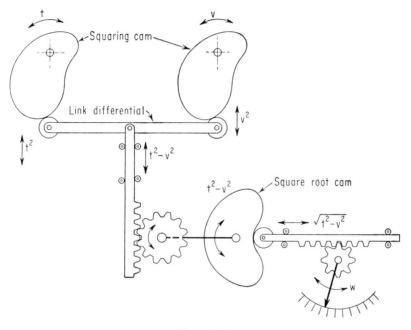

Fig. 13.25

the design, it is necessary to understand that the linkage generates the portion
of the parabola shown in Fig. 13.27 (Q). Each point on the curve OP represents
the angular displacements ϕ and ψ of links b and d respectively from the starting
position, regardless of the numbers on the input and output scales.

The input and output scales for linkage (A), Fig. 13.26, are also shown at (A)
in Fig. 13.27.   Obviously these two scales are not the same, (the v^2 scale is five
times larger than the v scale) but this does not matter.   The t and t^2 scales on
linkage (B) are again not equal.   Note in Fig. 13.26 (B) that only a portion of
the ranges are used, but for determining gear ratios, it is convenient to consider
the entire ranges.   In order that the subtraction $(t^2 - v^2)$ have physical meaning,
it is necessary that the t^2 and v^2 scales be matched (e.g., one cannot successfully
use the slider from a five-inch slide rule in a ten-inch slide rule).   This can be
accomplished with a 9 to 1 gear ratio to step up the t^2 input to the differential.
The parabola OP', Fig. 13.27(B), represents the angular relationship of link b

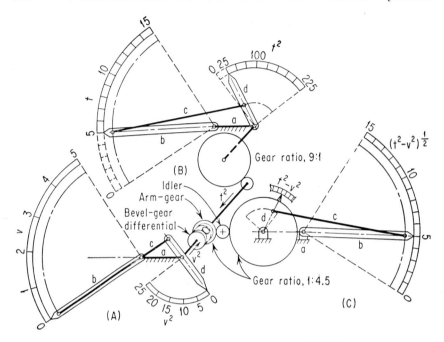

Fig. 13.26.   Computer for solving the equation $w = \sqrt{t^2 - V^2}$.   The drawing is expanded for clarity.   Note the compact design of the linkages in Fig. 13.28.

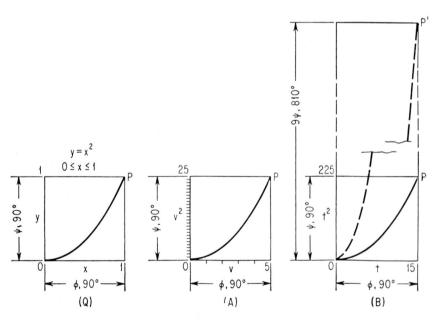

Fig. 13.27

and the stepped-up shaft to the differential. If the input of linkage (A) is set at zero, the output $(t^2 - v^2)^{1/2}$ of linkage (C) becomes t; i.e., the output reading of (C) should be identical with the input of (B). With linkage (A) fixed, the turns of the arm of the differential will be half that of the t^2 input shaft; hence, the gear ratio of the differential arm-gear and link d of linkage (C) must be 1 to

Fig. 13.28. Typical linkage computer. (Courtesy of Librascope, Inc.)

4.5. This results from the 9 to 1 gear ratio and the fact that the arm-gear turns only half as far as the t^2 input. When linkage (A) is in the starting position, links c and b are collinear, but this does not matter since link b is the driver. If $t = v = 5$, the output of linkage (C) is zero, which brings links b and c into a collinear position. This will not be satisfactory since b is the follower and not the driver, as is the case in linkage (A). For satisfactory operation it will be necessary to reduce one of the input ranges; e.g., the v range is to be from 0 to 4.5, or the t range is to be from 6 to 15. If it is necessary to use the original ranges, linkage (C) can be replaced with a square root cam. The ranges in this example were purposely chosen to illustrate this possible difficulty.

PROBLEMS

13.1. The range of an input variable is to be represented by a 1 in. displacement of a slider having rectilinear motion.   Design a simple linkage that transforms this to a rectilinear output with a 1.75 in. displacement; i.e., the input is to be multiplied by the constant 1.75.

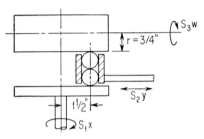

Fig. P 13.2

13.2. Let S_1, S_2, and S_3 be scale factors for the integrator, Fig. P 13.2.   The basic equation is

$$w = \frac{1}{r} \int y \, dx \qquad (P\ 13.1)$$

and with scale factors is

$$S_3 w = \frac{1}{r} \int S_2 y S_1 \, dx \qquad (P\ 13.2)$$

Then

$$S_3 = \frac{S_2 S_1}{r} \qquad (P\ 13.3)$$

Assume that the usable radius of the disc is 1.5 in., and that $0 \le y \le 18$.   If the 1.5 in. radius is used, the scale factor will be

$$S_2 = \frac{1.5}{18} = \frac{1}{12} \text{ in. per unit of } y$$

Assume

$$S_1 = \frac{1}{10} \text{ revolution per unit of } x$$

Then

$$S_3 = \frac{S_2 S_1}{r} = \frac{4}{3 \times 12 \times 10} = \frac{1}{90} \text{ revolution per unit of } w$$

Assume that y remains constant with a value of 6 and that x changes from 0 to 5. Determine the value of w from Eq. (P 13.1).   The value of r is included in a scale factor and should be neglected in this calculation.   It is usually included in the basic equation because it is built into the integrator and cannot be changed. Check the value of w by using the theory of rolling bodies.

13.3. The product of two variables may be obtained by mechanizing the equation

$$w = xy = \int_{y_0}^{y} x \, dy + \int_{x_0}^{x} y \, dx$$

The arrangement of the components is shown in Fig. P 13.3. Assume that the integrators and scales are the same as in Prob. 13.2. The inputs to the adder have been increased by the ratio 2 to 1. While this is not necessary, it will make the scale of the adder output (the turns of the arm) the same as the scales for the cylinders of the integrators.

(a) Let $x = 4$ and $y = 5$. Check the multiplication by using the theory of rolling bodies. Assume that the balls are on the centers of the discs, then apply the x factor followed by the y factor.

(b) Same as (a), except apply the y factor followed by the x factor.

(c) Same as (a), except apply $x = 2$, then $y = 5$, followed by a change of x from 2 to 4.

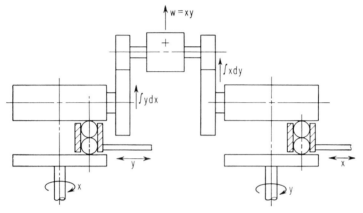

Fig. P 13.3

13.4. Mechanize the function $w = (xy)^{1.5}$. The ranges are $5 \leq x \leq 20$ and $0 \leq y \leq 5$. Use only gears, adders, and four-bar linkages from Table 13.1. Note that

$$xy = \frac{1}{4}[(x + y)^2 - (x - y)^2]$$

Make a sketch, similar to Fig. 13.26, of the mechanism.

CHAPTER 14

Constrained Motion, Number Synthesis

14.1. Constrained motion, plane mechanisms.

Grubler's equations for mechanisms, which apply in most designs, (exceptions will be considered later) have been derived by Bottema in a simple manner by subtracting the number of constraints at the joints from the total number of degrees of freedom of all the links.[*] Plane mechanisms, which require all the axes to be perpendicular to the plane of motion, will be considered first. When the movement of a rigid body is confined to a plane, it has three degrees of freedom: one of rotation, and two of translation, i.e., an angle and two rectangular coordinates are required to specify its position in a plane.

Let L = number of links

J = number of joints

X = degrees of freedom (or constraint) of a linkage

Constrained motion corresponds to one degree of freedom, $X = 1$. If $X < 1$, the linkage is locked and there can be no relative motion. If $X > 1$, the motion is unconstrained. The total number of degrees of freedom of the links which are detached from each other in a plane linkage is $3L$. In a hinge joint a point in one link must coincide permanently with a point in the other link which eliminates the two translational degrees of freedom and leaves only the single rotational freedom of one link relative to the other. The total number of degrees of freedom of the linkage is then

$$X = 3L - 2J$$

In order to use a chain, it must be made into a mechanism by fixing one

---

[*] O. Bottema, "On Grubler's Formulae for Mechanisms," *Applied Scientific Research*, Vol. A2, The Hague, Martinus Nijhoff, 1951. Other references include P. Grodzinski and E. M'Ewen, "Link Mechanisms in Modern Kinematics," *Proceedings*, The Institution of Mechanical Engineers, Vol. 168, 1954; N. Rosenauer and A. H. Willis, *Kinematics of Mechanisms*, Associated General Publications, Sydney, Australia, 1953; J. S. Beggs, *Mechanism*, McGraw-Hill Book Company, Inc., 1955.

of the links.* Before a link is fixed, the linkage can be moved freely in a plane; hence, the fixing of a link removes three degrees of freedom. The degrees of freedom in the mechanism are then

$$X = 3L - 2J - 3$$

or

$$X = 3(L - 1) - 2J \qquad (14.1)$$

The following computation shows that the six-bar linkage, Fig. 14.1,

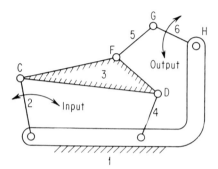

Fig. 14.1

has constrained motion.

$$X = 3(6 - 1) - 2 \times 7 = 1$$

This means that for each position of the input link, there is a definite position for the output link.

Assume that the reversing lever for the Walschaert valve gear, Fig. 4.23, is fixed and is therefore a part of the frame. This leaves twelve links with thirteen turning pairs and three sliding pairs, each with one degree of freedom. Application of Eq. (14.1) gives

$$X = 3(12 - 1) - 2 \times 16 = 1$$

Eq. (1), when applied to Fig. 14.2, gives

$$X = 3(7 - 1) - 2 \times 8 = 2$$

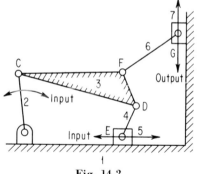

Fig. 14.2

With two degrees of freedom, there must be two input links to produce constrained motion of the output link. In general, the number of input links must equal the number of degrees of freedom that are indicated by Eq. (14.1).

* The terms *kinematic chain* (defined in Art. 1.7) and *kinematic linkage* are used interchangeably. In the previous discussion chains or linkages were assumed to be kinematic. In this chapter we are dealing with the criterion for constraint, and the terms *chain* and *linkage* may or may not be understood to be kinematic.

When several links are attached at the same joint, the number of joints is one less than the number of links; i.e., two links form a joint and each additional link adds a joint. Applying Eq. (14.1) to Fig. P4.25 gives

$$X = 3(13 - 1) - 2 \times 17 = 2$$

Here, 6 and 12 are input links, and 9 is the output link. Multiple input mechanisms are often used in computers.

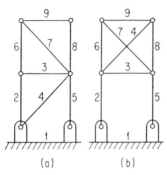

One case where the equation fails is shown in Fig. 14.3(b). Eq. (14.1) when applied to (a) and (b), gives the same results,

$$X = 3(9 - 1) - 2 \times 12 = 0$$

At (b) the upper cell is overconstrained, while the lower cell has one degree of freedom. Since the equation subtracts the total number of constraints from the total number of degrees of freedom, it indicates that both (a) and (b) are structures.

Fig. 14.3

14.2. Space mechanisms. A rigid body in space has six degrees of freedom: three of rotation and three of translation. For a space linkage, the total degrees of freedom of the links when detached from each other is $6L$. In a spherical joint, translation is eliminated leaving three degrees of rotation; the equation for constraint for a mechanism containing only spherical joints is then

$$X = 6L - 3J - 6$$

or

$$X = 6(L - 1) - 3J \tag{14.2}$$

If a space linkage contains only hinge joints, five degrees of freedom are removed from each joint leaving one degree of rotation. This gives the following equation for constraint.

$$X = 6(L - 1) - 5J \tag{14.3}$$

The application of this equation to Sarrut's mechanism, Fig. 15.14 gives

$$X = 6(6 - 1) - 5 \times 6 = 0$$

The equation fails as it did for Fig. 14.3(b) but for a different reason. In this case constrained motion is possible because parallelism of the axes removes one of the constraints. The equations are derived for general cases; the dimensions and orientation of the links are arbitrary. From these two examples it can be seen that the equations must be used with caution. A linkage must be examined for special relationships of its parts.

The required number of binary, hinge-joined links for the general case can be determined from Eq. (14.3).   If we let $J = L$ and $X = 1$, we find that $L = 7$.   The model, Fig. 14.4, is made from hinges that are twisted so that no two axes lie in the same plane.   When any one of the links is held, and an adjacent link is moved, the remaining links have constrained motion.   In a screw pair there is a fixed relationship between the translation and rotation displacements.   Therefore, only one coordinate is required to specify the displacements; a screw joint has

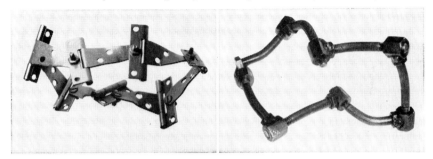

Fig. 14.4   Fig. 14.5

one degree of freedom.   Equation (14.3) therefore applies to a space linkage with screw pairs.   The model, Fig. 14.5, corresponds to Fig. 14.4 except that screw pairs have replaced the hinge pairs.

For a hinged pair that allows axial sliding, there are two degrees of freedom.   The equation for a space linkage with this type of joint is

$$X = 6(L - 1) - 4J \qquad (14.4)$$

Hinge-jointed links of a spherical chain, Fig. 14.6(a), move on the surfaces of spheres having a common center, O.   This motion excludes translation which leaves three degrees of rotation for each link, giving

$$X = 3(L - 1) - 2J \qquad (14.5)$$

This equation and Eq. (14.1) are identical.   In fact, motion in a plane can be considered as a special case of motion on the surface of an infinite sphere.   The Hooke coupling, Figs. 15.4 and 15.5, is kinematically equivalent to the four-bar spherical linkage, Fig. 14.6(b).   The above equations can be summarized by

$$X = P(L - 1) - QJ \qquad (14.6)$$

where P = number of degrees of freedom of the rigid body under the imposed condition (3 for plane motion, and 6 for motion in space).

Q = number of degrees of constraint at the joints.

In many cases, chains include different types of joints.   For these cases Eq. (14.6) can be written

$$X = P(L - 1) - \Sigma \, Q_i J_i \qquad (14.7)$$

where J_i is the number of joints with constraint Q_i.

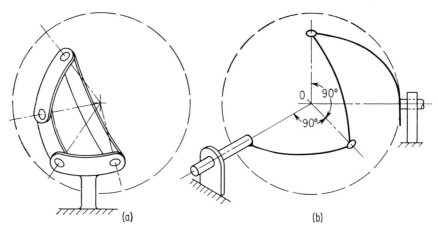

Fig. 14.6

The space linkage, Fig. 14.7, has two hinge joints (5 degrees of freedom removed) and two spherical joints (3 degrees of freedom removed). Applying Eq. (14.7)

$$X = 6(4 - 1) - 5 \times 2 - 3 \times 2 = 2$$

For most practical purposes, the linkage has constrained motion because one of the degrees of freedom is an undefined rotation of the coupler link about its own axis which does not affect the motion of the other

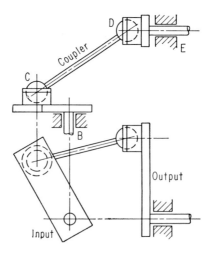

Fig. 14.7

links. For each position of the input link, there is a definite position of the output link. If, at one of the spherical joints, the coupler link is prevented from rotating about its own axis relative to the attached link, there will be left two degrees of freedom at this joint and Eq. (14.7) will indicate constrained motion. The absolute rotation of the coupler link about its own axis will then be defined.

In the example above of a space mechanism, $P = 6$ was used in Eq. (14.7). A plane mechanism, which has parallel axes, becomes a special case when space equations are used to analyze it. This is why the space equations fail when applied to plane mechanisms which must be analyzed in a plane with $P = 3$.

14.3. Plane mechanisms having direct contact. The direct contact linkage, Fig. 14.8 is often called an incomplete four-bar linkage. The point of contact, C, is a joint having two degrees of freedom, one of

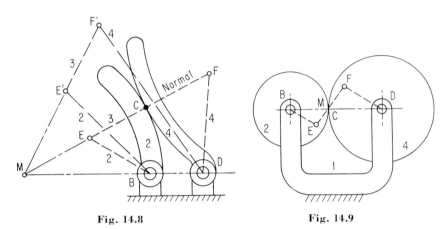

Fig. 14.8   Fig. 14.9

translation along the common tangent (sliding), and rotation because of rolling. The substitution of the values for this joint and the two hinge joints into Eq. (14.7) gives

$$X = 3(3 - 1) - 2 \times 2 - 1 \times 1 = 1$$

Eq. (14.1) can be used if an equivalent four-bar linkage, $BEFD$ or $BE'F'D$, is substituted for the original linkage. For a velocity analysis, all that is required of the equivalent linkage is that the line of transmission intersect the line of centers at M.

Pure rolling contact, Fig. 14.9, is a special case of a direct contact mechanism where the point of contact lies on the line of center. Here there is no sliding and, therefore, only one degree of freedom. The equivalent linkage, $BEFD$, does indicate that there is constrained motion; hence, for purposes of making an analysis, a rolling contact can be considered to have two degrees of freedom as in the general case, Fig. 14.8.

As another way of envisioning this, consider that rolling curves can always be replaced by gears with at least two pairs of teeth in contact at all times. A pair of teeth not in contact on the line of centers can then be selected for analysis, and the theory pertaining to Fig. 14.8 can be applied without question.

When all of the links of a chain have pure sliding contact, Fig. 14.10(a), Eq. (14.1) fails. An equation for this type of linkage can be developed as follows. Since the blocks have only sliding contact, assume that a free block has two degrees of translational freedom and

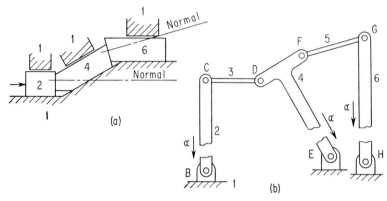

Fig. 14.10

no rotational freedom. When a block is confined to rectilinear translation, it has only one degree of freedom. Proceeding as before, we get

$$X = 2(L - 1) - J \tag{14.8}$$

Applying this to Fig. 14.10(a), gives

$$X = 2(4 - 1) - 5 = 1$$

Eq. (14.1) will apply to this type of chain if the equivalent linkage, Fig. 14.10(b) is used. In this example the sliding blocks are represented by links pivoted at infinity, and the coupler links are parallel to the normals or lines of transmission.

No trouble was encountered with the sliding blocks in Fig. 14.2 when an analysis was made. There are no missing links in this figure. A link with one element of a turning pair and one element of a sliding pair can always be replaced by an equivalent link with two elements of turning pairs without introducing an additional link.

14.4. Number synthesis. Grubler's equations have been used to analyse linkages. The links and joints of an existing linkage are counted, then substituted into the proper equation for determination of the number of degrees of freedom. In the remainder of this chapter the equations will be used for number synthesis. By assuming $X = 1$ and the number of links, the required number of joints can be determined. With this information the possible linkages can be determined. The theory will be confined to plane-motion linkages with turning pairs having only two links attached at each joint. After the basic linkages are obtained, some of the turning pairs may be replaced by sliding pairs, and single joints may be combined to form multiple joints.

First it will be shown that plane linkages having turning pairs must have an even number of links. Eq. (14.1) is written below for reference.

$$X = 3(L - 1) - 2J \qquad (14.9)$$

When $X = 1$, this can be written in the form

$$J = \frac{3}{2}L - 2 \qquad (14.10)$$

In order that there be no half joints, which are meaningless, L must be even.

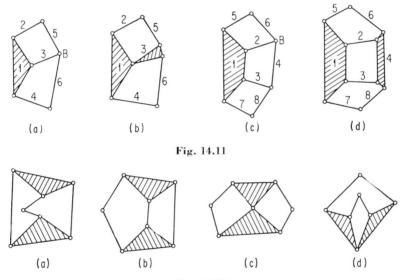

Fig. 14.11

Fig. 14.12

The maximum number of joints in a link is one-half the number of links in the linkage. Let

$$J = L + E$$

where E is the number of joints in excess of the number of links. This and the value $X = 1$ are substituted in Eq. (14.9), which gives

$$E = \frac{L}{2} - 2 \qquad (14.11)$$

This number is in excess of the number of joints that the linkage would contain if all of the links were binary. If the excess is added to one of the binary links which contains two joints, the number of joints is $L/2$. From Eq. (14.11), a four-bar linkage has no excess joints and therefore can contain only binary links. For a six-bar linkage $E = 1$ giving a ternary link. One such linkage is shown in Fig. 14.11(a). Earlier it

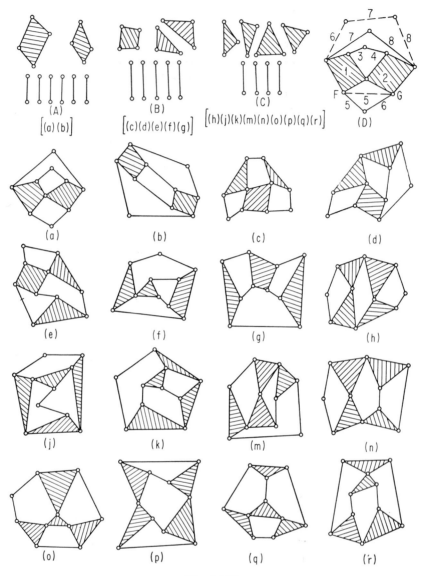

Fig. 14.13

was stated that in the basic types of linkages only two links are to connect at one joint. The double joint at B can be separated as shown at (b) giving a linkage with two ternary links.

One possible eight-bar linkage containing the maximum four-joint link is shown in Fig. 14.11(c). The double joints at B and C can be separated as shown at (d) giving a linkage with two quaternary links. This follows for all linkages; i.e., a linkage can contain two links with the maximum number of joints.

All linkages must have at least four binary links. Multiplication of Eq. (14.11) by 2 gives the number of elements (each joint has two elements) in excess of the number that would result if all links were binary.

$$2E = L - 4 \tag{14.12}$$

From Eq. (14.12), the excess is four less than the number of links. If

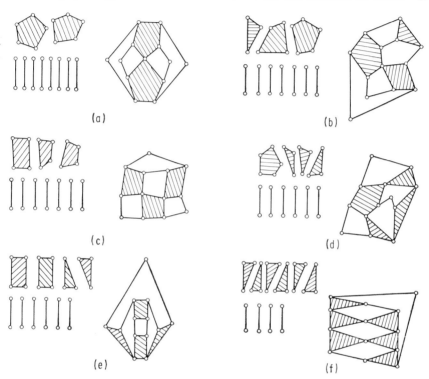

(a)

(b)

(c)

(d)

(e)

(f)

Fig. 14.14

these excess elements are added one to a link, four binary links will be left. This is shown for an eight-bar linkage, Fig. 14.13(n), and for a ten-bar linkage, Fig. 14.14(f). The two basic types of six-bar linkages are Stephenson's, Fig. 14.12(a) and (b), and Watt's, Fig. 14.12(c) and (d). The latter has the two ternary links connected to each other.

The number of joints in an eight-bar linkage is

$$J = \tfrac{3}{2}L - 2 = \tfrac{3}{2} \times 8 - 2 = 10$$

In determining the basic types of linkages, it is convenient to work with the number of links (eight) and the number of elements (twenty). Any combination of eight links having twenty elements (no link can contain more than $L/2$ elements) will be satisfactory. The three sets of links (A), (B), and (C), Fig. 14.13, each containing eight links having twenty elements, can be connected to form different linkages. The arrangement

shown with solid lines at (D) is made from set (A). If link 5 is connected to F and G, and link 6 is moved to the dotted position, links 1, 2, 3,
4, and 5 become a single link, or structure, which connects with links
6, 7, and 8 to form a four-bar linkage. The connecting of three links
with each other, which forms a structure, should be avoided. The sixteen
possible arrangements for the three sets of links are shown in Fig. 14.13.

A ten-bar linkage, which contains thirteen joints or twenty-six elements, can be formed from any one of seven different sets of links. Six
of these sets, with one arrangement of each, are shown in Fig. 14.14.

PROBLEMS

14.1. Determine the degrees of freedom for the Davis engine mechanism
shown in Fig. P 14.1. Does the equation give the correct answer? Discuss
briefly.

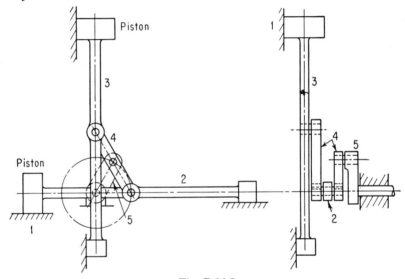

Fig. P 14.1

14.2. (a) Determine the degrees of freedom for the Walschaert mechanism,
Fig. 4.23. Assume that the reversing lever is fixed.

(b) Draw the set of links for the mechanism. Indicate a turning element
with a small circle, and a sliding element with a small rectangle.

(c) Replace the sliding elements with turning elements and reassemble the
linkage in a generalized form, (see Fig. 14.14). Number the links according to
Fig. 4.23.

14.3. One set of links is omitted in Fig. 14.14. Draw this set of links.

14.4. Draw all of the sets of links for the twelve-link mechanism. Assume
all of the connections are hinge joints. Draw a representative chain for each
set. The solution should be of the form shown in Fig. 14.14.

CHAPTER 15

Miscellaneous Mechanisms

15.1. Universal joints are used to connect intersecting shafts. One of the simplest types, Fig. 15.1, is used in toys. It is included here because of its simplicity and its basic theory. Shafts 2 and 3 are of very small diameter and are equally bent, $\phi_2 = \phi_3$. For the phase shown with solid lines the point of contact of 2 and 3, point B, lies in the plane of the paper. It also lies in the homokinetic plane. This is the plane that is normal to the plane containing the shafts and bisects the angle

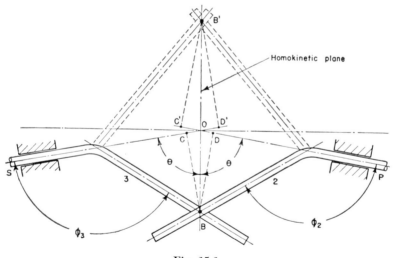

Fig. 15.1

between them. The velocity of B as a point in 3 coincides with that of B as a point in 2. The perpendiculars to the axes, BC and BD, are equal. These same conditions hold for the phase shown with broken lines. Because of symmetry the point of contact B will lie in the homokinetic plane for all other phases. Velocities V_{B_2} and V_{B_3} do not coincide for the phases that are not in the plane of the paper. Because of symmetry they will make equal angles with the homokinetic plane. The driving and driven components of these two vectors in the homokinetic plane must be

329

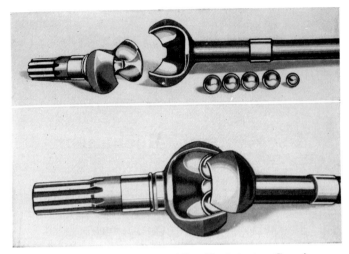

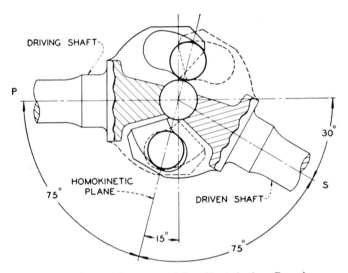

Fig. 15.2.   (Courtesy of Bendix Aviation Corp.)

Fig. 15.3.   (Courtesy of Bendix Aviation Corp.)

equal.   Then V_{B_2} and V_{B_3} are equal in magnitude.   The perpendiculars to the axes are also equal.   The angular velocity ratio of driver and follower is therefore unity for all phases.

The requirement of a universal joint to transmit motion with a constant velocity ratio is fulfilled if the power-transmitting elements (in the example above there is only one, the point of contact B) lie in the homokinetic plane for all phases.

The Bendix-Weiss joint is shown in Figs. 15.2 and 15.3.   Power is transmitted from one fork to the other through balls.   The small ball in Fig. 15.2 is used at the center for a spacer.   The principle of the joint is shown in Fig. 15.3.   Each ball fits in two grooves or races, one being in each fork.   The grooves are designed so that they always intersect in the homokinetic plane.   The balls can lie only at the intersection of the grooves.   This joint therefore transmits motion with a constant angular velocity ratio.

The Hooke or Cardan* joint is shown in Fig. 15.4.   A schematic diagram is shown in Fig. 15.5(a).   The nature of the motion can be determined by using Fig. 15.5(b) and (c).   At (b) fork P lies in the horizontal plane and fork S in the vertical plane.   The angle between

Fig. 15.4.   (Courtesy of Boston Gear Works.)

the shafts is β.   As P rotates, points B and C move in a circle as shown in (c).   Points D and E move in a circle of the same size.   This circle is projected in the plane of the paper in (c) and appears as an ellipse. When P is displaced by an angle ϕ, point B moves to B' and D to D'. Angle DOD' is equal to ϕ.   (A little consideration will show that this is correct.   At (d) right angle BOD lies in the plane of the paper.   Point D is swung out of the plane of the paper to position D_1.   Angle BOD_1 when projected back to the paper is equal to BOD.   Angle FOD when swung out and projected back is F_1OD_1 and is not equal to FOD.)   It appears that S has moved through the same angle as P.   This is not correct, since the true angle must be measured in a circle that represents the path of D.   This can be done most conveniently by using the circle in (c).   Point D' is projected vertically to D''.   The true angle turned through by S is θ.

This joint does not transmit motion with a constant angular velocity ratio.   The power transmission elements B, C, D, and E lie in a plane that passes through O, but the plane wobbles as motion takes place. From (b) it can be seen that when fork P turns 180°, fork S will also turn 180°.   When fork P is turned to the vertical position, fork S is horizontal.   Both have turned 90°.   For four phases in each cycle the

* An Italian, Cardan (1501–1576), was the first to describe this joint.   An Englishman, Robert Hooke (1635–1703), first applied it for the transmission of rotary motion. Hooke was a physicist, mathematician, and inventor.   He is most widely known for Hooke's law, which is stated in all strength of materials books.

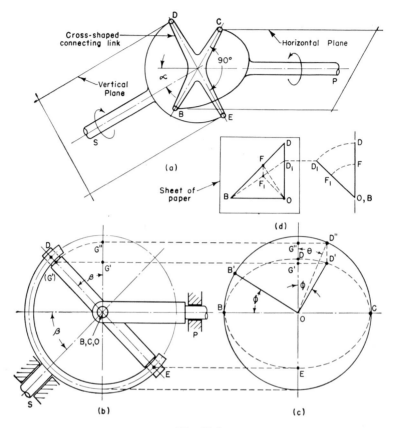

Fig. 15.5

displacements are equal. For all other phases they are not. Part of
the time the follower is ahead and part of the time it is behind the driver.

The relationship between θ and ϕ can be determined as follows, noting
that $G'D' = G''D''$ and $OG'' = O(G')$.

$$\frac{\tan \theta}{\tan \phi} = \frac{G''D''/G''O}{G^1D^1/G'O} = \frac{G'O}{G''O} = \frac{G''O \cos \beta}{G''O} = \cos \beta$$

or $\qquad \tan \phi = \dfrac{\tan \theta}{\cos \beta}$ $\qquad\qquad$ (15.1)

Angle β is usually a constant in a given application. It is assumed
constant in this development.

The angular velocity ratio is obtained by differentiating Eq. (15.1)
with respect to time.

$$\sec^2 \phi \, \frac{d\phi}{dt} = \frac{\sec^2 \theta}{\sec^2 \beta} \frac{d\theta}{dt}$$

Letting

$$\frac{d\phi}{dt} = \omega_p \quad \text{and} \quad \frac{d\theta}{dt} = \omega_s$$

gives

$$\frac{\omega_s}{\omega_p} = \frac{\sec^2 \phi \cos \beta}{\sec^2 \theta} = \frac{\sec^2 \phi \cos \beta}{1 + \tan^2 \theta}$$

Angle θ is eliminated, using Eq. (15.1), giving

$$\frac{\omega_s}{\omega_p} = \frac{\sec \phi \cos \beta}{1 + \sec^2 \beta \tan^2 \phi} = \frac{\cos \beta / \cos^2 \phi}{(\cos^2 \phi + \cos^2 \beta \sin^2 \phi)/\cos^2 \phi}$$

Letting $\cos^2 \beta = 1 - \sin^2 \beta$ gives

$$\frac{\omega_s}{\omega_p} = \frac{\cos \beta}{1 - \sin^2 \beta \sin^2 \phi} \tag{15.2}$$

For a constant angular velocity of P the angular acceleration of S is

$$\begin{aligned}
\alpha_s &= \frac{d\omega_s}{dt} = \frac{d}{dt}\left(\omega_p \frac{\cos \beta}{1 - \sin^2 \alpha \sin^2 \phi} \right) \\
&= \omega_p \left[\frac{\cos \beta \sin^2 \beta \, 2 \sin \phi \cos \phi (d\phi/dt)}{(1 - \sin^2 \beta \sin^2 \phi)^2} \right] \\
&= \omega_p^2 \frac{\cos \beta \sin^2 \beta \sin 2\phi}{(1 - \sin^2 \beta \sin^2 \phi)^2} \tag{15.3}
\end{aligned}$$

If an intermediate shaft R (Fig. 15.6) and two Hooke's joints are used to connect shafts P and S, one joint can be made to compensate

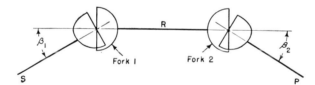

Fork I   Fork 2

Fig. 15.6

for the other. Shafts P and S do not have to intersect. The angular velocity ratio of P and S will be unity for all phases if R is placed so that the angle between R and S is equal to that between R and P, and fork 1 is made to lie in the plane of R and S when fork 2 lies in the plane of R and P.

15.2. Oldham coupling [Fig. 15.7(a)] is used to connect parallel shafts. Member 1 has two tongues at right angles that fit into grooves in members 2 and 4. The only relative motion between 2 and 1 is translation. The same is true of 1 and 4. Therefore any angular motion of member 4 will be imparted exactly to member 2. The angular velocity ratio of this coupling is unity.

This mechanism is an inversion of the double slider mechanism shown at (b). If member 3 is fixed, 2 and 4 will rotate equally with 1.

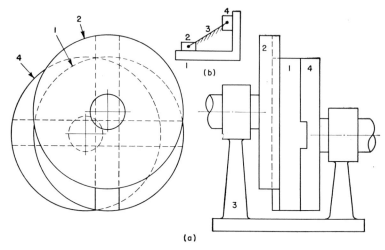

Fig. 15.7

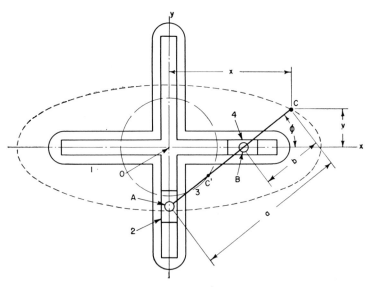

Fig. 15.8

15.3. The elliptic trammel (Fig. 15.8) is another application of the double-slider mechanism. It can be used for drawing ellipses. From Fig. 15.8,

$$x = a \cos \phi$$
$$y = b \sin \phi$$

Then $$\frac{x^2}{a^2} + \frac{y^2}{b^2} = \cos^2 \phi + \sin^2 \phi = 1 \qquad (15.4)$$

This is the equation of the ellipse with center at the origin, where a is the semimajor axis and b is the semiminor axis. Axes a and b are equal when C is chosen at C' midway between A and B. The path of C' is a circle of radius a. Equation (15.4) becomes

$$x^2 + y^2 = a^2$$

This mechanism, when made for drawing, carries a pen or pencil at C, and the lengths AB and BC are adjustable.

15.4. Generation of second-degree curves.* The general equation of the second degree is

$$Ax^2 + Bxy + Cy^2 + Dx + Ey + F = 0 \qquad (15.5)$$

By translation and rotation of the axes a second-degree equation can always be reduced to one of the conic equations.

Ellipse
$$\frac{x^2}{a^2} + \frac{y^2}{b^2} = 1$$

Hyperbola
$$\frac{x^2}{a^2} - \frac{y^2}{b^2} = 1$$

Parabola
$$y^2 = 2px$$

A machine based on theorems from projective geometry can be made to generate these curves.

Theorem 1. If a right angle moves in its plane in such a way that its vertex describes a fixed circle, while one of the arms passes always through a fixed point, the envelope of the other arm will be a conic section concentric with the given circle, and having one focus at the fixed point. The conic is an ellipse or a hyperbola according as the given point lies within or without the given circle.

Theorem 2. If a right angle moves in its plane so that its vertex describes a fixed straight line, while one of the arms passes always through a fixed point, the other arm will envelop a parabola having the fixed point for the focus and the fixed straight line for the tangent at the vertex. The fixed point or focus must not lie on the chosen fixed straight line.

Kinematical schemes for generating the ellipse, hyperbola, and parabola in accordance with the foregoing theorems are illustrated in Fig. 15.9(a), (b), and (c), respectively. Here F is a focus and FJK is a right angle. A curve that looks like a conic but actually is a conic less a constant dimension measured normal to the curve will be generated if the plane of the cutter is advanced, say to a position L-L as shown in (a). This property of parallel curves can be applied in allowing for roller radius in the generation of a conic-section cam to operate with a roller follower. Templates with an allowance for thickness of sheet metal

* This article is taken from "Generation of the Conic Sections with Machine Tools" by Rolland T. Hinkle, *Product Eng.*, August, 1947.

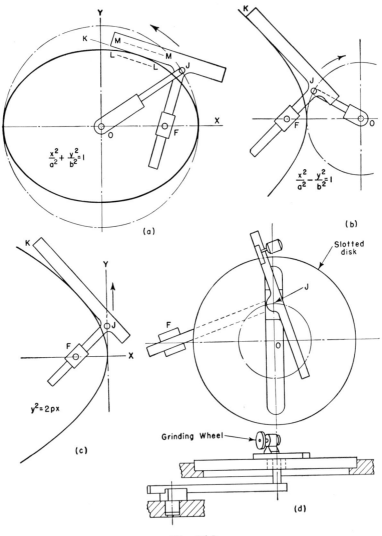

Fig. 15.9

might be made in this manner. Solids of revolution can be made by rotating the work during the machining operation.

A curve that is larger than a conic by a constant dimension measured normal to the curve would be generated by withdrawing the cutting surface to some position M-M. Thus a conic can be roughed out just slightly oversize before finish grinding exactly to size.

A machine for generating any conic is shown at (d). When the slotted wheel is fixed in the position shown and slider J is moved in the slot, the grinding wheel sweeps out a parabola. When the slider is

fixed in the slot and the disk is rotated the grinding wheel sweeps out
an ellipse or hyperbola depending on the location of F.

15.5. The pantograph is used to enlarge or reduce movements.
In Fig. 15.10(a) link ABC is parallel to OD, and OA is parallel to BD.
A line through C and O intersects BD at P. If C is moved to trace a
given path, point P will trace a path that is similar but of a different size.

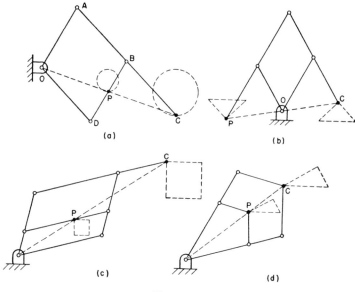

(a)   (b)

(c)   (d)

Fig. 15.10

In order that the movement of P be similar to that of C it is necessary
that triangles OPD and PBC be similar for all positions. Here OD and
BC are always parallel, as are PD and BP. For any position the line OC
will produce parallel sides OP and PC. Since OD and BC are fixed
lengths, PD and BP will also be fixed. The ratio of the sizes of the
motions will be

$$\frac{\text{motion of } C}{\text{motion of } P} = \frac{OC}{OP} = \frac{AC}{AB}$$

Other arrangements are shown at (b), (c), and (d).

Pantographs are used for reproducing drawings to a different scale.
Maps are a common example. They are also used to guide cutting tools.
Printing type is first drawn by hand several inches high. A pantograph
is used to reduce the type and cut the moulds.

15.6. Straight-line motions. Most of the mechanisms that produce straight-line motions without the use of sliders were developed
before plane surfaces could be machined accurately. At the present
time the need for these mechanisms is not so great as in the past but

they still have useful applications. The mechanisms can be classed in two groups, exact and approximate.

Peaucellier's Mechanism (Fig. 15.11) was developed in 1864 by a Frenchman, Peaucellier. Links of equal length are $AB = BC = CD = DA$, $OA = OC$, and $OE = ED$. From symmetry a line through

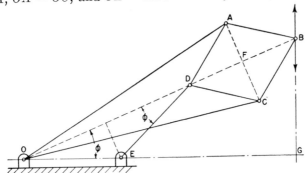

Fig. 15.11

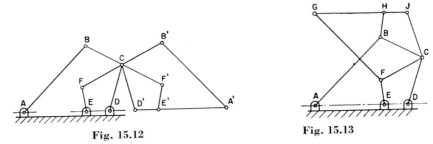

Fig. 15.12 **Fig. 15.13**

OB will pass through D and AC will bisect DB at F. It will be shown that point B moves in a straight line.

From right triangles OFA and DFA,

$$\overline{OF^2} = \overline{OA^2} - \overline{AF^2} \quad \text{and} \quad \overline{DF^2} = \overline{DA^2} - \overline{AF^2}$$

Eliminating $\overline{AF^2}$ from the equations gives

$$\overline{OF^2} - \overline{DF^2} = \overline{OA^2} - \overline{DA^2}$$

or

$$(OF + DF)(OF - DF) = \overline{OA^2} - \overline{DA^2}$$

But $OF + DF = OB = \dfrac{OG}{\cos \phi}$ and $OF - DF = OD = 2(OE) \cos \phi$

Then

$$\frac{OG}{\cos \phi} 2(OE) \cos \phi = \overline{OA^2} - \overline{DA^2}$$

or

$$OG = \frac{\overline{OA^2} - \overline{DA^2}}{2(OE)} = \text{a constant}$$

The projection of B on a line through OE is a fixed point G. Therefore B moves in a straight line perpendicular to OE.

Kempe's Mechanism (Fig. 15.12) produces rectilinear translation of a member with the use of pin-connected links. The proportions of the links are, $AB = AD = 2CD = 4FE = 4ED$. Links BCF' and FCB' are rigid members. Here $CB'A'E'F'D'$ is a duplication of the left half of the mechanism. If link AED is fixed, the only motion that link $D'E'A'$ can have is horizontal.

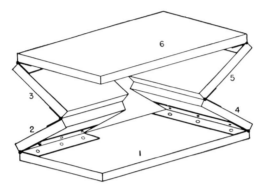

Fig. 15.14

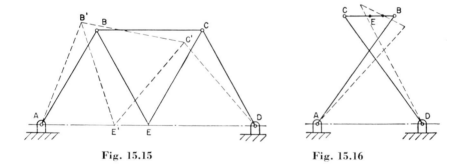

Fig. 15.15   Fig. 15.16

Another arrangement is shown in Fig. 15.13. The only motion that link GHJ can have is rectilinear translation in a vertical direction.

Sarrut's Mechanism (Fig. 15.14) is one of the simplest and perhaps the earliest mechanism to produce straight-line motion. When 1 is fixed, the only motion that 6 can have is rectilinear translation in a vertical direction.

Robert's Mechanism (Fig. 15.15) produces approximate straight-line motion. Here E moves very nearly along the line AD. The proportions of the links are $AB = BE = EC = CD$, and $AD = 2BC$. The accuracy of the motion is increased as the height of the mechanism is made greater in relation to its width.

Chebichev's Mechanism (Fig. 15.16) produces approximate straight-line motion. The mid-point E of CB moves very nearly along the line

CB. The proportions of the links are $AB = CD = 1.25\ AD$, and $AD = 2CB$.

The Scott-Russell and Watt straight-line mechanisms are shown in Figs. P 2.3 and P 2.4.

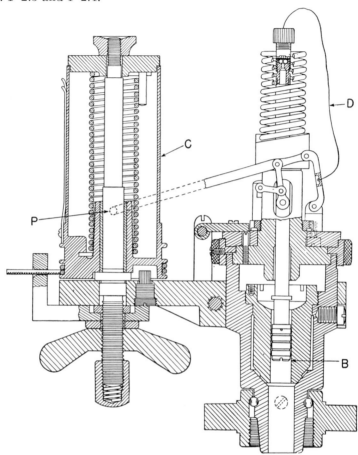

Fig. 15.17.   (Courtesy of Bacharach Industrial Instrument Co.)

An Engine Pressure Indicator is shown in Fig. 15.17.   Piston B moves against a spring and is displaced in proportion to the pressure in the cylinder.   This motion is transmitted through the linkage and produces a larger vertical motion of the pencil P.   A pressure displacement diagram is traced on a paper that is wrapped around cylinder C.   The cylinder is rotated in accordance with the piston displacement.   It is necessary not only that P move in an approximate straight line, but that its motion be proportional to that of B.   The wire D is used with spark ignition engines.   Ignition is recorded on the diagram by a hole burned through the paper at P.

15.7. Escapements are used to prevent a wheel from rotating in an uncontrolled manner and to cause it to rotate with a definite intermittent motion.   The Graham escapement that is used in clocks and watches is shown in Fig. 15.18.   A clockwise torque is applied to the escape wheel by means of a spring or weight.   The anchor oscillates on the axis E, which is called the verge.   A balance wheel or pendulum is attached to the anchor.   The ends of the anchor are called pallets. The pallets are close enough together so that there is no position of the

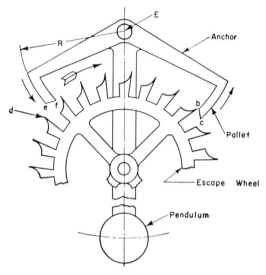

Fig. 15.18

anchor that allows the escape wheel to rotate continuously.   If the pendulum is displaced and then released, it will oscillate and allow the escape wheel to rotate intermittently as the pallets alternately pull out of the tooth spaces.   This motion will soon cease because of friction unless energy is supplied to the pendulum.   The required energy is supplied by the spring or weight by means of the escape wheel and the inclined surfaces bc and ef.   For the phase shown the pendulum is swinging to the right, and the end of a tooth is in contact with the right pallet at b. The torque on the escape wheel causes the end of the tooth to slide along the surface bc.   This pushes the pallet to the right and adds energy to the pendulum.   Before the end of the tooth reaches c, point e on the left pallet enters a tooth space and is in a position to catch the adjacent tooth and stop the motion.   When the pendulum swings to the left, point d slides along surface ef and supplies energy to the pendulum. During one cycle the pendulum receives two energy impulses, and the escape wheel has rotation corresponding to one tooth.   Surfaces of the pallets are circular arcs with E as center.   When these surfaces are in contact with the escape wheel, rotation of the anchor does not cause rotation of the escape wheel.

15.8. Ratchets are used to convert rotation or oscillation into intermittent rotation or translation. In Fig. 15.19 rotations of crank 6 in either direction cause intermittent counterclockwise rotation of the

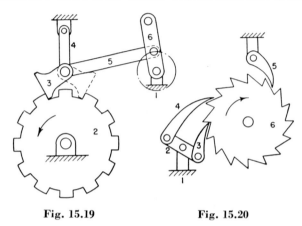

Fig. 15.19   Fig. 15.20

ratchet wheel 2. If the pawl 3 is changed to the dotted position, the ratchet wheel will rotate in a clockwise direction.

In Fig. 15.20, oscillation of 2 causes intermittent clockwise rotation of 6. Two pawls 3 and 4, are used to produce rotation for both directions of motion of 2. Member 5 is a holding pawl. It is sometimes necessary to use springs on the pawls to hold them against the ratchet wheel.

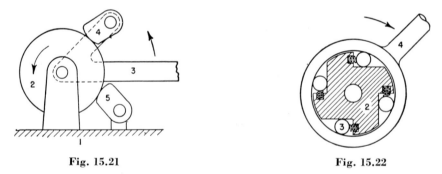

Fig. 15.21   Fig. 15.22

A silent or friction ratchet is shown in Fig. 15.21. Oscillation of 3 causes intermittent counterclockwise rotation of 2. Here 5 is a holding pawl.

Another type of silent ratchet is shown in Fig. 15.22. Light springs push balls 3 into the wedge-shaped spaces formed by 2 and 4. Here 2 can be the driver in a counterclockwise direction, or 4 can be the driver in a clockwise direction.

15.9. Zero backlash gears. A train of conventional gears with zero backlash would require that the gears and mountings be dimensionally perfect and that all parts change equally with a change in temperature. A practical way of eliminating backlash in a gear train is shown in Fig. 15.23. The pinion is made in two parts and the parts connected with a spring. In assembly the parts are rotated so that the spring is in tension. If the torque produced by the spring is greater than the torque

Fig. 15.23

applied to the shaft, the pinion can transmit motion in either direction with zero backlash. In a train with several gears, alternate gears are made in this manner.

15.10. Bennett's linkage.* Consider the four-bar space linkage $ABCD$, Fig. 15.24, in which the opposite links are of equal length. The length of one pair of opposite links is a, and the length of the other pair of opposite links is b. It is not yet apparent that such a hinge-jointed linkage is possible; so, for the present, assume that the four joints are of the ball and socket type. For any configuration triangles ABD and CDB will be congruent, and triangles ADC and CBA will be congruent,

* M. Goldberg, "New Five-Bar and Six-Bar Linkages in Three Dimensions," *ASME Transactions*, August 1943, p. 645; G. T. Bennett, "A New Mechanism," *Engineering*, Vol. 76, 1903, pp. 777–778. Bennett was a fellow of Emmanuel College, Cambridge. Other references on space linkage include F. R. E. Crossley, "3–D Mechanisms," *Machine Design*, August 1955; J. S. Beggs, *Mechanism*, McGraw-Hill Book Company, Inc., New York 1955; J. E. Shigley, *Kinematic Analysis of Mechanisms*, McGraw-Hill Book Company, Inc., New York, 1959.

hence

$$\text{angle } BAD = \text{angle } BCD = \theta$$

and

$$\text{angle } ADC = \text{angle } ABC = \phi$$

The volume of a tetrahedron is one third of the area of the base times the altitude. The area of the base $ACD = \dfrac{1}{2} ab \sin \phi$, and the altitude $GB = b \sin \theta \sin \alpha$, hence

$$6V = (ab \sin \phi)(b \sin \theta \sin \alpha) \qquad (15.6)$$

Similarly

$$6V = (ab \sin \theta)(a \sin \phi \sin \beta) \qquad (15.7)$$

When Eqs. (15.6) and (15.7) are equated, we obtain

$$b \sin \alpha = a \sin \beta \qquad (15.8)$$

This relation is independent of angles θ and ϕ. Therefore, the angles α and β can be fixed twists while θ and ϕ vary. The twist α in link AD

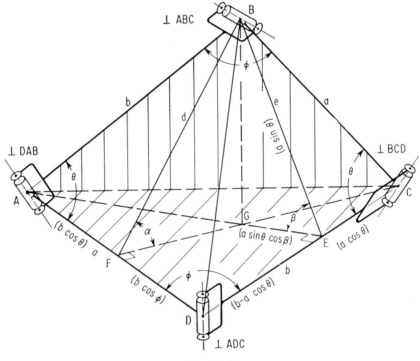

Fig. 15.24

can be obtained by making the hinge axis at D perpendicular to plane ADC, and the hinge axis at A perpendicular to plane DAB. If the hinge axis at C is perpendicular to plane DCB, the angle of twist in link DC will be β. Because of symmetry about the line AC, Eq. (15.8) can be obtained in exactly the same manner by taking ABC as the reference plane and dropping a perpendicular from D to this plane. Hence, the twists of links AB and BC are β and α respectively. If Eq. (15.8) is satisfied, hinge joints can replace the ball and socket joints assumed earlier. In design, three of the four variables, a, b, α, and β, can be assumed and the fourth obtained from Eq. (15.8).

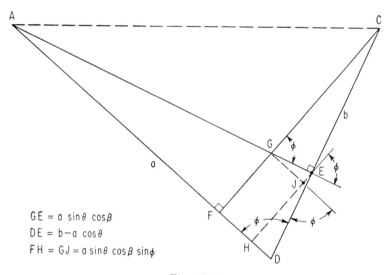

$GE = a \sin\theta \cos\beta$

$DE = b - a \cos\theta$

$FH = GJ = a \sin\theta \cos\beta \sin\phi$

Fig. 15.25

A Bennett linkage, with hinges on the b links twisted 90°, is shown in Fig. (15.26). Link b shown with broken lines can be considered the fixed link.

The relation between θ and ϕ can be obtained from Figs. (15.24) and (15.25) as follows

$$FD = b \cos \phi = a - b \cos \theta = (b - a \cos \theta) \cos \phi + a \sin \theta \cos \beta \sin \phi$$

or

$$a(1 + \cos \theta \cos \phi) - b \cos \theta - b \cos \phi = a \sin \theta \cos \beta \sin \phi \quad (15.9)$$

and

$$DE = a \cos \phi = b - a \cos \theta = (a - b \cos \theta) \cos \phi + b \sin \theta \cos \alpha \sin \phi$$

or

$$b(1 + \cos \theta \cos \phi) - a \cos \theta - a \cos \phi = b \sin \theta \cos \alpha \sin \phi \quad (15.10)$$

Add Eqs. (15.9) and (15.10)

$$(a + b)(1 - \cos \theta)(1 - \cos \phi) = \sin \theta \sin \phi (a \cos \beta + b \cos \alpha)$$

The above can be written in the form

$$\frac{(1 - \cos \theta)}{\sin \theta} \frac{(1 - \cos \phi)}{\sin \phi} = \frac{a \cos \beta + b \cos \alpha}{a + b}$$

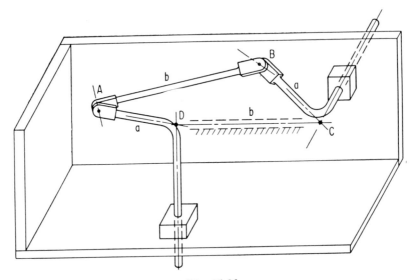

Fig. 15.26

Use Eq. (15.8) to eliminate a, then multiply numerator and denominator of the right side by $\sin \beta$

$$\tan \frac{\theta}{2} \tan \frac{\phi}{2} = \frac{\sin \alpha \cos \beta + \cos \alpha \sin \beta}{\sin \alpha + \sin \beta} = \frac{\sin (\alpha + \beta)}{\sin \alpha + \sin \beta}$$

$$= \frac{2 \sin \frac{1}{2} (\alpha + \beta) \cos \frac{1}{2} (\alpha + \beta)}{2 \sin \frac{1}{2} (\alpha + \beta) \cos \frac{1}{2} (\alpha - \beta)} = \frac{\cos \frac{1}{2} (\alpha + \beta)}{\cos \frac{1}{2} (\alpha - \beta)} = \text{constant}$$

$$(15.11)$$

Index